LABORATORY MANUAL

ANATOMY & PHYSIOLOGY

Elaine N. Marieb

Revised Custom Edition for Westchester Community College

Taken from:
*Human Anatomy & Physiology Laboratory Manual
Cat Version*, Eighth Edition
by Elaine N. Marieb

PEARSON
Custom
Publishing

PEARSON
Benjamin
Cummings

Taken from:

Human Anatomy & Physiology Laboratory Manual, Cat Version, Eighth Edition
by Elaine N. Marieb
Copyright © 2006 by Pearson Education, Inc.
Published by Benjamin Cummings
San Francisco, California 94111

This special edition published in cooperation with Pearson Custom Publishing.

Printed in the United States of America

10   9   8   7   6   5   4   3   2   1

ISBN 0-536-12272-5

2005140507

EC

Please visit our web site at *www.pearsoncustom.com*

PEARSON CUSTOM PUBLISHING
75 Arlington Street, Suite 300, Boston, MA 02116
A Pearson Education Company

Contents

Preface to the Instructor

The philosophy behind the eighth edition update of this manual mirrors that of all earlier editions. It reflects a still-developing sensibility for the way teachers teach and students learn engendered by years of teaching the subject, and by listening to the suggestions of other instructors as well as those of students enrolled in multifaceted health-care programs. *Human Anatomy & Physiology Laboratory Manual: Cat Version* was originally developed to facilitate and enrich the laboratory experience for both teachers and students. This, its eighth edition, retains those same goals.

This manual, intended for students in introductory human anatomy and physiology courses, presents a wide range of laboratory experiences for students concentrating in nursing, physical therapy, dental hygiene, pharmacology, respiratory therapy, health and physical education, as well as biology and premedical programs. It differs from *Human Anatomy & Physiology Laboratory Manual, Main Version* (Seventh Edition, 2005) in that it contains detailed guidelines for dissecting a laboratory animal. The manual's coverage is intentionally broad, allowing it to serve both one- and two-semester courses.

Basic Pedagogical Approach

The generous variety of experiments in this manual provides flexibility that enables instructors to gear their laboratory approach to specific academic programs, or to their own teaching preferences. The manual is still independent of any textbook, so it contains the background discussions and terminology necessary to perform all experiments. Such a self-contained learning aid eliminates the need for students to bring a textbook into the laboratory.

Each of the 46 exercises leads students toward a coherent understanding of the structure and function of the human body. The manual begins with anatomical terminology and an orientation to the body, which together provide the necessary tools for studying the various body systems. The exercises that follow reflect the dual focus of the manual—both anatomical and physiological aspects receive considerable attention. As the various organ systems of the body are introduced, the initial exercises focus on organization, from the cellular to the organ system level. As indicated by the table of contents, the anatomical exercises are usually followed by physiological experiments that familiarize students with various aspects of body functioning and promote the critical understanding that function follows structure. Homeostasis is continually emphasized as a requirement for optimal health. Pathological conditions are viewed as a loss of homeostasis; these discussions can be recognized by the homeostasis imbalance logo within the descriptive material of each exercise. This holistic approach encourages an integrated understanding of the human body.

Features and Changes

In this revision, I have continued to try to respond to reviewers' and users' feedback concerning trends that are having an impact on the anatomy and physiology laboratory experience, most importantly:

- the growing reluctance of students to perform experiments using living laboratory animals, the declining popularity of animal dissection exercises, and the growing demand for student-based experimentation

- the increased use of computers in the laboratory, and hence the subsequent desire for more computer simulation exercises

- the replacement of older recording equipment with computerized data acquisition and compilation systems

- the continued importance of visual learning for today's student

- the need to reinforce writing, computation, and critical thinking skills across the curriculum

The specific changes implemented to address these trends fall neatly into two areas: pedagogical and multimedia. Changes made in each of these areas are described next.

Pedagogical Features

1. Design Enhancements

A color-coded heading design enhances the lab manual pedagogy and distinguishes important features of the text. Opening pages of exercises are enriched with colored background screens that highlight descriptions of exercise objectives and lists of required materials. Red *Activity* heads are used throughout the manual, alerting the student that "hands-on" learning is to follow. *Activity* heads for experiments involving BIOPAC® and other apparatus are also set off in red. A scissors icon and blue-green *Dissection* head herald sections that entail dissection of isolated organs. The conclusion of each *Activity* and *Dissection* is indicated by a block symbol, which is of the same hue as the section heading. Tables and charts are framed in blue and beige, and are placed near relevant text.

2. Art Program Revisions

A completely revitalized art program is offered with this new edition. Several new figures have been added, and many illustrations have been revised for more detail, improved line quality, and stronger color. The tissue figures in Exercise 6 have been reformatted and now include photomicrographs that are much larger. Selected tables have been embellished with new full-color drawings. Several new photographs have been added to accompany diagrammatic figures, and many new photomicrographs are offered throughout the main exercises and in the Histology Atlas.

3. Updated Anatomical Terminology
The anatomical terminology in this eighth edition has been updated to match that in *Human Anatomy & Physiology, Sixth Edition* (main text authored by Elaine N. Marieb).

4. Content Changes
Activities that have proven to be of limited pedagogical value because of unpredictability of results, difficult implementation, or general unpopularity have been deleted from the manual. These include the filtration demonstration in Exercise 5A, mapping rods and cones in Exercise 24, and estimating venous pressure in Exercise 33A.

A number of new activities, many of which depend on student-student interaction, have been added to this edition. The following are representative of these additions:

- Dermagraphics: Fingerprinting in Exercise 7

- Several changes in Exercise 13: for example, a new activity demonstrating the importance of friction reducing structures; the addition of a new joint (temporomandibular) to study; manipulating models to demonstrate hip and knee movements

- Making a muscle painting using water-based paints to paint the skin over specific muscles on a classmate's body in Exercise 15

- Demonstrating the galvanic skin response (lie detector test) using BIOPAC® in Exercise 21

- Per user request, adding the Tallquist method for determining hemoglobin back into Exercise 29A

5. Organization Changes
As in the previous edition of the manual, the principal laboratory lessons, Exercises 1 through 46, appear first and are followed by corresponding Review Sheets and the excellent Histology and Human Anatomy Atlases. Within the main section are 11 exercises designated with the letter "A." The "A" indicates that the exercise has a correlating "B" exercise—a PhysioEx™ computer simulation that can be used along with or in place of a wet lab activity. All 13 PhysioEx™ modules, as well as PhysioEx™ Review Sheets, are contained in a separate section located near the end of the manual.

All instructions for dissection of the major laboratory animal (cat in this case) have been moved to a special section of the manual. In this section, the laboratory review sections are made part of the individual dissection exercises to encourage the student to look at questions during the laboratory when the dissection specimen is still in front of them. Four-color photographs are integrated in the dissection exercises and additional photographs have been taken to ensure that nearly all diagrams in this section are accompanied by a corresponding photo. This approach provides students with both a realistic (photographs in real color) and an idealized (diagrams in four-color) art program to guide their dissection experiences.

Multimedia Features

1. PhysioEx™ Version 6.0 Computer Simulations
The PhysioEx™ CD-ROM, shrink-wrapped with every lab manual, has been expanded in the Eighth Edition Update of the manual to include a new lab on serological testing, more data variability, and online worksheets. Unlike the typical tutorial-based computer supplements that usually target anatomy, the 40 physiology experiments on PhysioEx™ Version 6.0 allow students to explore with different variables while being guided through the process of discovery within the structure and security of a written lab exercise. Particularly advantageous is the fact that the students can conduct or review the experiments and slides at home on a personal computer. PhysioEx™ Version 6.0 also provides convenient "laboratory access" for students enrolled in Internet-based distance education courses and now is available online at www. physioex.com. (Use the access code found at the front of your lab manual to log onto the site.)

PhysioEx™ Version 6.0 topics include:

- Exercise 5B, *The Cell: Transport Mechanisms and Permeability—Computer Simulation.* Explores how substances cross the cell's membrane. Simple and facilitated diffusion, osmosis, filtration, and active transport are covered.

- Exercise 6B, *Histology Tutorial.* Includes over 200 histology images, viewable at various magnifications, with accompanying descriptions and labels.

- Exercise 16B, *Skeletal Muscle Physiology: Computer Simulation.* Provides insights into the complex physiology of skeletal muscle. Electrical stimulation, isometric contractions, and isotonic contractions are investigated.

- Exercise 18B, *Neurophysiology of Nerve Impulses: Computer Simulation.* Investigates stimuli that elicit action potentials, stimuli that inhibit action potentials, and factors affecting nerve conduction velocity.

- Exercise 28B, *Endocrine System Physiology: Computer Simulation.* Investigates the relationship between hormones and metabolism; the effect of estrogen replacement therapy; and the effect of insulin on diabetes.

- Exercise 29B, *Blood Analysis: Computer Simulation.* Covers hematocrit determination, erythrocyte sedimentation rate determination, hemoglobin determination, blood typing, and total cholesterol determination.

- Exercise 33B, *Cardiovascular Dynamics: Computer Simulation.* Allows students to perform experiments that would be difficult if not impossible to do in a traditional laboratory. Topics of inquiry include vessel resistance and pump (heart) mechanics.

- Exercise 34B, *Frog Cardiovascular Physiology: Computer Simulation.* Variables influencing heart activity are examined. Topics include setting up and recording baseline heart activity, the refractory period of cardiac muscle, and an investigation of physical and chemical factors that affect enzyme activity.

- Exercise 35B, *Serological Testing: Computer Simulation.* Investigates antigen-antibody reactions and their role in clinical tests used to diagnose a disease or infection.

- Exercise 37B, *Respiratory System Mechanics: Computer Simulation.* Investigates physical and chemical aspects of pulmonary function. Students collect data simulating normal lung volumes. Other activities examine factors such as airway resistance and the effect of surfactant on lung function.

- Exercise 39B, *Chemical and Physical Processes of Digestion: Computer Simulation.* Turns the student's computer into a virtual chemistry lab where enzymes, reagents, and incubation conditions can be manipulated (in compressed time) to examine factors that affect enzyme activity.

• Exercise 41B, *Renal Physiology: The Function of the Nephron—Computer Simulation*. Simulates the function of a single nephron. Topics include factors influencing glomerular filtration, the effect of hormones on urine function, and glucose transport maximum.

• Exercise 47, *Acid-Base Balance: Computer Simulation*. Topics include respiratory and metabolic acidosis/alkalosis, and renal and respiratory compensation.

2. BIOPAC® Instructions
Instructions for the use of the BIOPAC® Student Lab System are included in the lab manual: Exercises 16A, 20, 21, 22, 31, 33A, 34A, and 37A.

3. PowerLab® Instructions
Instructions for use of the PowerLab® data acquisition and compilation system for Exercises 16A, 22, 31, 33A, 34A, and 37A can be found in Appendix B of the Instructor's Guide.

4. Intelitool® Instructions
Four physiological experiments (Exercises 16i, 22i, 31i, and 37i) using Intelitool® equipment are available in the *Instructor's Guide*. Instructors using Intelitool® equipment in their laboratory may copy these exercises for student handouts.

5. Videotapes
Human Anatomy & Physiology videotapes are available to qualified adopters. These excellent videotapes reinforce many of the concepts covered in this manual and will represent a valuable addition to any multimedia library.

Special Features Retained

Virtually all the special features appreciated by the adopters of the last edition are retained.

• The prologue, "Getting Started—What to Expect, The Scientific Method, and Metrics," explains the scientific method, the logical, practical, and reliable way of approaching and solving problems in the laboratory and reviews metric units and interconversions. A format for writing lab reports is also included.

• Each exercise begins with learning objectives.

• Key terms appear in boldface print, and each term is defined when introduced.

• Illustrations are large and of exceptional quality. Full-color photographs and drawings highlight, differentiate, and focus student attention on important structures.

• Body structures are studied from simple-to-complex levels, and physiological experiments allow ample opportunity for student observation and experimentation.

• The numerous physiological experiments for each organ system range from simple experiments that can be performed without specialized tools to more complex ones using laboratory equipment computers and instrumentation techniques.

• Tear-out laboratory review sheets, located toward the end of the manual, are designed to accompany each lab exercise. The review sheets provide space for recording and interpreting experimental results and require students to label diagrams and answer multiple-choice and short-answer questions.

• In addition to the figures, isolated animal organs such as the sheep heart and pig kidney are employed because of their exceptional similarity to human organs. If no major dissection animal is used in your course, the laboraory manual version entitled *Human Anatomy & Physiology, Main Version*, Seventh Edition, is recommended.

• The Histology Atlas has 63 color photomicrographs, and the edges of its pages are colored purple for quick location. The photomicrographs selected are those deemed most helpful to students because they correspond closely with slides typically viewed in the lab. Most such tissues are stained with hematoxylin and eosin (H & E), but a few depicted in the Histology Atlas are stained with differential stains to allow selected cell populations to be identified in a given tissue. Line drawings, corresponding to selected plates in the Histology Atlas, appear in appropriate places in the text and add to the utility of the atlas. The student can color these diagrams to replicate the stains of the slides; thus they provide a valuable learning aid.

• All exercises involving body fluids (blood, urine, saliva) incorporate current Centers for Disease Control (CDC) guidelines for handling human body fluids. Because it is important that nursing students, in particular, learn how to safely handle bloodstained articles, the human focus has been retained. However, the decision to allow testing of human (student) blood or to use animal blood in the laboratory is left to the discretion of the instructor in accordance with institutional guidelines. The CDC guidelines for handling body fluids are reinforced by the laboratory safety procedures described on the inside front cover of this text, in Exercise 29A: Blood, and in the *Instructor's Guide*. The inside cover can be photocopied and posted in the lab to help students become well versed in laboratory safety.

• Appendix B correlates some of the required anatomical laboratory observations with the corresponding sections of A.D.A.M.® Interactive Anatomy. Using A.D.A.M.® to complement the printed manual descriptions of anatomical structures provides an extremely useful study method for visually oriented students.

• Four logos alert students to special features or instructions. These include:

The dissection scissors icon appears at the beginning of activities that entail the dissection of isolated animal organs.

The homeostasis imbalance icon directs the student's attention to conditions representing a loss of homeostasis.

A safety icon notifies students that specific safety precautions must be observed when using certain equipment or conducting particular lab procedures. (For example, when working with ether, a hood is to be used, or when handling body fluids such as blood, urine, or saliva, gloves are to be worn.)

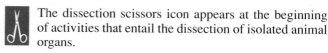 The A.D.A.M.® icon indicates where use of the A.D.A.M.® software would enhance the study and comprehension of laboratory topics.

Supplements

• The *Instructor's Guide* that accompanies all versions of the *Human Anatomy & Physiology Laboratory Manual* contains a wealth of information for those teaching this course.

Instructors can find help in planning the experiments, ordering equipment and supplies, anticipating pitfalls and problem areas, and locating audiovisual material. The probable in-class time required for each lab is indicated by an hour-glass icon. Other useful resources are the Trends in Instrumentation section that describes the latest laboratory equipment and technological teaching tools available and directions for using PowerLab data acquisition and compilation system and Intelitool® instrumentation. Additional supplements include the following videos, which are available free of charge to qualified adopters:

- *Selected Actions of Hormones and Other Chemical Messengers* videotape by Rose Leigh Vines and Juanita Barrena (0-8053-4155-2)

- *Human Musculature* videotape by Rose Leigh Vines and Allan Hinderstein (0-8053-0106-2)

- The *Human Cardiovascular System: The Heart* videotape by Rose Leigh Vines and Rosalee Carter, University Media Services, California State University, Sacramento (0-8053-4289-3)

- *The Human Cardiovascular System: The Blood Vessels* videotape by Rose Leigh Vines, University Media Services, California State University, Sacramento (0-8053-4297-4)

- The *Human Nervous System: Human Brain and Cranial Nerves* videotape by Rose Leigh Vines and Rosalee Carter, University Media Services, California State University, Sacramento (0-8053-4012-2)

- The *Human Nervous System: The Spinal Cord and Nerves* videotape by Rose Leigh Vines and Rosalee Carter, University Media Services, California State University, Sacramento (0-8053-4013-0)

- *The Human Respiratory System* videotape by Rose Leigh Vines and Ann Motekaitis (0-8053-4822-0)

- *The Human Digestive System* videotape by Rose Leigh Vines and Ann Motekaitis (0-8053-4823-9)

- *The Human Urinary System* videotape by Rose Leigh Vines and Ann Motekaitis (0-8053-4915-4)

- *The Human Reproductive Systems* videotape by Rose Leigh Vines and Ann Motekaitis (0-8053-4914-6)

- Student Video Series Vol. I (0-8053-4110-2)

- Student Video Series Vol. II (0-8053-6115-4)

A.D.A.M.® Software

Available for purchase from Benjamin Cummings to enhance student learning are the following:

A.D.A.M.® Interactive Anatomy Student Package, Third Edition, with Windows DVD
(ISBN 0-8053-7232-6)

A.D.A.M.® Interactive Anatomy Student Lab Guide, Third Edition
(ISBN 0-8053-5911-7)

Contact your Benjamin Cummings sales representative for more information, or visit our web site at www.aw-bc.com.

Acknowledgments

I wish to thank the following reviewers for their contributions to this edition: Bert Atsma, Union County College; Lynne Anderson, Meridian Community College; Maj Angarano, University of Texas at Arlington; Julie Baugh, Community College of Baltimore County Essex; Moges Bizuneh, Ivy Tech State College, Central Campus; Mike Gehner, Xavier University; Edwin Gines-Candelaria, Miami Dade Community College, Wolfson Campus; Ewa Gorski, Community College of Baltimore County at Catonsville; David Hall, Kirkwood Community College; Douglas Hirzel, Canada College; Ted Namm, University of Massachusetts Lowell; Janice Meeking, Mount Royal College; Elizabeth Murray, College of Mount St. Joseph; Julie Pilcher, University of Southern Indiana; Colin Pursche, Southern Cross University; Tim Roye, San Jacinto College South; Eugene Rutheny, Westchester Community College; Larry Seaman, Miami Dade Community College North Campus; Lori Smith, American River College; Charles Weitze, Mount Wachusett Community College.

My continued thanks to my colleagues and friends at Benjamin Cummings who worked with me in the production of this edition, especially Daryl Fox, Publisher; Serina Beauparlant, Executive Editor; and Mary Ann Murray, Project Editor, who steered the manuscript every inch of the way. Applause also to Barbara Yien, PhysioEx™ Project Editor, who managed the new version of PhysioEx™, and to Sarah Kaminker, Editorial Assistant, who provided expert assistance. Many thanks to Stacey Weinberger for her manufacturing expertise, and to Lauren Harp, for keeping the team informed on the needs of the market.

The excellence of PhysioEx™ reflects the expertise of Peter Zao, Timothy Stabler, and Greta Peterson. They generated the ideas behind the equipment graphics and envisioned the animations that would be needed. Credit also goes to the team at Cadre Design, including Ian Shakeshaft, David Hegarty, Robert Bleeker, and Chris Kemmett, for their expert programming and wonderful graphics produced in PhysioEx™.

Kudos to Wendy Earl and her production team. Sharon Montooth got the job done in jig time. Laura Southworth, Art Manager, oversaw the art program, Claudia Durrell acted as art and photo coordinator, and Diane Austin conducted photo research. Just-right interior and cover designs were created by tani hasegawa. Carla Breidenbach brought her lab experience to copyediting the text, and improved its presentation as a result.

Many thanks to Susan Baxley, who checked the currency of equipment included in the lab manual. Much appreciation for a job well done by J. Michael Reynolds, who contributed eight new BIOPAC® activities to select exercises in this edition, and to his assistant, Vorapong Nimnual, who carefully tested each activity for accuracy. Thanks also to Janice Meeking, Mount Royal College, and to Douglas Hirzel, Canada College, who consulted in their development. Finally, a tremendous dollop of gratitude to the team at BIOPAC®, especially to Jocelyn Kremer, who was extremely helpful in contributing her expertise to these activities.

Last but not least, thanks to Linda S. Kollett for her contribution to the lab manual. She came up with ideas for revising selected activities, illustrations, and photographs for the last edition and wrote the informative *Instructor's Guide* that accompanies this lab manual. We sincerely appreciate her efforts.

Preface to the Student

Hopefully, your laboratory experiences will be exciting times for you. Like any unfamiliar experience, it really helps if you know in advance what to expect and what will be expected of you.

Laboratory Activities

The A&P laboratory exercises in this manual are designed to help you gain a broad understanding of both anatomy and physiology. You can anticipate examining models, dissecting an animal, and using a microscope to look at tissue slides (anatomical approaches). You will also investigate chemical conditions or observe changes in both living and nonliving systems, manipulate variables in computer simulations, and conduct experiments that examine responses of living organisms to various stimuli (physiological approaches).

Because some students question the use of animals in the laboratory setting, their concerns need to be addressed. Be assured that the preserved organ specimens used in the anatomy and physiology labs are *not* harvested from animals raised specifically for dissection purposes. Organs that are of no use to the meat packing industry (such as the brain, heart, or lungs) are sent from slaughterhouses to biological supply houses for preparation.

Every effort is being made to find alternative methods that do not use living animals to study physiological concepts. For example, included in this edition is the PhysioEx™ CD-ROM. The ten simulation exercises on this CD allow you to convert a computer into a virtual laboratory. You will be able to manipulate variables to investigate physiological phenomena. Such computer-based simulations provide you with alternatives to the use of real animals.

There is little doubt that computer simulations offer certain advantages: (1) they allow you to experiment at length without time constraints of traditional experiments, and (2) they make it possible to investigate certain concepts that would be difficult or impossible to explore in traditional exercises. Yet, the main disadvantage of computer simulations is that the real-life aspects of experimentation are sacrificed. An animated frog muscle or heart on a computer screen is not really a substitute for observing the responses of actual muscle tissue. Consequently, living animal experiments remain an important part of the approach of this manual to the study of human anatomy and physiology. However, wherever possible, the minimum number of animals needed to demonstrate a particular point is used. Furthermore, some instructor-delivered and videotaped demonstrations of live animal experiments are suggested.

If you use living animals for experiments, you will be expected to handle them humanely. Inconsiderate treatment of laboratory animals will not be tolerated in your anatomy and physiology laboratory.

A.D.A.M.® Interactive Anatomy

If the A.D.A.M.® CD-ROM software is available for your use, Appendix B of the manual will help you link the various laboratory topics with specific frames of the A.D.A.M.® software to help you in your studies.

Icons/Visual Mnemonics

I have tried to make this manual very easy for you to use, and to this end two colored section heads and four different icons (visual mnemonics) are used throughout:

The *Dissection* head is blue-green and is accompanied by the **dissection scissors icon** at the beginning of activities that require you to dissect isolated animal organs.

The *Activity* head is red. Because most exercises have some explanatory background provided before the experiment(s), this visual cue alerts you that your lab involvement is imminent.

The **homeostasis imbalance icon** appears where a clinical disorder is described to indicate what happens when there is a structural abnormality or physiological malfunction (e.g., a loss of homeostasis).

The **A.D.A.M.® Interactive Anatomy icon** alerts you where the use of the A.D.A.M.® CD-ROM would enhance your laboratory experience.

The **safety icon** alerts you to special precautions that should be taken when handling lab equipment or conducting certain procedures. For example, it alerts you to use a ventilating hood when using volatile chemicals and signifies that you should take special measures to protect yourself when handling blood or other body fluids (e.g., saliva, urine).

Hints for Success in the Laboratory

With the possible exception of those who have photographic memories, most students can use helpful hints and guidelines to ensure that they have successful lab experiences.

1. Perhaps the best bit of advice is to attend all your scheduled labs and to participate in all the assigned exercises. Learning is an *active* process.

2. Scan the scheduled lab exercise and the questions in the review section in the back of the manual that pertain to it *before* going to lab.

3. Be on time. Most instructors explain what the lab is about, pitfalls to avoid, and the sequence or format to be followed at the beginning of the lab session. If you are late, not only will you miss this information, you will not endear yourself to the instructor.

4. Follow the instructions in the order in which they are given. If you do not understand a direction, ask for help.

5. Review your lab notes after completing the lab session to help you focus on and remember the important concepts.

6. Keep your work area clean and neat. Move books and coats out of the way. This reduces confusion and accidents.

7. Assume that all lab chemicals and equipment are sources of potential danger to you. Follow directions for equipment use and observe the laboratory safety guidelines provided inside the front cover of this manual.

8. Keep in mind the real value of the laboratory experience—a place for you to observe, manipulate, and experience hands-on activities that will dramatically enhance your understanding of the lecture presentations.

I really hope that you enjoy your A&P laboratories and that this lab manual makes learning about intricate structures and functions of the human body a fun and rewarding process. I'm always open to constructive criticism and suggestions for improvement in future editions. If you have any, please write to me.

Elaine N. Marieb
Anatomy and Physiology
Benjamin Cummings
1301 Sansome Street
San Francisco, CA 94111

The Microscope

With the invention of the microscope, biologists gained a valuable tool to observe and study structures (like cells) that are too small to be seen by the unaided eye. The information gained helped in establishing many of the theories basic to the understanding of biological sciences. This exercise will familiarize you with the workhorse of microscopes—the compound microscope—and provide you with the necessary instructions for its proper use.

Care and Structure of the Compound Microscope

The **compound microscope** is a precision instrument and should always be handled with care. *At all times you must observe the following rules for its transport, cleaning, use, and storage:*

- When transporting the microscope, hold it in an upright position with one hand on its arm and the other supporting its base. Avoid swinging the instrument during its transport and jarring the instrument when setting it down.
- Use only special grit-free lens paper to clean the lenses. Use a circular motion to wipe the lenses, and clean all lenses before and after use.
- Always begin the focusing process with the lowest-power objective lens in position, changing to the higher-power lenses as necessary.
- Use the coarse adjustment knob only with the lowest power lens.
- Always use a coverslip with temporary (wet mount) preparations.
- Before putting the microscope in the storage cabinet, remove the slide from the stage, rotate the lowest-power objective lens into position, wrap the cord neatly around the base, and replace the dust cover or return the microscope to the appropriate storage area.
- Never remove any parts from the microscope; inform your instructor of any mechanical problems that arise.

Objectives

1. To identify the parts of the microscope and list the function of each.
2. To describe and demonstrate the proper techniques for care of the microscope.
3. To define *total magnification* and *resolution*.
4. To demonstrate proper focusing technique.
5. To define *parfocal, field,* and *depth of field.*
6. To estimate the size of objects in a field.

Materials

- ❑ Compound microscope
- ❑ Millimeter ruler
- ❑ Prepared slides of the letter *e* or newsprint
- ❑ Immersion oil
- ❑ Lens paper
- ❑ Prepared slide of grid ruled in millimeters (grid slide)
- ❑ Prepared slide of three crossed colored threads
- ❑ Clean microscope slide and coverslip
- ❑ Toothpicks (flat-tipped)
- ❑ Physiologic saline in a dropper bottle
- ❑ Iodine or methylene blue stain (dilute) in a dropper bottle
- ❑ Filter paper or paper towels
- ❑ Beaker containing fresh 10% household bleach solution for wet mount disposal
- ❑ Disposable autoclave bag
- ❑ Prepared slide of cheek epithelial cells
- ❑ Stereomicroscope
- ❑ Coins

Note to the Instructor: The slides and coverslips used for viewing cheek cells are to be soaked for 2 hours (or longer) in 10% bleach solution and then drained. The slides and disposable autoclave bag (containing coverslips, lens paper, and used toothpicks) are to be autoclaved for 15 min at 121°C and 15 pounds pressure to ensure sterility. After autoclaving, the disposable autoclave bag may be discarded in any disposal facility and the slides and glassware washed with laboratory detergent and reprepared for use. These instructions apply as well to any bloodstained glassware or disposable items used in other experimental procedures.

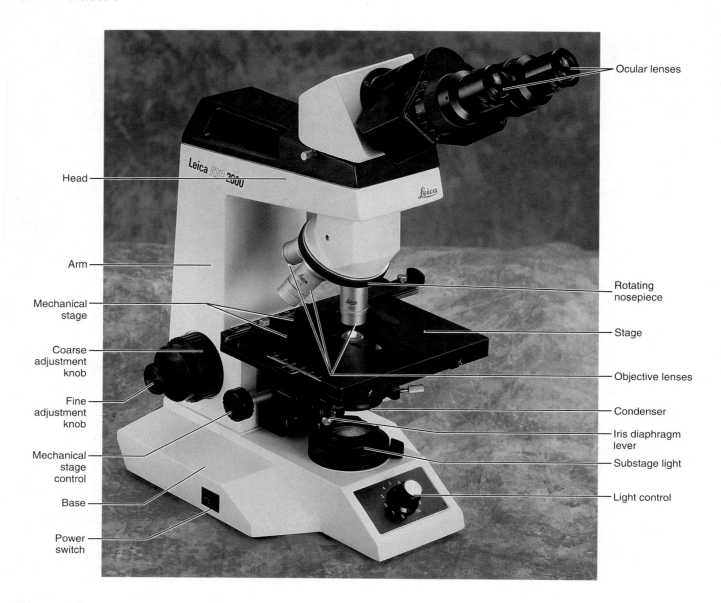

Labels on figure:
- Ocular lenses
- Head
- Arm
- Mechanical stage
- Coarse adjustment knob
- Fine adjustment knob
- Mechanical stage control
- Base
- Power switch
- Rotating nosepiece
- Stage
- Objective lenses
- Condenser
- Iris diaphragm lever
- Substage light
- Light control

Figure 3.1 Compound microscope and its parts.

Activity 1:
Identifying the Parts of a Microscope

1. Obtain a microscope and bring it to the laboratory bench. (Use the proper transport technique!)

• Record the number of your microscope in the summary chart on page 24.

Compare your microscope with the illustration in Figure 3.1 and identify the following microscope parts:

Base: Supports the microscope. (**Note:** Some microscopes are provided with an inclination joint, which allows the instrument to be tilted backward for viewing dry preparations.)

Substage light or **mirror**: Located in the base. In microscopes with a substage light source, the light passes directly upward through the microscope: light controls are located on the microscope base. If a mirror is used, light must be reflected from a separate free-standing lamp.

Stage: The platform the slide rests on while being viewed. The stage has a hole in it to permit light to pass through both it and the specimen. Some microscopes have a stage equipped with *spring clips;* others have a clamp-type *mechanical stage* as shown in Figure 3.1. Both hold the slide in position for viewing; in addition, the mechanical stage has two adjustable knobs that control precise movement of the specimen.

Condenser: Small substage lens that concentrates the light on the specimen. The condenser may have a height-adjustment knob that raises and lowers the condenser to vary light delivery. Generally, the best position for the condenser is close to the inferior surface of the stage.

Iris diaphragm lever: Arm attached to the base of the condenser that regulates the amount of light passing through the condenser. The iris diaphragm permits the best possible contrast when viewing the specimen.

Coarse adjustment knob: Used to focus on the specimen.

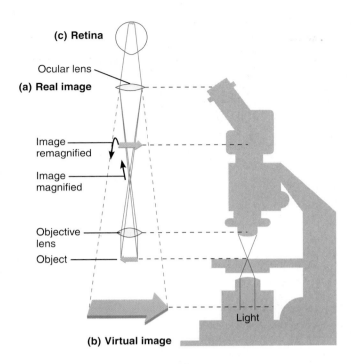

(c) Retina

Ocular lens

(a) Real image

Image remagnified

Image magnified

Objective lens

Object

Light

(b) Virtual image

Figure 3.2   Image formation in light microscopy. (a) Light passing through the objective lens forms a real image. **(b)** The real image serves as the object for the ocular lens, which remagnifies the image and forms the virtual image. **(c)** The virtual image passes through the lens of the eye and is focused on the retina.

Fine adjustment knob: Used for precise focusing once coarse focusing has been completed.

Head or **body tube:** Supports the objective lens system (which is mounted on a movable nosepiece) and the ocular lens or lenses.

Arm: Vertical portion of the microscope connecting the base and head.

Ocular (or *eyepiece*): Depending on the microscope, there are one or two lenses at the superior end of the head or body tube. Observations are made through the ocular(s). An ocular lens has a magnification of 10×. (It increases the apparent size of the object by ten times or ten diameters). If your microscope has a **pointer** (used to indicate a specific area of the viewed specimen), it is attached to one ocular and can be positioned by rotating the ocular lens.

Nosepiece: Rotating mechanism at the base of the head. Generally carries three or four objective lenses and permits sequential positioning of these lenses over the light beam passing through the hole in the stage. Use the nosepiece to change the objective lenses. Do not directly grab the lenses.

Objective lenses: Adjustable lens system that permits the use of a **scanning lens,** a **low-power lens,** a **high-power lens,** or an **oil immersion lens.** The objective lenses have different magnifying and resolving powers.

2.   Examine the objective lenses carefully; note their relative lengths and the numbers inscribed on their sides. On many microscopes, the scanning lens, with a magnification between 4× and 5×, is the shortest lens. If there is no scan-

ning lens, the low-power objective lens is the shortest and typically has a magnification of 10×. The high-power objective lens is of intermediate length and has a magnification range from 40× to 50×, depending on the microscope. The oil immersion objective lens is usually the longest of the objective lenses and has a magnifying power of 95× to 100×. Some microscopes lack the oil immersion lens.

•   Record the magnification of each objective lens of your microscope in the first row of the chart on page 24. Also, cross out the column relating to a lens that your microscope does not have. Plan on using the same microscope for all microscopic studies.

3.   Rotate the lowest-power objective lens until it clicks into position, and turn the coarse adjustment knob about 180 degrees. Notice how far the stage (or objective lens) travels during this adjustment. Move the fine adjustment knob 180 degrees, noting again the distance that the stage (or the objective lens) moves. ■

Magnification and Resolution

The microscope is an instrument of magnification. In the compound microscope, magnification is achieved through the interplay of two lenses—the ocular lens and the objective lens. The objective lens magnifies the specimen to produce a **real image** that is projected to the ocular. This real image is magnified by the ocular lens to produce the **virtual image** seen by your eye (Figure 3.2).

The **total magnification** (TM) of any specimen being viewed is equal to the power of the ocular lens multiplied by the power of the objective lens used. For example, if the ocular lens magnifies 10× and the objective lens being used magnifies 45×, the total magnification is 450× (or 10 × 45).

•   Determine the total magnification you may achieve with each of the objectives on your microscope, and record the figures on the second row of the chart.

The compound light microscope has certain limitations. Although the level of magnification is almost limitless, the **resolution** (or resolving power), that is, the ability to discriminate two close objects as separate, is not. The human eye can resolve objects about 100 μm apart, but the compound microscope has a resolution of 0.2 μm under ideal conditions. Objects closer than 0.2 μm are seen as a single fused image.

Resolving power is determined by the amount and physical properties of the visible light that enters the microscope. In general, the more light delivered to the objective lens, the greater the resolution. The size of the objective lens aperture (opening) decreases with increasing magnification, allowing less light to enter the objective. Thus, you will probably find it necessary to increase the light intensity at the higher magnifications.

Activity 2:
Viewing Objects Through the Microscope

1.   Obtain a millimeter ruler, a prepared slide of the letter *e* or newsprint, a dropper bottle of immersion oil, and some lens paper. Adjust the condenser to its highest position and switch on the light source of your microscope. (If the light

Summary Chart for Microscope # _____

	Scanning	Low power	High power	Oil immersion
Magnification of objective lens	_____ ×	_____ ×	_____ ×	_____ ×
Total magnification	_____ ×	_____ ×	_____ ×	_____ ×
Working distance	_____ mm	_____ mm	_____ mm	_____ mm
Detail observed Letter *e*				
Field size (diameter)	——mm ——μm	——mm ——μm	——mm ——μm	——mm ——μm

source is not built into the base, use the curved surface of the mirror to reflect the light up into the microscope.)

2. Secure the slide on the stage so that you can read the slide label and the letter *e* is centered over the light beam passing through the stage. If you are using a microscope with spring clips, make sure the slide is secured at both ends. If your microscope has a mechanical stage, open the jaws of its slide retainer (holder) by using the control lever (typically) located at the rear left corner of the mechanical stage. Insert the slide squarely within the confines of the slide retainer. Check to see that the slide is resting on the stage (and not on the mechanical stage frame) before releasing the control lever.

3. With your lowest-power (scanning or low-power) objective lens in position over the stage, use the coarse adjustment knob to bring the objective lens and stage as close together as possible.

4. Look through the ocular lens and adjust the light for comfort using the iris diaphragm. Now use the coarse adjustment knob to focus slowly away from the *e* until it is as clearly focused as possible. Complete the focusing with the fine adjustment knob.

5. Sketch the letter *e* in the circle on the summary chart above just as it appears in the **field** (the area you see through the microscope).

What is the total magnification? _____ ×

How far is the bottom of the objective lens from the specimen? In other words, what is the **working distance**? Use a millimeter ruler to make this measurement.

_____ mm

Record the TM detail observed and the working distance in the summary chart.

How has the apparent orientation of the *e* changed top to bottom, right to left, and so on?

_____

_____

6. Move the slide slowly away from you on the stage as you view it through the ocular lens. In what direction does the image move?

_____

Move the slide to the left. In what direction does the image move?

_____

At first this change in orientation may confuse you, but with practice you will learn to move the slide in the desired direction with no problem.

7. Today most good laboratory microscopes are **parfocal**; that is, the slide should be in focus (or nearly so) at the higher magnifications once you have properly focused. *Without touching the focusing knobs,* increase the magnification by rotating the next higher magnification lens (low-power or high-power) into position over the stage. Make sure it clicks into position. Using the fine adjustment only, sharpen the focus.* Note the decrease in working distance. As you can see, focusing with the coarse adjustment knob could drive the

*If you are unable to focus with a new lens, your microscope is not parfocal. Do not try to force the lens into position. Consult your instructor.

objective lens through the slide, breaking the slide and possibly damaging the lens. Sketch the letter *e* in the summary chart (page 24). What new details become clear?

_____

_____

What is the total magnification now? _____ ×

Record the TM, detail observed, and working distance in the summary chart.

As best you can, measure the distance between the objective and the slide (the working distance), and record it on the chart (page 24).

Is the image larger or smaller? _____

Approximately how much of the letter *e* is visible now?

_____

Is the field larger or smaller? _____

Why is it necessary to center your object (or the portion of the slide you wish to view) before changing to a higher power?

_____

_____

Move the iris diaphragm lever while observing the field. What happens?

_____

Is it more desirable to increase *or* decrease the light when changing to a higher magnification?

_____ Why? _____

_____

8. If you have just been using the low-power objective, repeat the steps given in direction 7 using the high-power objective lens.

Record the TM, detail observed, and working distance in the summary chart (page 24).

9. Without touching the focusing knob, rotate the high-power lens out of position so that the area of the slide over the opening in the stage is unobstructed. Place a drop of immersion oil over the *e* on the slide and rotate the oil immersion lens into position. Set the condenser at its highest point (closest to the stage), and open the diaphragm fully. Adjust the fine focus and fine-tune the light for the best possible resolution.

Note: If for some reason the specimen does not come into view after adjusting the fine focus, do not go back to the 40× lens to recenter. You do not want oil from the oil immersion lens to cloud the 40× lens. Turn the revolving nosepiece in the other direction to the low-power lens and recenter and

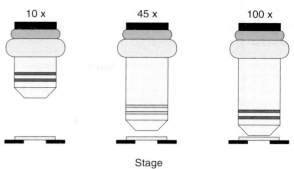

Figure 3.3 Relative working distances of the 10×, 45×, and 100× objectives.

refocus the object. Then move the immersion lens back into position, again avoiding the 40× lens.

Is the field again decreased in size? _____

What is the total magnification with the oil immersion lens?

_____ ×

Is the working distance less *or* greater than it was when the high-power lens was focused?

_____

Compare your observations on the relative working distances of the objective lenses with the illustration in Figure 3.3. Explain why it is desirable to begin the focusing process in the lowest power.

_____

_____

_____

10. Rotate the oil immersion lens slightly to the side and remove the slide. Clean the oil immersion lens carefully with lens paper, and then clean the slide in the same manner with a fresh piece of lens paper. ■

The Microscope Field

By this time you should know that the size of the microscope field decreases with increasing magnification. For future microscope work, it will be useful to determine the diameter of each of the microscope fields. This information will allow you to make a fairly accurate estimate of the size of the objects you view in any field. For example, if you have calculated the field diameter to be 4 mm and the object being observed extends across half this diameter, you can estimate the length of the object to be approximately 2 mm.

Table 3.1	Comparison of Metric Units of Length*	
Metric unit	**Abbreviation**	**Equivalent**
Meter	m	(about 39.3 in.)
Centimeter	cm	10^{-2} m
Millimeter	mm	10^{-3} m
Micrometer (or micron)	μm (μ)	10^{-6} m
Nanometer (or millimicrometer or millimicron)	nm (mμ)	10^{-9} m
Ångstrom	Å	10^{-10} m

*Refer to the "Getting Started" exercise (page xii) for tips on metric conversions.

Microscopic specimens are usually measured in micrometers and millimeters, both units of the metric system. You can get an idea of the relationship and meaning of these units from Table 3.1. A more detailed treatment appears in Appendix A.

Activity 3:
Estimating the Diameter of the Microscope Field

1. Obtain a grid slide (a slide prepared with graph paper ruled in millimeters). Each of the squares in the grid is 1 mm on each side. Use your lowest-power objective to bring the grid lines into focus.

2. Move the slide so that one grid line touches the edge of the field on one side, and then count the number of squares you can see across the diameter of the field. If you can see only part of a square, as in the accompanying diagram, estimate the part of a millimeter that the partial square represents.

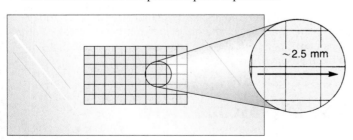

~2.5 mm

Record this figure in the appropriate space marked "field size" on the summary chart (page 24). (If you have been using the scanning lens, repeat the procedure with the low-power objective lens.)

Complete the chart by computing the approximate diameter of the high-power and oil immersion fields. The general formula for calculating the unknown field diameter is:

Diameter of field $A \times$ total magnification of field $A =$ diameter of field $B \times$ total magnification of field B

where A represents the known or measured field and B represents the unknown field. This can be simplified to

Diameter of field $B =$

$$\frac{\text{diameter of field } A \times \text{ total magnification of field } A}{\text{total magnification of field } B}$$

For example, if the diameter of the low-power field (field A) is 2 mm and the total magnification is 50×, you would compute the diameter of the high-power field (field B) with a total magnification of 100× as follows:

Field diameter $B = (2$ mm $\times 50)/100$
Field diameter $B = 1$ mm

3. Estimate the length (longest dimension) of the following microscopic objects. *Base your calculations on the field sizes you have determined for your microscope.*

a. Object seen in low-power field:

approximate length:

_____ mm

b. Object seen in high-power field:
approximate length:

_____ mm

or _____ μm

c. Object seen in oil immersion field:
approximate length:

_____ μm

4. If an object viewed with the oil immersion lens looked as it does in the field depicted just below, could you determine its approximate size from this view?

If not, then how could you determine it? _____

_____

_____

_____ ■

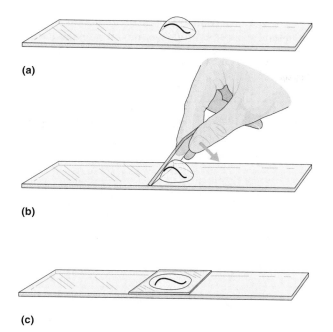

(a)

(b)

(c)

Figure 3.4 Procedure for preparation of a wet mount. (a) The object is placed in a drop of water (or saline) on a clean slide, **(b)** a coverslip is held at a 45° angle with the fingertips, and **(c)** it is lowered carefully over the water and the object.

Perceiving Depth

Any microscopic specimen has depth as well as length and width; it is rare indeed to view a tissue slide with just one layer of cells. Normally you can see two or three cell thicknesses. Therefore, it is important to learn how to determine relative depth with your microscope. In microscope work the **depth of field** (the depth of the specimen clearly in focus) is greater at lower magnifications.

Activity 4:
Perceiving Depth

1.   Obtain a slide with colored crossed threads. Focusing at low magnification, locate the point where the three threads cross each other.

2.   Use the iris diaphragm lever to greatly reduce the light, thus increasing the contrast. Focus down with the coarse adjustment until the threads are out of focus, then slowly focus upward again, noting which thread comes into clear focus first. (You will see two or even all three threads, so you must be very careful in determining which one first comes into clear focus.) Observe: As you rotate the adjustment knob forward (away from you), does the stage rise or fall? If the stage rises, then the first clearly focused thread is the top one; the last clearly focused thread is the bottom one.

If the stage falls, how is the order affected? _____

Record your observations, relative to which color of thread is uppermost, middle, or lowest:

Top thread _____

Middle thread _____

Bottom thread _____ ■

Viewing Cells Under the Microscope

There are various ways to prepare cells for viewing under a microscope. Cells and tissues can look very different with different stains and preparation techniques. One method of preparation is to mix the cells in physiologic saline (called a wet mount) and stain them with methylene blue stain.

   If you are not instructed to prepare your own wet mount, obtain a prepared slide of epithelial cells to make the observations in step 10 of Activity 5.

Activity 5:
Preparing and Observing a Wet Mount

1.   Obtain the following: a clean microscope slide and coverslip, two flat-tipped toothpicks, a dropper bottle of physiologic saline, a dropper bottle of iodine or methylene blue stain, and filter paper (or paper towels). Handle only your own slides throughout the procedure.

2.   Place a drop of physiologic saline in the center of the slide. Using the flat end of the toothpick, *gently* scrape the inner lining of your cheek. Transfer your cheek scrapings to the slide by agitating the end of the toothpick in the drop of saline (Figure 3.4a).

⚠ *Immediately* discard the used toothpick in the disposable autoclave bag provided at the supplies area.

3.   Add a tiny drop of the iodine or methylene blue stain to the preparation. (These epithelial cells are nearly transparent and thus difficult to see without the stain, which colors the nuclei of the cells and makes them look much darker than the cytoplasm.) Stir again.

⚠ *Immediately* discard the used toothpick in the disposable autoclave bag provided at the supplies area.

4.   Hold the coverslip with your fingertips so that its bottom edge touches one side of the fluid drop (Figure 3.4b), then *carefully* lower the coverslip onto the preparation (Figure 3.4c). *Do not just drop the coverslip,* or you will trap large air bubbles under it, which will obscure the cells. *A coverslip should always be used with a wet mount* to prevent soiling the lens if you should misfocus.

5.   Examine your preparation carefully. The coverslip should be closely apposed to the slide. If there is excess fluid around its edges, you will need to remove it. Obtain a piece of filter paper, fold it in half, and use the folded edge to absorb the excess fluid. (You may use a twist of paper towel as an alternative.)

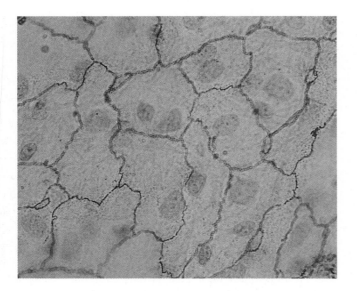

Figure 3.5 Epithelial cells of the cheek cavity (surface view, 400×).

⚠️ Before continuing, discard the filter paper in the disposable autoclave bag.

6.   Place the slide on the stage, and locate the cells in low power. You will probably want to dim the light with the iris diaphragm to provide more contrast for viewing the lightly stained cells. Furthermore, a wet mount will dry out quickly in bright light because a bright light source is hot.

7.   Cheek epithelial cells are very thin, six-sided cells. In the cheek, they provide a smooth, tilelike lining, as shown in Figure 3.5. Move to high power to examine the cells more closely.

8.   Make a sketch of the epithelial cells that you observe.

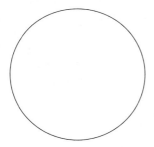

Use information on your summary chart (page 24) to estimate the diameter of cheek epithelial cells.

_____ mm

Why do *your* cheek cells look different than those illustrated in Figure 3.5? (Hint: what did you have to *do* to your cheek to obtain them?)

_____

_____

⚠️ 9. When you complete your observations of the wet mount, dispose of your wet mount preparation in the beaker of bleach solution, and put the coverslips in an autoclave bag.

10. Obtain a prepared slide of cheek epithelial cells, and view them under the microscope.

Estimate the diameter of one of these cheek epithelial cells using information from the summary chart (page 24).

_____ mm

Why are these cells more similar to those seen in Figure 3.5 and easier to measure than those of the wet mount?

_____

_____

11. Before leaving the laboratory, make sure all other materials are properly discarded or returned to the appropriate laboratory station. Clean the microscope lenses and put the dust cover on the microscope before you return it to the storage cabinet. ▪

The Stereomicroscope (Dissecting Microscope)

Occasionally biologists look at specimens too large to observe with the compound microscope but too small to observe easily with the unaided eye. The **stereomicroscope,** sometimes called a **dissecting microscope,** can be helpful in these situations. It works basically like a large magnifying glass.

Activity 6: Identifying the Parts of a Stereomicroscope

1.   Obtain a stereomicroscope, and put it on the lab bench.

2.   Using what you have learned about the compound microscope and Figure 3.6, identify the following parts:

Adjustment focus knob: Used to focus on the specimen.

Arm: Connects the base to the head of the microscope.

Base: Supports the microscope.

Oculars (or *eyepieces*): Magnify the images from the objective lenses.

Head (or **body tube**): Supports the ocular and objective lenses.

Light control: Switch that allows you to choose transmitted light, reflected light, or both.

Objective lenses: Adjustable lens system used to increase or decrease magnification.

Stage: Platform that holds the specimen.

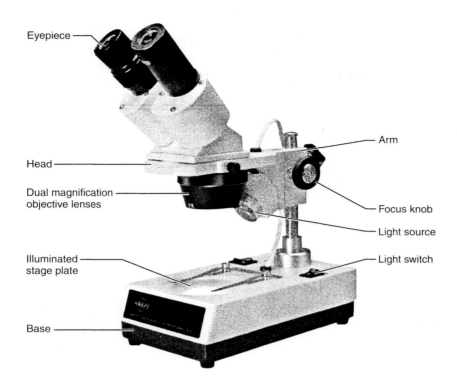

Eyepiece

Head

Dual magnification
objective lenses

Illuminated
stage plate

Base

Arm

Focus knob

Light source

Light switch

Figure 3.6 Stereomicroscope and its parts.

Substage light: Located in the base; sends light up through the specimen; the source of transmitted light.

Upper light source: Located above the stage; directs light onto the surface of the specimen; the source of reflected light. ■

Activity 7:
Using the Stereomicroscope

1.   Place a coin on the stage of the microscope. Turn on the light source, and adjust the oculars until you can see a single image of the specimen.

2.   Focus the microscope on the coin.

3.   Experiment with transmitted and reflected light until you get the best image. Which works best in this situation, the transmitted or reflected light?

_____

4.   Increase and decrease the magnification to familiarize yourself with the controls.

5.   Each coin has a small letter indicating where it was minted. See if you can determine the initial of the mint that produced your coin.

Where was your coin produced? _____

What is the total magnification you used? _____ ■

The Cell: Transport Mechanisms and Cell Permeability—Wet Lab

Objectives

1. To define *differential permeability; diffusion* (*simple diffusion* and *osmosis*); *isotonic, hypotonic,* and *hypertonic solutions; active transport processes*—*exocytosis, phagocytosis, pinocytosis,* and *solute pump*.

2. To describe the processes that account for the movement of substances across the plasma membrane and to indicate the driving force for each.

3. To determine which way substances will move passively through a differentially permeable membrane (given appropriate information on concentration differences).

Materials

Passive Processes

Brownian Movement, and Diffusion of Dye through Agar Gel

- Toothpicks (flat-tipped)
- Forceps
- Carmine dye crystals
- Clean microscope slides and coverslips
- Compound microscope
- Petri dish containing 12 ml of 1.5% agar-agar
- Millimeter-ruled graph paper
- Wax marking pencil
- 3.5% methylene blue solution (approximately 0.1 *M*) in dropper bottles
- 1.6% potassium permanganate solution (approximately 0.1 *M*) in dropper bottles
- Medicine dropper

Diffusion Through Nonliving Membranes

- Four dialysis sacs or small Hefty "alligator" sandwich bags
- Small funnel
- 25-ml graduated cylinder
- Wax marking pencil
- Fine twine or dialysis tubing clamps
- 250-ml beakers
- Distilled water

- 40% glucose solution
- 10% sodium chloride (NaCl) solution
- 40% sucrose solution colored with Congo red dye
- Laboratory balance
- Paper towels
- Hot plate and large beaker for hot water bath
- Benedict's solution in dropper bottle
- Silver nitrate ($AgNo_3$) in dropper bottle
- Test tubes in rack, test tube holder

Diffusion Through Living Membranes

- Yeast suspension in dropper bottle
- Congo red dye in dropper bottle
- Forceps
- 15-ml graduated cylinder
- Clean microscope slides and coverslips
- Glass stirring rod
- Test tubes in racks, test tube holder
- Compound microscope
- Vials of animal (mammalian) blood obtained from a biological supply house or veterinarian—at option of instructor
- Freshly prepared physiologic (mammalian) saline solution in dropper bottle
- 1.5% sodium chloride solution in dropper bottle
- Distilled water
- Filter paper
- Disposable gloves
- Basin and wash bottles containing 10% household bleach solution
- Disposable autoclave bag
- Paper towels

Diffusion demonstrations:

1: Diffusion of a dye through water

Prepared the morning of the laboratory session with setup time noted. Potassium permanganate crystals are placed in a 1,000-ml graduated cylinder, and distilled water is added slowly and with as little turbulence as possible to fill to the 1,000-ml mark.

2: Osmometer

Just before the laboratory begins, the broad end of a thistle tube is closed with a differentially permeable dialysis membrane, and the tube is secured to a ring stand. Molasses is added to approximately 5 cm above the thistle tube bulb and the bulb is immersed in a beaker of distilled water. At the beginning of the lab session, the level of the molasses in the tube is marked with a wax pencil.

Active processes:

❑ Culture of starved amoeba (*Amoeba proteus*)

❑ Medicine dropper

❑ Depression slide

❑ Coverslip (glass)

❑ *Tetrahymena pyriformis* culture

❑ Compound microscope

❑ Videotape showing phagocytosis (if available)

❑ Videotape viewing box

PhysioEx™ 6.0 Computer Simulation on page P–4

Note to the Instructor: See directions for handling wet mount preparations and disposable supplies on page 27, Exercise 3.

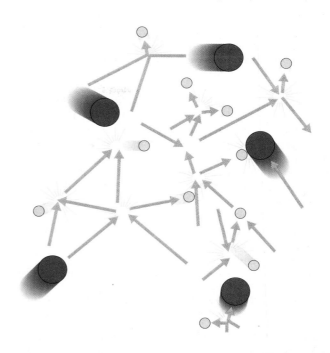

Figure 5A.1   Random movement and numerous collisions cause molecules to become evenly distributed. The small spheres represent water molecules; the large spheres represent glucose molecules.

Because of its molecular composition, the plasma membrane is selective about what passes through it. It allows nutrients to enter the cell but keeps out undesirable substances. By the same token, valuable cell proteins and other substances are kept within the cell, and excreta or wastes pass to the exterior. This property is known as **differential,** or **selective, permeability.** Transport through the plasma membrane occurs in two basic ways. In **passive processes,** concentration or pressure differences drive the movement. In **active processes,** the cell provides energy (ATP) to power the transport process.

Passive Processes

The two important passive processes of membrane transport are *diffusion* and *filtration.* Diffusion is an important transport process for every cell in the body. By contrast, filtration usually occurs only across capillary walls. Only diffusion will be considered here.

Recall that all molecules possess *kinetic energy* and are in constant motion. At a specific temperature, given molecules have about the same average kinetic energy. Since kinetic energy is directly related to both mass and velocity (KE − ½mv²), smaller molecules tend to move faster. As molecules move about randomly at high speeds, they collide and ricochet off one another, changing direction with each collision (Figure 5A.1).

Although individual molecules cannot be seen, the random motion of small particles suspended in water can be observed. This is called **Brownian movement.**

Activity 1:
Observing Brownian Movement

1.   Using the blunt end of a toothpick, add a small amount of water-insoluble carmine dye to a drop of water on a microscope slide and stir to mix.

2.   Add a coverslip and observe under high power (400×).

Does the movement appear to be directed or random?

_____

What effect would a change in temperature have on the speed of the movement?

_____ ■

Diffusion

When a **concentration gradient** (difference in concentration) exists, the net effect of this random molecular movement is that the molecules eventually become evenly distributed throughout the environment, that is, the process called diffusion occurs. Hence, **diffusion** is the movement of molecules from a region of their higher concentration to a region of their lower concentration. Its driving force is the kinetic energy of the molecules themselves.

There are many examples of diffusion in nonliving systems. For example, if a bottle of ether was uncorked at the front of the laboratory, very shortly thereafter you would be nodding as the ether molecules become distributed throughout the room. The ability to smell a friend's cologne shortly after he or she has entered the room is another example.

The diffusion of particles into and out of cells is modified by the plasma membrane, which constitutes a physical barrier. In general, molecules diffuse passively through the plasma membrane if they can dissolve in the lipid portion of the membrane (as in the case of CO_2 and O_2). The diffusion of solutes (particles dissolved in water) through a differentially permeable membrane is called **simple diffusion**. The diffusion of water through a differentially permeable membrane is called **osmosis**. Both simple diffusion and osmosis involve the movement of a substance from an area of its higher concentration to one of its lower concentration, that is, down its concentration gradient.

Facilitated diffusion occurs when certain molecules, for example glucose, combine with protein carrier molecules in the plasma membrane and move from one side of the membrane to the other down a concentration gradient. Passive movement of molecules through protein membrane channels is also facilitated diffusion. Like simple diffusion, facilitated diffusion does not require ATP.

Diffusion of Dye Through Agar Gel and Water

The relationship between molecular weight and the rate of diffusion can be examined easily by observing the diffusion of two different types of dye molecules through an agar gel. The dyes used in this experiment are methylene blue, which has a molecular weight of 320 and is deep blue in color, and potassium permanganate, a purple dye with a molecular weight of 158. Although the agar gel appears quite solid, it is primarily (98.5%) water and allows free movement of the dye molecules through it.

Activity 2:
Observing Diffusion of Dye Through Agar Gel

1.   Work with members of your group to formulate a hypothesis about the rates of diffusion of methylene blue and potassium permanganate through the agar gel. Justify your hypothesis.

2.   Obtain a petri dish containing agar gel, a piece of millimeter-ruled graph paper, a wax marking pencil, dropper bottles of methylene blue and potassium permanganate, and a medicine dropper. (See Figure 5A.2.)

3.   Using the wax marking pencil, draw a line on the bottom of the petri dish dividing it into two sections. Place the petri dish on the ruled graph paper.

4.   Create a well in the center of each section using the medicine dropper. To do this, squeeze the bulb of the medicine dropper, and push it down into the agar. Release the bulb as you slowly pull the dropper vertically out of the agar. This should remove an agar plug, leaving a well in the agar.

5.   Carefully fill one well with the methylene blue solution and the other well with the potassium permanganate solution.

Record the time. _____

6.   At 15-minute intervals, measure the distance the dye has diffused from each well. These observations should be continued for 1 hour, and the results recorded in the chart above.

Which dye diffused more rapidly? _____

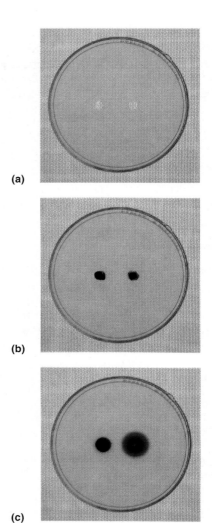

(a)

(b)

(c)

Figure 5A.2 Comparing diffusion rates. Agar-plated petri dish as it appears after the diffusion of 0.1 *M* methylene blue placed in one well and 0.1 *M* potassium permanganate placed in another.

Time (min)	Diffusion of methylene blue (mm)	Diffusion of potassium permanganate (mm)
15		
30		
45		
60		

What is the relationship between molecular weight and rate of molecular movement (diffusion)?

_____

Why did the dye molecules move? _____

_____

Compute the rate of diffusion of the potassium permanganate molecules in millimeters per minute (mm/min) and record.

_____ mm/min

Compute the rate of diffusion of the methylene blue molecules in mm/min and record.

_____ mm/min

7.   Prepare a lab report for these experiments. (See Getting Started: Writing a Lab Report, page xii.) ◼

Make a mental note to yourself to go to demonstration area 1 at the end of the laboratory session to observe the extent of diffusion of the potassium permanganate dye through water. At that time, follow the directions given next.

Activity 3:
Observing Diffusion of Dye Through Water

1.   Go to diffusion demonstration area 1, and observe the cylinder containing dye crystals and water set up at the beginning of the lab.

2.   Measure the number of millimeters the dye has diffused from the bottom of the graduated cylinder and record.

_____ mm

3.   Record the time the demonstration was set up and the time of your observation. Then compute the rate of the dye's diffusion through water and record below.

Time of setup _____

Time of observation _____

Rate of diffusion _____ mm/min

4.   Does the potassium permanganate dye move (diffuse) more rapidly through water or the agar gel? (Explain your answer.)

_____

_____   ◼

Activity 4:
Observing Diffusion Through Nonliving Membranes

The following experiment provides information on the diffusion of water and solutes through differentially permeable membranes, which may be applied to the study of transport mechanisms in living membrane-bound cells.

1.   Read through the experiments in this activity, and develop a hypothesis for each part.

2.   Obtain four dialysis sacs,* a small funnel, a 25-ml graduated cylinder, a wax marking pencil, fine twine or dialysis tubing clamps, and four beakers (250 ml). Number the beakers 1 to 4 with the wax marking pencil, and half fill all of them with distilled water except beaker 2, to which you should add 40% glucose solution.

3.   Prepare the dialysis sacs one at a time. Using the funnel, half fill each with 20 ml of the specified liquid (see below). Press out the air, fold over the open end of the sac, and tie it securely with fine twine or clamp it. Before proceeding to the next sac, rinse it under the tap, and quickly and carefully blot the sac dry by rolling it on a paper towel. Weigh it with a laboratory balance. Record the weight in the data chart on page 44, and then drop the sac into the corresponding beaker. Be sure the sac is completely covered by the beaker solution, adding more solution if necessary.

- Sac 1: 40% glucose solution. Weight: _____ g

- Sac 2: 40% glucose solution. Weight: _____ g

- Sac 3: 10% NaCl solution. Weight: _____ g

- Sac 4: Congo red dye in 40% sucrose solution. Weight:

    _____ g

Allow sacs to remain undisturbed in the beakers for 1 hour. (Use this time to continue with other experiments.)

4.   After an hour, get a beaker of water boiling on the hot plate. Obtain the supplies you will need to determine your experimental results: dropper bottles of Benedict's solution and silver nitrate solution, a test tube rack, four test tubes, and a test tube holder.

5.   Quickly and gently blot sac 1 dry and weigh it. (**Note:** Do not squeeze the sac during the blotting process.) Record in the data chart.

Weight of sac 1: _____ g

Has there been any change in weight? _____

Conclusions? _____

_____

_____

Place 5 ml of Benedict's solution in each of two test tubes. Put 4 ml of the beaker fluid into one test tube and 4 ml of the sac fluid into the other. Mark the tubes for identification and then place them in a beaker containing boiling water. Boil 2 minutes.

*Dialysis sacs are differentially permeable membranes with pores of a particular size. The selectivity of living membranes depends on more than just pore size, but using the dialysis sacs will allow you to examine selectivity due to this factor.

Data from Experiments on Diffusion Through Nonliving Membranes

Beaker	Contents of sac	Initial weight	Final weight	Weight change	Tests— beaker fluid	Tests—sac fluid
Beaker 1 ½ filled with distilled water	20 ml 40% glucose solution				Benedict's test:	Benedict's test:
Beaker 2 ½ filled with 40% glucose solution	20 ml 40% glucose solution					
Beaker 3 ½ filled with distilled water	20 ml 10% NaCl solution				AgNO₃ test:	
Beaker 4 ½ filled with distilled water	20 ml sucrose solution containing Congo red dye				Benedict's test:	

Cool slowly. If a green, yellow, or rusty red precipitate forms, the test is positive, meaning that glucose is present. If the solution remains the original blue color, the test is negative. Record results in the data chart.

Was glucose still present in the sac? _____

Was glucose present in the beaker? _____

Conclusions? _____

_____

_____

6.   Blot gently and weigh sac 2: _____ g
Record weight in the data chart.

Was there an *increase* or *decrease* in weight? _____

With 40% glucose in the sac and 40% glucose in the beaker, would you expect to see any net movement of water (osmosis) or of glucose molecules (simple diffusion)?

_____ Why or why not? _____

_____

7.   Blot gently and weigh sac 3: _____ g
Record weight in the data chart.

Was there any change in weight? _____

Conclusions? _____

_____

Take a 5-ml sample of beaker 3 solution and put it in a clean test tube. Add a drop of silver nitrate. The appearance of a white precipitate or cloudiness indicates the presence of silver chloride (AgCl), which is formed by the reaction of AgNO₃ with NaCl (sodium chloride). Record results in the data chart.

Results? _____

Conclusions? _____

8.   Blot gently and weigh sac 4: _____ g
Record weight in the data chart.

Was there any change in weight? _____

Did the beaker water turn pink? _____

Conclusions? _____

_____

Take a 1-ml sample of beaker 4 solution and put the test tube in boiling water in a hot water bath. Add 5 drops of Benedict's solution to the tube and boil for 5 minutes. The presence of glucose (one of the hydrolysis products of sucrose) in the bath water is indicated by the presence of a green, yellow, or rusty colored precipitate.

Did sucrose diffuse from the sac into the bath water?

_____ Explain your conclusion. _____

_____

9.   In which of the test situations did net osmosis occur?

_____

In which of the test situations did net simple diffusion occur?

_____

What conclusions can you make about the relative size of glucose, sucrose, Congo red dye, NaCl, and water molecules?

_____

_____

_____

With what cell structure can the dialysis sac be compared?

_____

10. Prepare a lab report for the experiment. (See Getting Started: Writing a Lab Report, page xii.) Be sure to include in your discussion the answers to the questions proposed in this activity.

Activity 5:
Observing Osmometer Results

Before leaving the laboratory, observe demonstration 2, the *osmometer demonstration* set up before the laboratory session to follow the movement of water through a membrane (osmosis). Measure the distance the water column has moved during the laboratory period and record below. (The position of the meniscus in the thistle tube at the beginning of the laboratory period is marked with wax pencil.)

Distance the meniscus has moved: _____ mm ■

Activity 6:
Investigating Diffusion Through Living Membranes

To examine permeability properties of plasma membranes, conduct the following two experiments.

Experiment 1:
1.   Go to the supply area and obtain a dropper bottle of yeast suspension, a dropper bottle of Congo red dye, a 15-ml graduated cylinder, three slides and coverslips, a glass stirring rod, two test tubes and a test tube rack, and bring them to your laboratory bench.

2.   Make a wet mount by adding a drop of the yeast suspension to a slide and observe the cells under high power. Draw a few cells that record your observations below.

3.   Prepare two test tubes by placing 3 ml of the yeast suspension in each. Boil one of the tubes in a hot water bath for 15 seconds.

4.   Remove the boiled tube from the water bath. Add eight drops of Congo red dye to both the boiled and the unboiled preparations. Stir each tube with the glass stirring rod.

5.   Prepare a wet mount from each tube and observe the yeast cells in each preparation. Respond to the following questions, based on your observations.

Was the dye accepted by the unboiled cells? _____

By the boiled cells? _____ What are your conclusions about the selectivity of living and nonliving (boiled) cell

membranes? _____

_____

Experiment 2:
Now you will conduct a microscopic study of red blood cells suspended in solutions of varying tonicities. The objective is to determine if these solutions have any effect on cell shape by promoting net osmosis.

1.   The following supplies should be available at your laboratory bench to conduct this experimental series: two clean slides and coverslips, a vial of animal blood, a medicine dropper, physiologic saline, 1.5% sodium chloride solution, distilled water, filter paper, and disposable gloves.

⚠   Wear disposable gloves at all times when handling blood (steps 2–5).

2.   Place a very small drop of physiologic saline on a slide. Using the medicine dropper, add a small drop of animal blood to the saline on the slide. Tilt the slide to mix, cover with a coverslip, and immediately examine the preparation under the high-power lens. Notice that the red blood cells retain their normal smooth disclike shape (see Figure 5A.3a). This is because the physiologic saline is **isotonic** to the cells. That is, it contains a concentration of nonpenetrating solutes (e.g., proteins and some ions) equal to that in the cells (same solute-solvent ratio). Consequently, the cells neither gain nor lose water by osmosis. Set this slide aside.

3.   Prepare another wet mount of animal blood, but this time use 1.5% sodium chloride (saline) solution as the suspending medium. After 5 minutes, carefully observe the red blood cells under high power. What is happening to the normally smooth disc shape of the red blood cells?

_____

_____

_____

This crinkling-up process, called **crenation**, is due to the fact that the 1.5% sodium chloride solution is slightly hypertonic to the cytosol of the red blood cell. A **hypertonic** solution contains more nonpenetrating solutes (thus less water) than are present in the cell. Under these circumstances, water

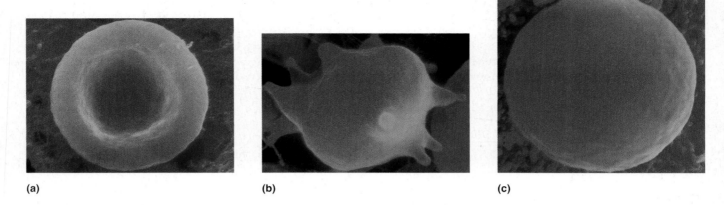

(a)   (b)   (c)

Figure 5A.3   Influence of isotonic, hypertonic, and hypotonic solutions on red blood cells. (a) Red blood cells suspended in an isotonic solution, where the cells retain their normal size and shape. **(b)** Red blood cells suspended in hypertonic solution. As the cells lose water to the external environment, they shrink and become prickly, a phenomenon called crenation. **(c)** Red blood cells suspended in a hypotonic solution. Notice their spherical bloated shape, a result of excessive water intake.

tends to leave the cells by osmosis. Compare your observations to Figure 5A.3b.

4.   Add a drop of distilled water to the edge of the coverslip. Fold a piece of filter paper in half and place its folded edge at the opposite edge of the coverslip; it will absorb the saline solution and draw the distilled water across the cells. Watch the red blood cells as they float across the field. After about 5 minutes have passed, describe the change in their appearance.

_____

_____

Distilled water contains *no* solutes (it is 100% water). Distilled water and *very* dilute solutions (that is, those containing less than 0.9% nonpenetrating solutes) are **hypotonic** to the cell. In a hypotonic solution, the red blood cells first "plump up" (Figure 5A.3c), but then they suddenly start to disappear. The red blood cells burst as the water floods into them, leaving "ghosts" in their wake—a phenomenon called **hemolysis.**

⚠️ 5. Place the blood-soiled slides and test tube in the bleach-containing basin. Put the coverslips you used into the disposable autoclave bag. Obtain a wash (squirt) bottle containing 10% bleach solution, and squirt the bleach liberally over the bench area where blood was handled. Wipe the bench down with a paper towel wet with the bleach solution and allow it to dry before continuing. Remove gloves, and discard in the autoclave bag.

6.   Prepare a lab report for experiments 1 and 2. (See Getting Started: Writing a Lab Report, page xii.) Be sure to include in the discussion answers to the questions proposed in this activity. ■

Filtration

Filtration is the process by which water and solutes are forced through a membrane from an area of higher hydrostatic (fluid) pressure into an area of lower hydrostatic pressure. Like diffusion, it is a passive process. For example, fluids and

solutes filter out of the capillaries in the kidneys into the kidney tubules because the blood pressure in the capillaries is greater than the fluid pressure in the tubules. Filtration is not a selective process. The amount of filtrate (fluids and solutes) formed depends almost entirely on the pressure gradient (difference in pressure on the two sides of the membrane) and on the size of the membrane pores. We will be studying filtration in conjunction with urinary system physiology.

Active Processes

Whenever a cell uses the bond energy of ATP to move substances across its boundaries, the process is an *active process.* Substances moved by active means are generally unable to pass by diffusion. They may not be lipid soluble; they may be too large to pass through the membrane channels; or they may have to move against rather than with a concentration gradient. There are two types of active processes: **active transport** and **vesicular transport.**

Active Transport

Active transport requires carrier proteins that combine specifically with the transported substance, which is similar to enzyme-substrate interactions described in your text. Active transport may be primary, driven directly by hydrolysis of ATP, or secondary, acting with a primary transport system as a coupled system. In most cases the substances move against concentration or electrochemical gradients or both. Some of the substances that are moved into the cells by such carriers, commonly called **solute pumps,** are amino acids and some sugars. Both solutes are lipid insoluble and too large to pass through the membrane channels but are necessary for cell life. On the other hand, sodium ions (Na^+) are ejected from cells by active transport. There is more Na^+ outside the cell than inside, so the Na^+ tends to remain in the cell unless actively transported out. Active transport, using solute pumps, is difficult to study in an A&P laboratory and will not be considered further here.

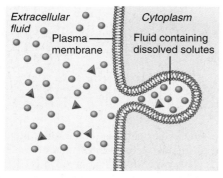

(a) Pinocytosis

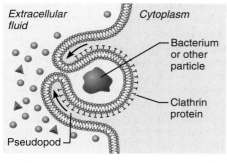

(b) Phagocytosis

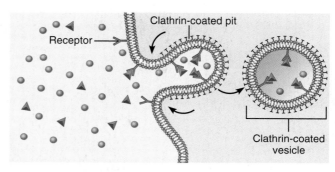

(c) Receptor-mediated endocytosis

Figure 5A.4   Three types of endocytosis.
(a) In pinocytosis, dissolved proteins gather on the external surface of the plasma membrane, causing the membrane to invaginate and to incorporate a droplet of the fluid. **(b)** In phagocytosis, cellular extensions (pseudopodia) flow around the external particle and enclose it within a vacuole. **(c)** In receptor-mediated endocytosis, plasma membrane proteins bind only with certain substances.

Vesicular Transport

Large particles and molecules are transported across the membrane by vesicular transport. Movement may be into the cell (**endocytosis**) or out of the cell (**exocytosis**).

Most types of endocytosis utilize clathrin protein-coated pits to engulf the substance to be carried into the cell. Once engulfed, the substance is transported in the cell within a clathrin-coated vesicle. In **pinocytosis,** also called **fluid-phase endocytosis,** the cell membrane sinks beneath the material to form a small vesicle, which then pinches off into the cell interior (see Figure 5A.4a). Pinocytosis is most common for taking in liquids containing protein or fat.

In **phagocytosis** (cell eating), parts of the plasma membrane and cytoplasm expand and flow around a relatively large or solid material (for example, bacteria or cell debris) and engulf it (Figure 5A.4b). The membranous sac thus formed, called a *phagosome,* is then fused with a lysosome and its contents are digested. In the human body, phagocytic cells are mainly found among the white blood cells and macrophages that act as scavengers and help protect the body from disease-causing microorganisms and cancer cells.

A more selective type of endocytosis uses plasma membrane receptors and is called **receptor-mediated endocytosis** (Figure 5A.4c). As opposed to the phagocytosis used by the body's scavenger cells (see below), this type of endocytosis is exquisitely selective and is used primarily for cellular uptake of specific molecules, such as cholesterol, iron, and some hormones, and for transfer of substances from one side of the cell to the other.

Activity 7:
Observing Phagocytosis in Amoeba

1.   Obtain a drop of starved *Amoeba proteus* culture and place it on a coverslip. Add a drop of *Tetrahymena pyriformis* culture (an amoeba "meal") to the amoeba-containing drop, and then quickly but gently invert the coverslip over the well of a depression slide.

2.   Locate an amoeba under low power. Keep the light as dim as possible; otherwise the amoeba will "ball up" and begin to disintegrate.

3.   Watch as the amoeba phagocytizes the *Tetrahymena* by forming pseudopods that engulf it. As mentioned, in unicellular organisms like the amoeba, phagocytosis is an important food-getting mechanism, but in higher organisms, it is more important as a protective device.

4.   Return all equipment to the appropriate supply areas and rinse glassware used. ■

Note: If you have not already done so, complete Activity 3 ("Observing Diffusion of Dye Through Water," page 43), and Activity 5 ("Observing Osmometer Results," page 45).

Objectives

1. To name the four major types of tissues in the human body and the major subcategories of each.

2. To identify the tissue subcategories through microscopic inspection or inspection of an appropriate diagram or projected slide.

3. To state the location of the various tissue types in the body.

4. To list the general functions and structural characteristics of each of the four major tissue types.

Materials

❑ Compound microscope

❑ Immersion oil

❑ Prepared slides of simple squamous, simple cuboidal, simple columnar, stratified squamous (nonkeratinized), stratified cuboidal, stratified columnar, pseudostratified ciliated columnar, and transitional epithelium

❑ Prepared slides of mesenchyme; of adipose, areolar, reticular, and dense (both regular and irregular connective tissues); of hyaline and elastic cartilage; of fibrocartilage; of bone (x.s.); and of blood

❑ Prepared slides of skeletal, cardiac, and smooth muscle (l.s.)

❑ Prepared slide of nervous tissue (spinal cord smear)

PhysioEx™ 6.0 Computer Simulation on page P-15

Exercise 4 describes cells as the building blocks of life and the all-inclusive functional units of unicellular organisms. However, in higher organisms, cells do not usually operate as isolated, independent entities. In humans and other multicellular organisms, cells depend on one another and cooperate to maintain homeostasis in the body.

With a few exceptions (parthenogenetic organisms), even the most complex animal starts out as a single cell, the fertilized egg, which divides almost endlessly. The trillions of cells that result become specialized for a particular function; some become supportive bone, others the transparent lens of the eye, still others skin cells, and so on. Thus a division of labor exists, with certain groups of cells highly specialized to perform functions that benefit the organism as a whole. Cell specialization carries with it certain hazards, because when a small specific group of cells is indispensable, any inability to function on its part can paralyze or destroy the entire body.

Groups of cells that are similar in structure and function are called **tissues.** The four primary tissue types—epithelium, connective tissue, nervous tissue, and muscle—have distinctive structures, patterns, and functions. The four primary tissues are further divided into subcategories, as described shortly.

To perform specific body functions, the tissues are organized into **organs** such as the heart, kidneys, and lungs. Most organs contain several representatives of the primary tissues, and the arrangement of these tissues determines the organ's structure and function. Thus **histology,** the study of tissues, complements a study of gross anatomy and provides the structural basis for a study of organ physiology.

The main objective of this exercise is to familiarize you with the major similarities and dissimilarities of the primary tissues, so that when the tissue composition of an organ is described, you will be able to more easily understand (and perhaps even predict) the organ's major function. Because epithelium and some types of connective tissue will not be considered again, they are emphasized more than muscle, nervous tissue, and bone (a connective tissue), which are covered in more depth in later exercises.

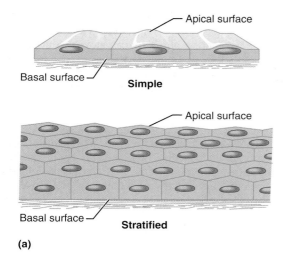

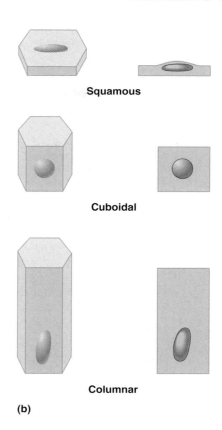

Figure 6.1 Classification of epithelia. (a) Classification on the basis of arrangement (relative number of layers). **(b)** Classification on the basis of cell shape. For each category, a whole cell is shown on the left and a longitudinal section is shown on the right.

Epithelial Tissue

Epithelial tissue, or **epithelium,** covers surfaces. For example, epithelium covers the external body surface (as the epidermis), lines its cavities and tubules, and generally marks off our "insides" from our outsides. Since the various endocrine (hormone-producing) and exocrine glands of the body almost invariably develop from epithelial membranes, glands, too, are logically classed as epithelium.

Epithelial functions include protection, absorption, filtration, excretion, secretion, and sensory reception. For example, the epithelium covering the body surface protects against bacterial invasion and chemical damage; that lining the respiratory tract is ciliated to sweep dust and other foreign particles away from the lungs. Epithelium specialized to absorb substances lines the stomach and small intestine. In the kidney tubules, the epithelium absorbs, secretes, and filters. Secretion is a specialty of the glands.

The following characteristics distinguish epithelial tissues from other types:

• Cellularity and specialized contacts. Cells fit closely together to form membranes, or sheets of cells, and are bound together by specialized junctions.

• Polarity. The membranes always have one free surface, called the *apical surface,* and typically that surface is significantly different from the *basal surface.*

• Supported by connective tissue. The cells are attached to and supported by an adhesive **basement membrane,** which is an amorphous material secreted partly by the epithelial

cells (*basal lamina*) and connective tissue cells (*reticular lamina*) that lie adjacent to each other.

• Avascularity. Epithelial tissues have no blood supply of their own (are avascular), but instead depend on diffusion of nutrients from the underlying connective tissue. (Glandular epithelia, however, are very vascular.)

• Regeneration. If well nourished, epithelial cells can easily regenerate themselves. This is an important characteristic because many epithelia are subjected to a good deal of friction.

The covering and lining epithelia are classified according to two criteria—arrangement or relative number of layers and cell shape (Figure 6.1). On the basis of arrangement, there are **simple** epithelia, consisting of one layer of cells attached to the basement membrane, and **stratified** epithelia, consisting of two or more layers of cells. The general types based on shape are **squamous** (scalelike), **cuboidal** (cubelike), and **columnar** (column-shaped) epithelial cells. The terms denoting shape and arrangement of the epithelial cells are combined to describe the epithelium fully. *Stratified epithelia are named according to the cells at the apical surface of the epithelial membrane,* not those resting on the basement membrane.

There are, in addition, two less easily categorized types of epithelia. **Pseudostratified epithelium** is actually a simple columnar epithelium (one layer of cells), but because its cells vary in height and the nuclei lie at different levels above the basement membrane, it gives the false appearance of being stratified. This epithelium is often ciliated. **Transitional**

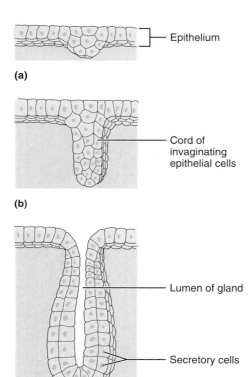

(a)

—— Epithelium

(b)

—— Cord of
invaginating
epithelial cells

—— Lumen of gland

—— Secretory cells

(c) Exocrine gland

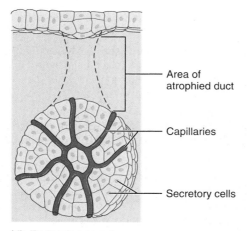

—— Area of
atrophied duct

—— Capillaries

—— Secretory cells

(d) Endocrine gland

Figure 6.2 Formation of endocrine and exocrine glands from epithelial sheets.
(a) Epithelial cells grow and push into the underlying tissue. **(b)** A cord of epithelial cells forms. **(c)** In an exocrine gland, a lumen (cavity) forms. The inner cells form the duct, the outer cells produce the secretion. **(d)** In a forming endocrine gland, the connecting duct cells atrophy, leaving the secretory cells with no connection to the epithelial surface. However, they do become heavily invested with blood and lymphatic vessels that receive the secretions.

epithelium is a rather peculiar stratified squamous epithelium formed of rounded, or "plump," cells with the ability to slide over one another to allow the organ to be stretched. Transitional epithelium is found only in urinary system organs subjected to periodic distension, such as the bladder. The superficial cells are flattened (like true squamous cells) when the organ is distended and rounded when the organ is empty.

Epithelial cells forming glands are highly specialized to remove materials from the blood and to manufacture them into new materials, which they then secrete. There are two types of glands, as shown in Figure 6.2. **Endocrine glands** lose their surface connection (duct) as they develop; thus they are referred to as ductless glands. Their secretions (all hormones) are extruded directly into the blood or the lymphatic vessels that weave through the glands. **Exocrine glands** retain their ducts, and their secretions empty through these ducts to an epithelial surface. The exocrine glands—including the sweat and oil glands, liver, and pancreas—are both external and internal; they will be discussed in conjunction with the organ systems to which their products are functionally related.

The most common types of epithelia, their characteristic locations in the body, and their functions are described in Figure 6.3.

Activity 1:
Examining Epithelial Tissue Under the Microscope

Obtain slides of simple squamous, simple cuboidal, simple columnar, stratified squamous (nonkeratinized), pseudostratified ciliated columnar, stratified cuboidal, stratified columnar, and transitional epithelia. Examine each carefully, and notice how the epithelial cells fit closely together to form intact sheets of cells, a necessity for a tissue that forms linings or covering membranes. Scan each epithelial type for modifications for specific functions, such as cilia (motile cell projections that help to move substances along the cell surface), and microvilli, which increase the surface area for absorption. Also be alert for goblet cells, which secrete lubricating mucus (see Plate 1 of the Histology Atlas). Compare your observations with the descriptions and photomicrographs in Figure 6.3.

While working, check the questions in the laboratory review section for this exercise. A number of the questions there refer to some of the observations you are asked to make during your microscopic study. ■

Text continues on page 55

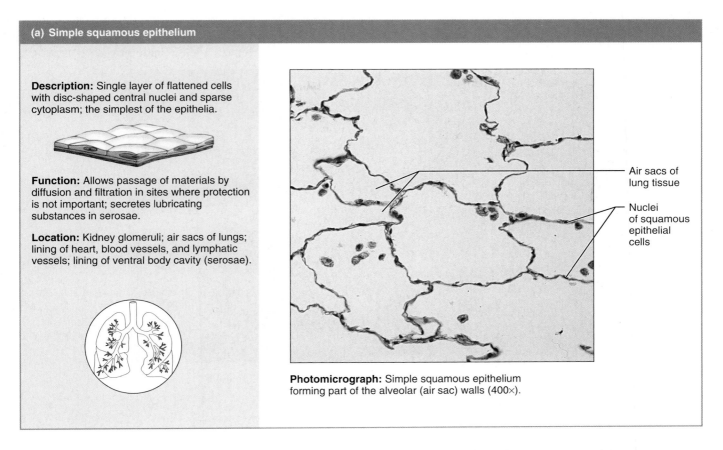

(a) Simple squamous epithelium

Description: Single layer of flattened cells with disc-shaped central nuclei and sparse cytoplasm; the simplest of the epithelia.

Function: Allows passage of materials by diffusion and filtration in sites where protection is not important; secretes lubricating substances in serosae.

Location: Kidney glomeruli; air sacs of lungs; lining of heart, blood vessels, and lymphatic vessels; lining of ventral body cavity (serosae).

Air sacs of lung tissue

Nuclei of squamous epithelial cells

Photomicrograph: Simple squamous epithelium forming part of the alveolar (air sac) walls (400×).

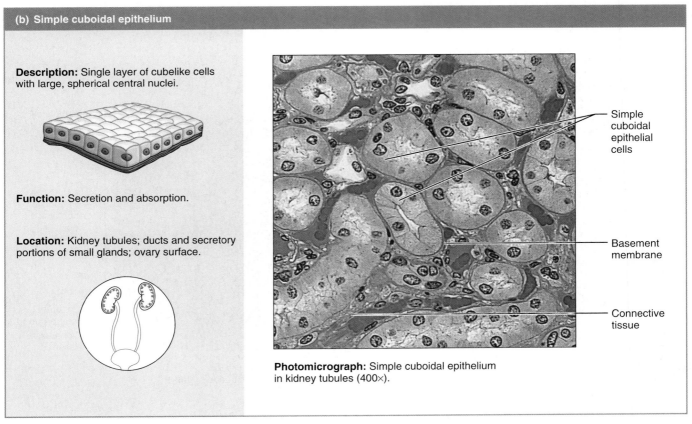

(b) Simple cuboidal epithelium

Description: Single layer of cubelike cells with large, spherical central nuclei.

Function: Secretion and absorption.

Location: Kidney tubules; ducts and secretory portions of small glands; ovary surface.

Simple cuboidal epithelial cells

Basement membrane

Connective tissue

Photomicrograph: Simple cuboidal epithelium in kidney tubules (400×).

Figure 6.3 Epithelial tissues. Simple epithelia **(a** and **b).**

(c) Simple columnar epithelium

Description: Single layer of tall cells with *round* to *oval* nuclei; some cells bear cilia; layer may contain mucus-secreting unicellular glands (goblet cells).

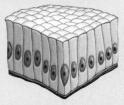

Function: Absorption; secretion of mucus, enzymes, and other substances; ciliated type propels mucus (or reproductive cells) by ciliary action.

Location: Nonciliated type lines most of the digestive tract (stomach to anal canal), gallbladder, and excretory ducts of some glands; ciliated variety lines small bronchi, uterine tubes, and some regions of the uterus.

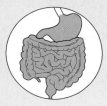

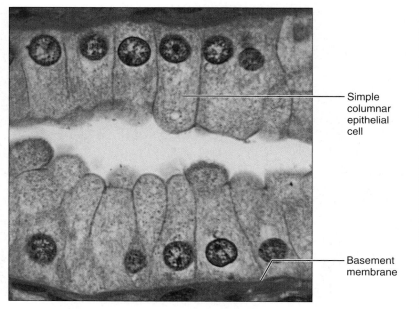

Simple columnar epithelial cell

Basement membrane

Photomicrograph: Simple columnar epithelium of the stomach mucosa (1300×).

(d) Pseudostratified columnar epithelium

Description: Single layer of cells of differing heights, some not reaching the free surface; nuclei seen at different levels; may contain goblet cells and bear cilia.

Function: Secretion, particularly of mucus; propulsion of mucus by ciliary action.

Location: Nonciliated type in male's sperm-carrying ducts and ducts of large glands; ciliated variety lines the trachea, most of the upper respiratory tract.

Trachea

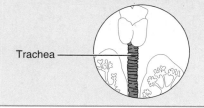

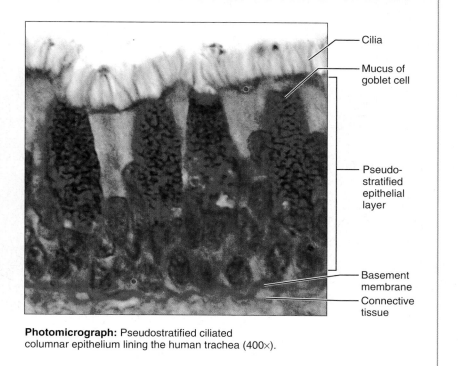

Cilia

Mucus of goblet cell

Pseudo-stratified epithelial layer

Basement membrane

Connective tissue

Photomicrograph: Pseudostratified ciliated columnar epithelium lining the human trachea (400×).

Figure 6.3 (*continued*) Epithelial tissues. Simple epithelia (**c** and **d**).

(e) Stratified squamous epithelium

Description: Thick membrane composed of several cell layers; basal cells are cuboidal or columnar and metabolically active; surface cells are flattened (squamous); in the keratinized type, the surface cells are full of keratin and dead; basal cells are active in mitosis and produce the cells of the more superficial layers.

Function: Protects underlying tissues in areas subjected to abrasion.

Location: Nonkeratinized type forms the moist linings of the esophagus, mouth, and vagina; keratinized variety forms the epidermis of the skin, a dry membrane.

Nuclei

Stratified squamous epithelium

Basement membrane

Connective tissue

Photomicrograph: Stratified squamous epithelium lining of the esophagus (300×).

(f) Stratified cuboidal epithelium

Description: Generally two layers of cubelike cells.

Function: Protection

Location: Largest ducts of sweat glands, mammary glands, and salivary glands.

Basement membrane

Cuboidal epithelial cells

Duct lumen

Photomicrograph: Stratified cuboidal epithelium forming a salivary gland duct.

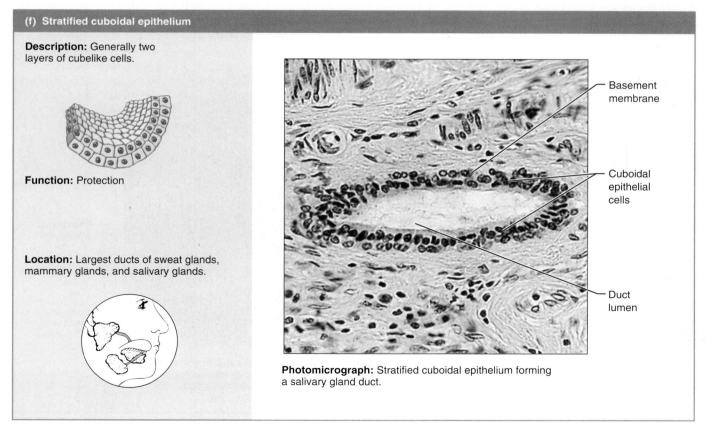

Figure 6.3 (*continued*)   Stratified epithelia (**e** and **f**).

(g) Stratified columnar epithelium

Description: Several cell layers; basal cells usually cuboidal; superficial cells elongated and columnar.

Function: Protection; secretion.

Location: Rare in the body; small amounts in male urethra and in large ducts of some glands.

Urethra

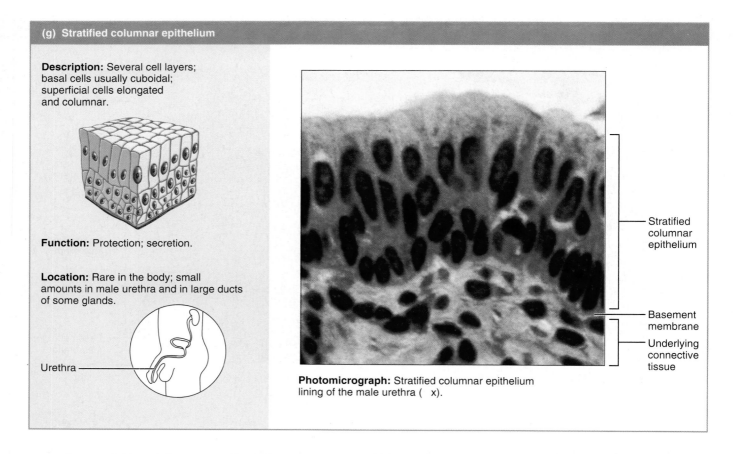

Stratified columnar epithelium

Basement membrane

Underlying connective tissue

Photomicrograph: Stratified columnar epithelium lining of the male urethra (x).

(h) Transitional epithelium

Description: Resembles both stratified squamous and stratified cuboidal; basal cells cuboidal or columnar; surface cells dome shaped or squamouslike, depending on degree of organ stretch.

Function: Stretches readily and permits distension of urinary organ by contained urine.

Location: Lines the ureters, bladder, and part of the urethra.

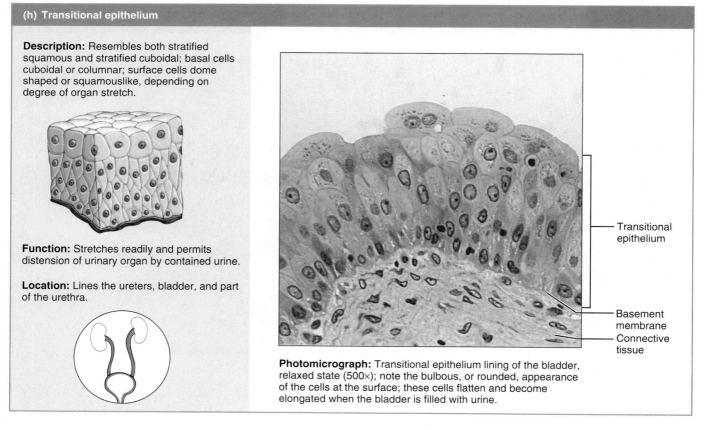

Transitional epithelium

Basement membrane

Connective tissue

Photomicrograph: Transitional epithelium lining of the bladder, relaxed state (500×); note the bulbous, or rounded, appearance of the cells at the surface; these cells flatten and become elongated when the bladder is filled with urine.

Figure 6.3 (*continued*)   Epithelial tissues. Stratified epithelia **(g** and **h).**

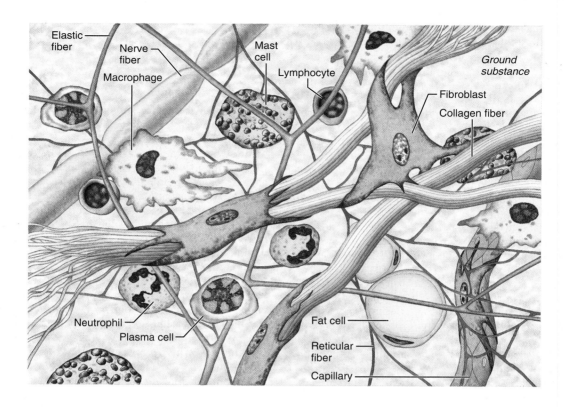

Figure 6.4   Areolar connective tissue: A prototype (model) connective tissue. This tissue underlies epithelia and surrounds capillaries. Note the various cell types and the three classes of fibers (collagen, reticular, elastic) embedded in the ground substance.

Connective Tissue

Connective tissue is found in all parts of the body as discrete structures or as part of various body organs. It is the most abundant and widely distributed of the tissue types.

Connective tissues perform a variety of functions, but they primarily protect, support, and bind together other tissues of the body. For example, bones are composed of connective tissue (**bone, or osseous tissue**), and they protect and support other body tissues and organs. The ligaments and tendons (**dense connective tissue**) bind the bones together or bind skeletal muscles to bones.

Areolar connective tissue (Figure 6.4) is a soft packaging material that cushions and protects body organs. **Adipose** (fat) tissue provides insulation for the body tissues and a source of stored food. Blood-forming (**hematopoietic**) tissue replenishes the body's supply of red blood cells. Connective tissue also serves a vital function in the repair of all body tissues since many wounds are repaired by connective tissue in the form of scar tissue.

The characteristics of connective tissue include the following:

- With a few exceptions (cartilages, which are avascular, and tendons and ligaments, which are poorly vascularized), connective tissues have a rich supply of blood vessels.

- Connective tissues are composed of many types of cells.

- There is a great deal of noncellular, nonliving material (matrix) between the cells of connective tissue.

The nonliving material between the cells—the **extracellular matrix**—deserves a bit more explanation because it distinguishes connective tissue from all other tissues. It is produced by the cells and then extruded. The matrix is primarily responsible for the strength associated with connective tissue, but there is variation. At one extreme, adipose tissue is composed mostly of cells. At the opposite extreme, bone and cartilage have few cells and large amounts of matrix.

The matrix has two components—ground substance and fibers. The **ground substance** is composed chiefly of interstitial fluid, cell adhesion proteins, and proteoglycans. Depending on its specific composition, the ground substance may be liquid, semisolid, gel-like, or very hard. When the matrix is firm, as in cartilage and bone, the connective tissue cells reside in cavities in the matrix called *lacunae*. The fibers, which provide support, include **collagen** (white) **fibers, elastic** (yellow) **fibers,** and **reticular** (fine collagen) **fibers.** Of these, the collagen fibers are most abundant.

Generally speaking, the ground substance functions as a molecular sieve, or medium, through which nutrients and other dissolved substances can diffuse between the blood capillaries and the cells. The fibers in the matrix hinder diffusion somewhat and make the ground substance less pliable. The properties of the connective tissue cells and the makeup and arrangement of their matrix elements vary tremendously, accounting for the amazing diversity of this tissue type. Nonetheless, the connective tissues have a common structural plan seen best in *areolar connective tissue* (Figure 6.4), a soft packing tissue that occurs throughout the body. Since all other connective tissues are variations of areolar, it is considered the model or prototype of the connective tissues. Notice in Figure 6.4 that areolar tissue has all three varieties of fibers, but they are sparsely arranged in its transparent gel-like ground substance. The cell type that secretes its matrix is the *fibroblast,* but a wide variety of other cells including phagocytic cells like macrophages and certain white blood cells and mast cells that act in the inflammatory response are present as well. The more durable connective tissues, such as bone, cartilage, and the dense fibrous varieties, characteristically have a firm ground substance and many more fibers.

There are four main types of adult connective tissue, all of which typically have large amounts of matrix. These are **connective tissue proper** (which includes areolar, adipose, reticular, and dense [fibrous] connective tissues), **cartilage, bone,** and **blood.** All of these derive from an embryonic tissue called *mesenchyme.* Figure 6.5 lists the general characteristics, location, and function of some of the connective tissues found in the body.

Activity 2:
Examining Connective Tissue Under the Microscope

Obtain prepared slides of mesenchyme; of adipose, areolar, reticular, dense regular and irregular connective tissue; of hyaline and elastic cartilage and fibrocartilage; of osseous connective tissue (bone); and of blood. Compare your observations with the views illustrated in Figure 6.5.

Distinguish between the living cells and the matrix and pay particular attention to the denseness and arrangement of the matrix. For example, notice how the matrix of the dense fibrous connective tissues, making up tendons and the dermis of the skin, is packed with collagen fibers, and that in the *regular* variety (tendon), the fibers are all running in the same direction, whereas in the dermis (a dense *irregular* connective tissue) they appear to be running in many directions.

While examining the areolar connective tissue, notice how much empty space there appears to be (*areol* = small empty space), and distinguish between the collagen fibers and the coiled elastic fibers. Identify the starlike fibroblasts. Also, try to locate a **mast cell,** which has large, darkly staining granules in its cytoplasm (*mast* = stuffed full of granules). This cell type releases histamine that makes capillaries more permeable during inflammatory reactions and allergies and thus is partially responsible for that "runny nose" of some allergies.

In adipose tissue, locate a "signet ring" cell, a fat cell in which the nucleus can be seen pushed to one side by the large, fat-filled vacuole that appears to be a large empty space. Also notice how little matrix there is in adipose (fat) tissue. Distinguish between the living cells and the matrix in the dense fibrous, bone, and hyaline cartilage preparations.

Scan the blood slide at low and then high power to examine the general shape of the red blood cells. Then, switch to the oil immersion lens for a closer look at the various types of white blood cells. How does blood differ from all other connective tissues?

Text continues on page 62

(a) Embryonic connective tissue: Mesenchyme

Description: Embryonic connective tissue; gel-like ground substance containing fibers; star-shaped mesenchymal cells.

Function: Gives rise to all other connective tissue types.

Location: Primarily in embryo.

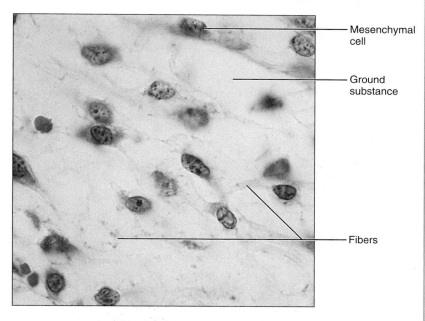

Mesenchymal cell

Ground substance

Fibers

Photomicrograph: Mesenchymal tissue, an embryonic connective tissue (400×); the clear-appearing background is the fluid ground substance of the matrix; notice the fine, sparse fibers.

(b) Connective tissue proper: Loose connective tissue, areolar

Description: Gel-like matrix with all three fiber types; cells: include fibroblasts, macrophages, mast cells, and some white blood cells.

Function: Wraps and cushions organs; its macrophages phagocytize bacteria; plays important role in inflammation; holds and conveys tissue fluid.

Location: Widely distributed under epithelia of body, e.g., forms lamina propria of mucous membranes; packages organs; surrounds capillaries.

Epithelium

Lamina propria

Elastic fibers

Collagen fibers

Fibroblast nuclei

Photomicrograph: Areolar connective tissue, a soft packaging tissue of the body (400×).

Figure 6.5   Connective tissues. Embryonic connective tissue **(a)** and connective tissue proper **(b)**.

(c) Connective tissue proper: Loose connective tissue, adipose

Description: Matrix as in areolar, but very sparse; closely packed adipocytes, or fat cells, have nucleus pushed to the side by large fat droplet.

Function: Provides reserve food fuel; insulates against heat loss; supports and protects organs.

Location: Under skin; around kidneys and eyeballs; within abdomen; in breasts.

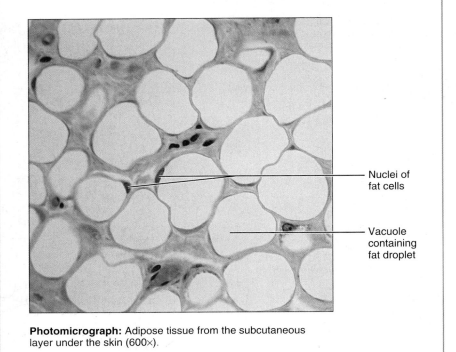

Nuclei of fat cells

Vacuole containing fat droplet

Photomicrograph: Adipose tissue from the subcutaneous layer under the skin (600×).

(d) Connective tissue proper: Loose connective tissue, reticular

Description: Network of reticular fibers in a typical loose ground substance; reticular cells lie on the network.

Function: Fibers form a soft internal skeleton (stroma) that supports other cell types including white blood cells, mast cells, and macrophages.

Location: Lymphoid organs (lymph nodes, bone marrow, and spleen).

Spleen

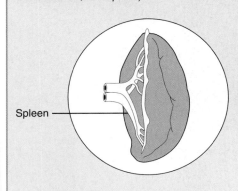

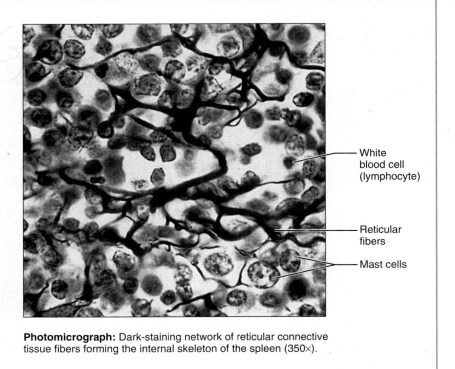

White blood cell (lymphocyte)

Reticular fibers

Mast cells

Photomicrograph: Dark-staining network of reticular connective tissue fibers forming the internal skeleton of the spleen (350×).

Figure 6.5 (*continued*) Connective tissues. Connective tissue proper (**c** and **d**).

(e) Connective tissue proper: Dense connective tissue, dense regular

Description: Primarily parallel collagen fibers; a few elastin fibers; major cell type is the fibroblast.

Function: Attaches muscles to bones or to muscles; attaches bones to bones; withstands great tensile stress when pulling force is applied in one direction.

Location: Tendons, most ligaments, aponeuroses.

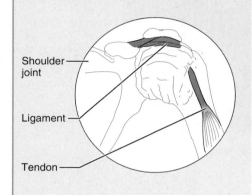

Shoulder joint

Ligament

Tendon

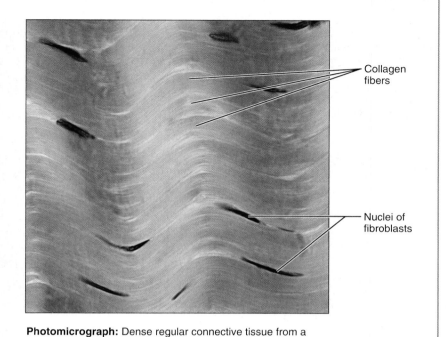

Collagen fibers

Nuclei of fibroblasts

Photomicrograph: Dense regular connective tissue from a tendon (1000×).

(f) Connective tissue proper: Dense connective tissue, dense irregular

Description: Primarily irregularly arranged collagen fibers; some elastic fibers; major cell type is the fibroblast.

Function: Able to withstand tension exerted in many directions; provides structural strength.

Location: Dermis of the skin; submucosa of digestive tract; fibrous capsules of organs and of joints.

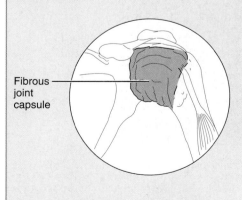

Fibrous joint capsule

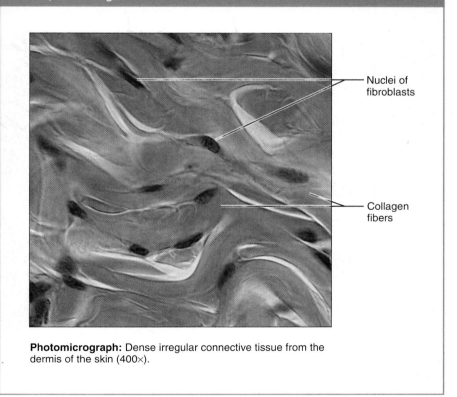

Nuclei of fibroblasts

Collagen fibers

Photomicrograph: Dense irregular connective tissue from the dermis of the skin (400×).

Figure 6.5 (*continued*)   Connective tissue proper (**e** and **f**).

(g) Cartilage: Hyaline

Description: Amorphous but firm matrix; collagen fibers form an imperceptible network; chondroblasts produce the matrix and when mature (chondrocytes) lie in lacunae.

Function: Supports and reinforces; has resilient cushioning properties; resists compressive stress.

Location: Forms most of the embryonic skeleton; covers the ends of long bones in joint cavities; forms costal cartilages of the ribs; cartilages of the nose, trachea, and larynx.

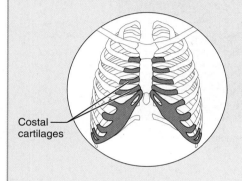

Costal cartilages

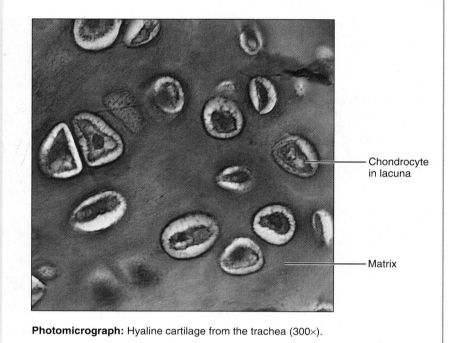

Chondrocyte in lacuna

Matrix

Photomicrograph: Hyaline cartilage from the trachea (300×).

(h) Cartilage: Elastic

Description: Similar to hyaline cartilage, but more elastic fibers in matrix.

Function: Maintains the shape of a structure while allowing great flexibility.

Location: Supports the external ear (pinna); epiglottis.

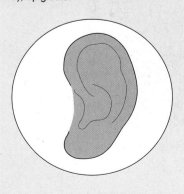

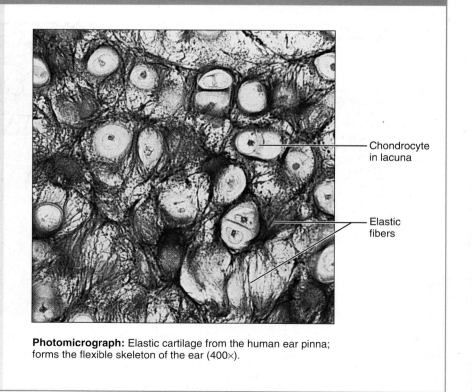

Chondrocyte in lacuna

Elastic fibers

Photomicrograph: Elastic cartilage from the human ear pinna; forms the flexible skeleton of the ear (400×).

Figure 6.5 (*continued*) Connective tissues. Cartilage (**g** and **h**).

(i) Cartilage: Fibrocartilage

Description: Matrix similar to but less firm than that in hyaline cartilage; thick collagen fibers predominate.

Function: Tensile strength with the ability to absorb compressive shock.

Location: Intervertebral discs; pubic symphysis; discs of knee joint.

Intervertebral discs

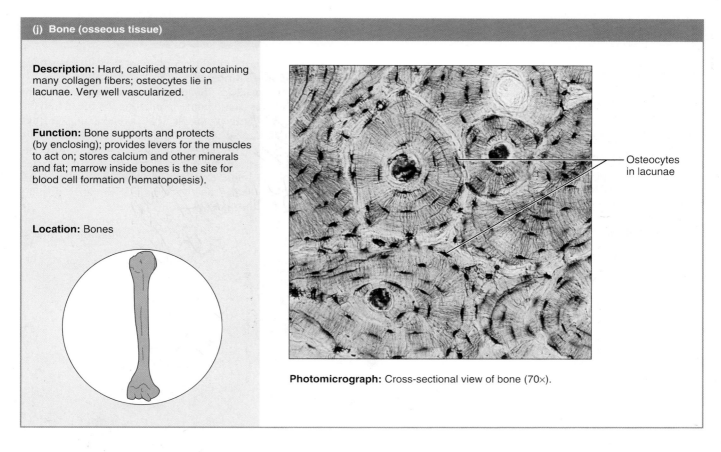

Chondrocytes in lacunae

Collagen fiber

Photomicrograph: Fibrocartilage of an intervertebral disc (200×).

(j) Bone (osseous tissue)

Description: Hard, calcified matrix containing many collagen fibers; osteocytes lie in lacunae. Very well vascularized.

Function: Bone supports and protects (by enclosing); provides levers for the muscles to act on; stores calcium and other minerals and fat; marrow inside bones is the site for blood cell formation (hematopoiesis).

Location: Bones

Osteocytes in lacunae

Photomicrograph: Cross-sectional view of bone (70×).

Figure 6.5 (*continued*) Cartilage **(i)** and bone **(j)**.

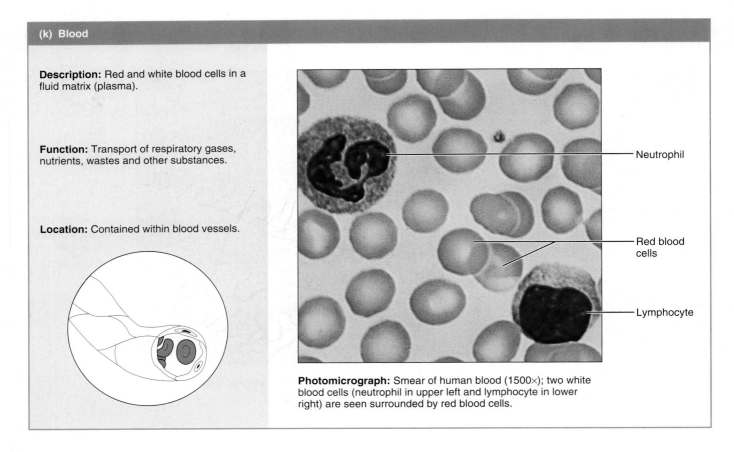

(k) Blood

Description: Red and white blood cells in a fluid matrix (plasma).

Function: Transport of respiratory gases, nutrients, wastes and other substances.

Location: Contained within blood vessels.

Neutrophil

Red blood cells

Lymphocyte

Photomicrograph: Smear of human blood (1500×); two white blood cells (neutrophil in upper left and lymphocyte in lower right) are seen surrounded by red blood cells.

Figure 6.5 (*continued*)   Connective tissues. Blood **(k).**

Muscle Tissue

Muscle tissue (Figure 6.6) is highly specialized to contract and produces most types of body movement. As you might expect, muscle cells tend to be elongated, providing a long axis for contraction. The three basic types of muscle tissue are described briefly here. Cardiac and skeletal muscles are treated more completely in later exercises.

Skeletal muscle, the "meat," or flesh, of the body, is attached to the skeleton. It is under voluntary control (consciously controlled), and its contraction moves the limbs and other external body parts. The cells of skeletal muscles are long, cylindrical, and multinucleate (several nuclei per cell),

with the nuclei pushed to the periphery of the cells; they have obvious *striations* (stripes).

Cardiac muscle is found only in the heart. As it contracts, the heart acts as a pump, propelling the blood into the blood vessels. Cardiac muscle, like skeletal muscle, has striations, but cardiac cells are branching uninucleate cells that interdigitate (fit together) at junctions called **intercalated discs.** These structural modifications allow the cardiac muscle to act as a unit. Cardiac muscle is under involuntary control, which means that we cannot voluntarily or consciously control the operation of the heart.

Text continues on page 64

(a) Skeletal muscle

Description: Long, cylindrical, multinucleate cells; obvious striations.

Function: Voluntary movement; locomotion; manipulation of the environment; facial expression; voluntary control.

Location: In skeletal muscles attached to bones or occasionally to skin.

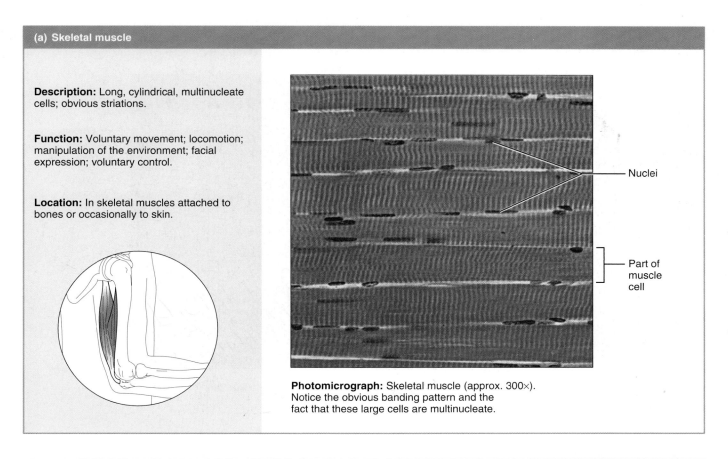

Nuclei

Part of muscle cell

Photomicrograph: Skeletal muscle (approx. 300×). Notice the obvious banding pattern and the fact that these large cells are multinucleate.

(b) Cardiac muscle

Description: Branching, striated, generally uninucleate cells that interdigitate at specialized junctions (intercalated discs).

Function: As it contracts, it propels blood into the circulation; involuntary control.

Location: The walls of the heart.

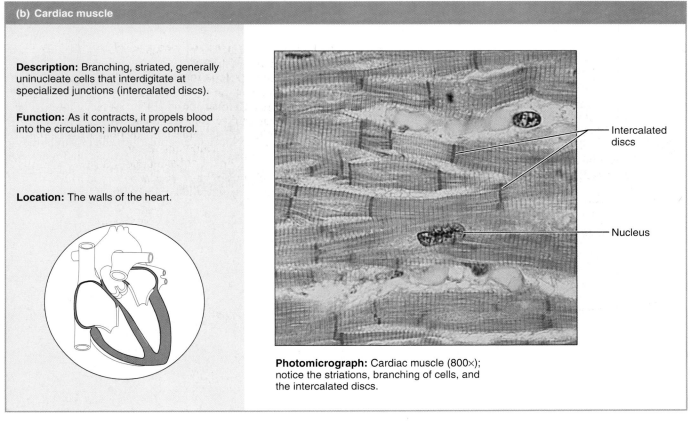

Intercalated discs

Nucleus

Photomicrograph: Cardiac muscle (800×); notice the striations, branching of cells, and the intercalated discs.

Figure 6.6 **Muscle tissues.** Skeletal **(a)** and cardiac **(b)** muscles.

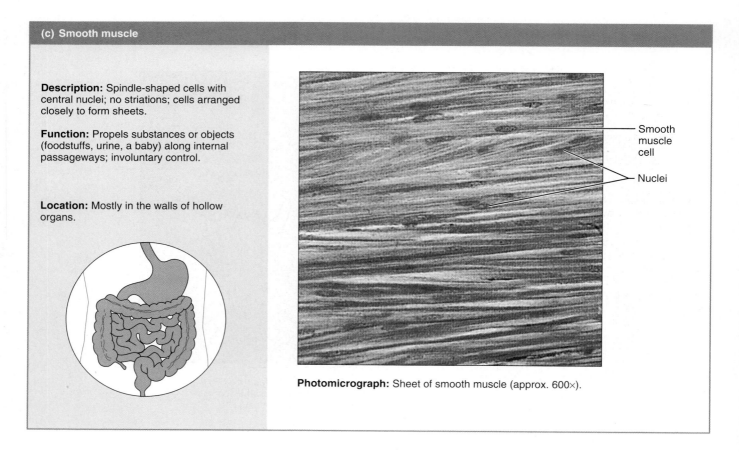

(c) Smooth muscle

Description: Spindle-shaped cells with central nuclei; no striations; cells arranged closely to form sheets.

Function: Propels substances or objects (foodstuffs, urine, a baby) along internal passageways; involuntary control.

Location: Mostly in the walls of hollow organs.

Smooth muscle cell

Nuclei

Photomicrograph: Sheet of smooth muscle (approx. 600×).

Figure 6.6 (continued) Muscle tissues. Smooth muscle **(c).**

Smooth muscle, or *visceral muscle,* is found mainly in the walls of hollow organs (digestive and urinary tract organs, uterus, blood vessels). Typically it has two layers that run at right angles to each other; consequently its contraction can constrict or dilate the lumen (cavity) of an organ and propel substances along predetermined pathways. Smooth muscle cells are quite different in appearance from those of skeletal or cardiac muscle. No striations are visible, and the uninucleate smooth muscle cells are spindle-shaped.

Activity 3:
Examining Muscle Tissue Under the Microscope

Obtain and examine prepared slides of skeletal, cardiac, and smooth muscle. Notice their similarities and dissimilarities in your observations and in the illustrations in Figure 6.6. Teased smooth muscle shows individual cell shape clearly (see Plate 3, Histology Atlas). ■

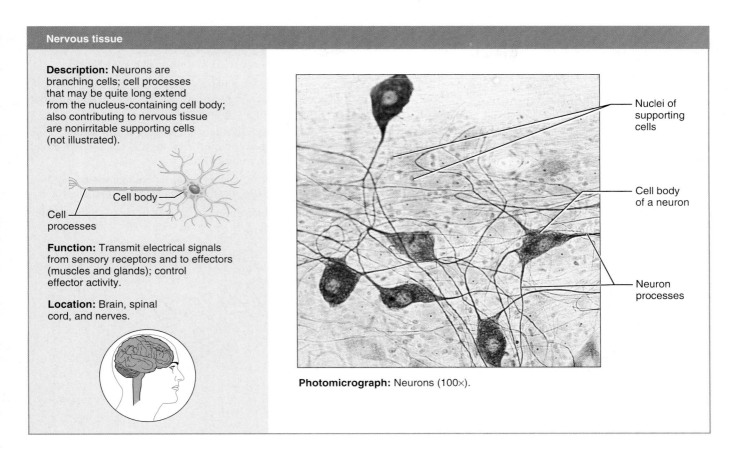

Nervous tissue

Description: Neurons are branching cells; cell processes that may be quite long extend from the nucleus-containing cell body; also contributing to nervous tissue are nonirritable supporting cells (not illustrated).

Cell body

Cell processes

Function: Transmit electrical signals from sensory receptors and to effectors (muscles and glands); control effector activity.

Location: Brain, spinal cord, and nerves.

Nuclei of supporting cells

Cell body of a neuron

Neuron processes

Photomicrograph: Neurons (100×).

Figure 6.7   Nervous tissue.

Nervous Tissue

Nervous tissue is composed of two major cell populations. The **neuroglia** are special supporting cells that protect, support, and insulate the more delicate neurons. The **neurons** are highly specialized to receive stimuli (irritability) and to conduct waves of excitation, or impulses, to all parts of the body (conductivity). They are the cells that are most often associated with nervous system functioning.

The structure of neurons is markedly different from that of all other body cells. They all have a nucleus-containing cell body, and their cytoplasm is drawn out into long extensions (cell processes)—sometimes as long as 1 m (about 3 feet), which allows a single neuron to conduct an impulse over relatively long distances. More detail about the anatomy of the different classes of neurons and neuroglia appears in Exercise 17.

Activity 4:
Examining Nervous Tissue Under the Microscope

Obtain a prepared slide of a spinal cord smear. Locate a neuron and compare it to Figure 6.7. Keep the light dim—this will help you see the cellular extensions of the neurons. See also Plates 5 and 6 in the Histology Atlas. ■

Activity 5:
Constructing a Concept Map of the Tissues

Constructing a **concept map** of the tissues will help you to organize the tissues logically and will be a useful tool for looking at slides throughout the course. A concept map aids in organism identification by a process of elimination based on observable traits. Each step of the map is a question with a yes or no answer. For example, tissues, our topic here, are separated based on observations made through the microscope.

Using the following steps, prepare a concept map that separates the tissues based on what is observed in the photomicrographs in Figures 6.3, 6.5, 6.6, and 6.7. Your instructor will give you a list of the tissue types to be included.

1. Read the sections on epithelial, connective, muscle, and nervous tissues. Carefully review the characteristics of the assigned tissues.

2. Prepare a series of questions based on features observed through the microscope that

   a. will have only two possible answers, yes or no.

   b. will separate the tissues in a logical manner. Figure 6.8 provides an example of a concept map separating out simple squamous epithelium.

3. A helpful first question is "Is there a free edge?" This question separates epithelial tissue from connective, muscle, and nervous tissue.

4. A branch of the concept map is complete when only a single tissue type is alone at the end of a branch.

5. When your concept map is complete, use it to help identify tissue types on prepared slides. ■

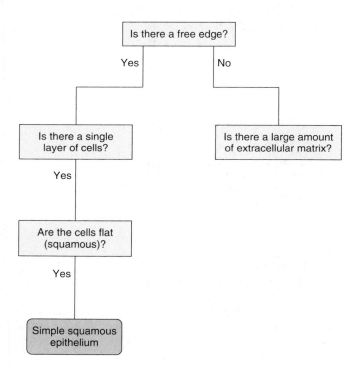

Figure 6.8 A concept map separating tissues based on observable characteristics. A map of simple squamous epithelium has been completed as an example. The map should continue until each tissue type is alone at the end of a branch.

Blood

Objectives

1. To name the two major components of blood, and to state their average percentages in whole blood.

2. To describe the composition and functional importance of plasma.

3. To define *formed elements* and list the cell types composing them, cite their relative percentages, and describe their major functions.

4. To identify red blood cells, basophils, eosinophils, monocytes, lymphocytes, and neutrophils when provided with a microscopic preparation or appropriate diagram.

5. To provide the normal values for a total white blood cell count and a total red blood cell count, and to state the importance of these tests.

6. To conduct the following blood test determinations in the laboratory, and to state their norms and the importance of each.

   hematocrit
   hemoglobin determination
   clotting time
   differential white blood cell count
   ABO and Rh blood typing
   plasma cholesterol concentration

7. To discuss the reason for transfusion reactions resulting from the administration of mismatched blood.

8. To define *anemia, polycythemia, leukopenia, leukocytosis,* and *leukemia* and to cite a possible reason for each condition.

Materials

*General supply area:**
- Disposable gloves
- Safety glasses (student-provided)
- Bucket or large beaker containing 10% household bleach solution for slide and glassware disposal
- Spray bottles containing 10% bleach solution
- Autoclave bag
- Designated lancet (sharps) disposal container
- Plasma (obtained from an animal hospital or prepared by centrifuging animal [for example, cattle or sheep] blood obtained from a biological supply house)

- Test tubes and test tube racks
- Wide-range pH paper
- Stained smears of human blood from a biological supply house or, if desired by the instructor, heparinized animal blood obtained from a biological supply house or an animal hospital (for example, dog blood), or EDTA-treated red cells (reference cells[†]) with blood type labels obscured (available from Immunocor, Inc.)
- Clean microscope slides
- Glass stirring rods
- Wright's stain in a dropper bottle
- Distilled water in a dropper bottle
- Sterile lancet
- Absorbent cotton balls
- Alcohol swabs (wipes)
- Paper towels
- Compound microscope
- Immersion oil
- Three-dimensional models (if available) and charts of blood cells
- Assorted slides of white blood count pathologies labeled "Unknown Sample ____"
- Timer

Because many blood tests are to be conducted in this exercise, it is advisable to set up a number of appropriately labeled supply areas for the various tests, as designated below. Some needed supplies are located in the general supply area.

Note: Artificial blood prepared by Ward's Natural Science can be used for differential counts, hematocrit, and blood typing.

Note to the Instructor: See directions for handling of soiled glassware and disposable items on page 313.

[†]The blood in these kits (each containing four blood cell types—A1, A2, B, and O—individually supplied in 10-ml vials) is used to calibrate cell counters and other automated clinical laboratory equipment. This blood has been carefully screened and can be safely used by students for blood typing and determining hematocrits. It is not usable for hemoglobin determinations or coagulation studies.

Text continues on next page

Activity 4: Hematocrit
- ❑ Heparinized capillary tubes
- ❑ Microhematocrit centrifuge and reading gauge (if the reading gauge is not available, a millimeter ruler may be used)
- ❑ Capillary tube sealer or modeling clay

Activity 5: Hemoglobin determination
- ❑ Hemoglobinometer, hemolysis applicator and lens paper or Tallquist hemoglobin scale and test paper

Activity 6: Sedimentation rate
- ❑ Landau Sed-rate pipettes with tubing and rack*
- ❑ Wide-mouthed bottle of 5% sodium citrate
- ❑ Mechanical suction device
- ❑ Millimeter ruler
- ❑ Pipette cleaning solutions: 10% household bleach, distilled water, 70% ethyl alcohol, acetone

Activity 7: Coagulation time
- ❑ Capillary tubes (nonheparinized)
- ❑ Fine triangular file

Activity 8: Blood typing
- ❑ Blood typing sera (anti-A, anti-B, and anti-Rh [anti-D])
- ❑ Rh typing box
- ❑ Wax marking pencil
- ❑ Toothpicks
- ❑ Blood test cards or microscope slides
- ❑ Medicine dropper

Activity 9: Demonstration
- ❑ Microscopes set up with prepared slides demonstrating the following bone (or bone marrow) conditions: macrocytic hypochromic anemia, microcytic hypochromic anemia, sickle cell anemia, lymphocytic leukemia (chronic), and eosinophilia

Activity 10: Cholesterol measurement
- ❑ Cholesterol test cards and color scale

 PhysioEx™ 6.0 Computer Simulation on page P-48

*An alternative is the Westergren ESR method. See Instructor's Guide for ordering information.

In this exercise you will study plasma and formed elements of blood and conduct various hematologic tests. These tests are useful diagnostic tools for the physician because blood composition (number and types of blood cells, and chemical composition) reflects the status of many body functions and malfunctions.

⚠ **ALERT: Special precautions when handling blood.** This exercise provides information on blood from several sources: human, animal, human treated, and artificial blood. The decision to use animal blood for testing or to have students test their own blood will be made by the instructor in accordance with the educational goals of the student group. For example, for students in the nursing or laboratory technician curricula, learning how to safely handle human blood or other human wastes is essential. Whenever blood is being handled, special attention must be paid to safety precautions. These precautions should be used regardless of the source of the blood. This will both teach good technique and ensure the safety of the students.

Follow exactly the safety precautions listed below.

1. Wear safety gloves at all times. Discard appropriately.

2. Wear safety glasses throughout the exercise.

3. Handle only your own, freshly let (human) blood.

4. Be sure you understand the instructions and have all supplies on hand before you begin any part of the exercise.

5. Do not reuse supplies and equipment once they have been exposed to blood.

6. Keep the lab area clean. Do not let anything that has come in contact with blood touch surfaces or other individuals in the lab. Pay attention to the location of any supplies and equipment that come into contact with blood.

7. Dispose of lancets immediately after use in a designated disposal container. Do not put them down on the lab bench, even temporarily.

8. Dispose of all used cotton balls, alcohol swabs, blotting paper, and so forth in autoclave bags and place all soiled glassware in containers of 10% bleach solution.

9. Wipe down the lab bench with 10% bleach solution when you are finished.

Composition of Blood

Circulating blood is a rather viscous substance that varies from bright scarlet to a dull brick red, depending on the amount of oxygen it is carrying. The average volume of blood in the body is about 5–6 L in adult males and 4–5 L in adult females.

Blood is classified as a type of connective tissue because it consists of a nonliving fluid matrix (the **plasma**) in which living cells (**formed elements**) are suspended. The fibers typical of a connective tissue matrix become visible in blood only when clotting occurs. They then appear as fibrin threads, which form the structural basis for clot formation.

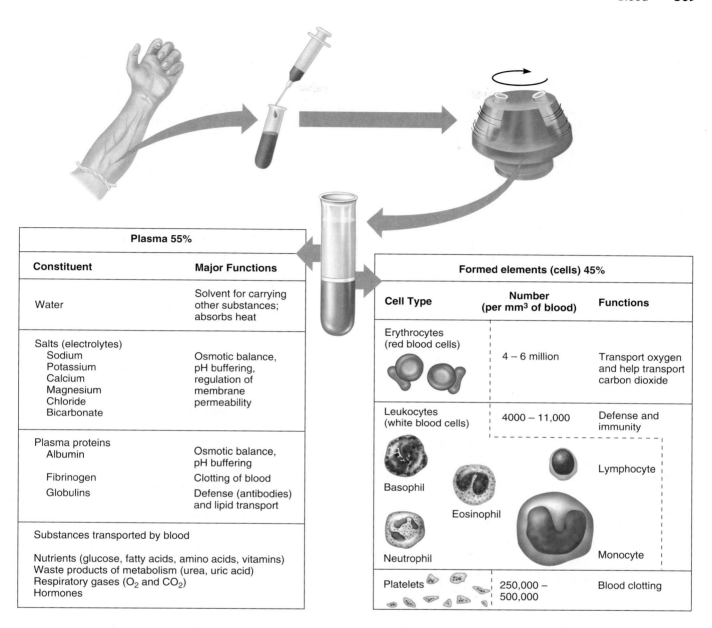

Figure 29.1   **The composition of blood.**

More than 100 different substances are dissolved or suspended in plasma (Figure 29.1), which is over 90% water. These include nutrients, gases, hormones, various wastes and metabolites, many types of proteins, and electrolytes. The composition of plasma varies continuously as cells remove or add substances to the blood.

Three types of formed elements are present in blood (Table 29.1). Most numerous are **erythrocytes,** or **red blood cells (RBCs),** which are literally sacs of hemoglobin molecules that transport the bulk of the oxygen carried in the blood (and a small percentage of the carbon dioxide). **Leukocytes,** or **white blood cells (WBCs),** are part of the body's nonspecific defenses and the immune system, and **platelets** function in hemostasis (blood clot formation). Formed elements normally constitute 45% of whole blood; plasma accounts for the remaining 55%.

Activity 1:
Determining the Physical Characteristics of Plasma

Go to the general supply area and carefully pour a few milliliters of plasma into a test tube. Also obtain some wide-range pH paper, and then return to your laboratory bench to make the following simple observations.

pH of Plasma

Test the pH of the plasma with wide-range pH paper. Record the pH observed. _____

Table 29.1	Summary of Formed Elements of the Blood

Cell type	Illustration	Description*	Number of cells/mm³ (μl) of blood	Duration of development (D) and life span (LS)	Function
Erythrocytes (red blood cells, RBCs)		Biconcave, anucleate disc; salmon-colored; diameter 7–8 μm	4–6 million	D: 5–7 days LS: 100–120 days	Transport oxygen and carbon dioxide
Leukocytes (white blood cells, WBCs)		Spherical, nucleated cells	4,800–10,800		
• **Granulocytes** Neutrophil		Nucleus multilobed; inconspicuous cytoplasmic granules; diameter 10–12 μm	3,000–7,000	D: 6–9 days LS: 6 hours to a few days	Phagocytize bacteria
Eosinophil		Nucleus bilobed; red cytoplasmic granules; diameter 10–14 μm	100–400	D: 6–9 days LS: 8–12 days	Kill parasitic worms; destroy antigen-antibody complexes; inactivate some inflammatory chemicals of allergy
Basophil		Nucleus lobed; large blue-purple cytoplasmic granules; diameter 8–10 μm	20–50	D: 3–7 days LS: ? (a few hours to a few days)	Release histamine and other mediators of inflammation; contain heparin, an anticoagulant
• **Agranulocytes** Lymphocyte		Nucleus spherical or indented; pale blue cytoplasm; diameter 5–17 μm	1,500–3,000	D: days to weeks LS: hours to years	Mount immune response by direct cell attack or via antibodies
Monocyte		Nucleus U- or kidney-shaped; gray-blue cytoplasm; diameter 14–24 μm	100–700	D: 2–3 days LS: months	Phagocytosis; develop into macrophages in tissues
• **Platelets**		Discoid cytoplasmic fragments containing granules; stain deep purple; diameter 2–4 μm	150,000–400,000	D: 4–5 days LS: 5–10 days	Seal small tears in blood vessels; instrumental in blood clotting

*Appearance when stained with Wright's stain.

Color and Clarity of Plasma

Hold the test tube up to a source of natural light. Note and record its color and degree of transparency. Is it clear, translucent, or opaque?

Color_____

Degree of transparency_____

Consistency

Dip your finger and thumb into plasma and then press them firmly together for a few seconds. Gently pull them apart. How would you describe the consistency of plasma (slippery, watery, sticky, granular)? Record your observations.

_____ ■

Activity 2:
Examining the Formed Elements of Blood Microscopically

In this section, you will observe blood cells on an already prepared (purchased) blood slide or on a slide prepared from your own blood or blood provided by your instructor.

• Those using the purchased blood slide are to obtain a slide and begin their observations at step 6.

• Those testing blood provided by a biological supply source or an animal hospital are to obtain a tube of the supplied blood, disposable gloves, and the supplies listed in step 1, except for the lancets and alcohol swabs. After donning gloves, those students will go to step 3b to begin their observations.

• If you are examining your own blood, you will perform all the steps described below *except* step 3b.

1.   Obtain two glass slides, a glass stirring rod, dropper bottles of Wright's stain and distilled water, two or three lancets, cotton balls, and alcohol swabs. Bring this equipment to the laboratory bench. Clean the slides thoroughly and dry them.

2.   Open the alcohol swab packet and scrub your third or fourth finger with the swab. (Because the pricked finger may be a little sore later, it is better to prepare a finger on the hand used less often.) Circumduct your hand (swing it in a cone-shaped path) for 10 to 15 seconds. This will dry the alcohol and cause your fingers to become engorged with blood. Then, open the lancet packet and grasp the lancet by its blunt end. Quickly jab the pointed end into the prepared finger to produce a free flow of blood. It is *not* a good idea to squeeze or "milk" the finger, as this forces out tissue fluid as well as blood. If the blood is not flowing freely, another puncture should be made.

⚠ _Under no circumstances is a lancet to be used for more than one puncture_. Dispose of the lancets in the designated disposal container immediately after use.

3a.   With a cotton ball, wipe away the first drop of blood; then allow another large drop of blood to form. Touch the blood to one of the cleaned slides approximately 1.3 cm, or ½ inch, from the end. Then quickly (to prevent clotting) use the second slide to form a blood smear as shown in Figure 29.2. When properly prepared, the blood smear is uniformly thin. If the blood smear appears streaked, the blood probably began to clot or coagulate before the smear was made, and another slide should be prepared. Continue at step 4.

3b.   Dip a glass rod in the blood provided, and transfer a generous drop of blood to the end of a cleaned microscope slide. For the time being, lay the glass rod on a paper towel on the bench. Then, as described in step 3a and Figure 29.2, use the second slide to make your blood smear.

4.   Dry the slide by waving it in the air. When it is completely dry, it will look dull. Place it on a paper towel, and flood it with Wright's stain. Count the number of drops of stain used. Allow the stain to remain on the slide for 3 to 4 minutes, and then flood the slide with an equal number of drops of distilled water. Allow the water and Wright's stain mixture to

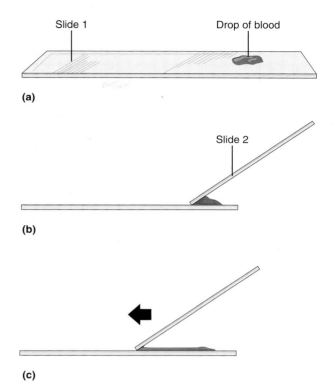

Figure 29.2   Procedure for making a blood smear. (a) Place a drop of blood on slide 1 approximately ½ inch from one end. **(b)** Hold slide 2 at a 30° to 40° angle to slide 1 (it should touch the drop of blood) and allow blood to spread along entire bottom edge of angled slide. **(c)** Smoothly advance slide 2 to end of slide 1 (blood should run out before reaching the end of slide 1). Then lift slide 2 away from slide 1 and place it on a paper towel.

remain on the slide for 4 or 5 minutes or until a metallic green film or scum is apparent on the fluid surface. Blow on the slide gently every minute or so to keep the water and stain mixed during this interval.

5.   Rinse the slide with a stream of distilled water. Then flood it with distilled water, and allow it to lie flat until the slide becomes translucent and takes on a pink cast. Then stand the slide on its long edge on the paper towel, and allow it to dry completely. Once the slide is dry, you can begin your observations.

6.   Obtain a microscope and scan the slide under low power to find the area where the blood smear is the thinnest. After scanning the slide in low power to find the areas with the largest numbers of nucleated WBCs, read the following descriptions of cell types, and find each one on Figure 29.1 and Table 29.1. (The formed elements are also shown in Plates 58 through 63 in the Histology Atlas.) Then, switch to the oil immersion lens, and observe the slide carefully to identify each cell type.

7.   Set your prepared slide aside for use in Activity 3.

Erythrocytes

Erythrocytes, or red blood cells, which average 7.5 μm in diameter, vary in color from a salmon red color to pale pink, depending on the effectiveness of the stain. They have a distinctive biconcave disk shape and appear paler in the center than at the edge (see Plate 59 in the Histology Atlas).

As you observe the slide, notice that the red blood cells are by far the most numerous blood cells seen in the field. Their number averages 4.5 million to 5.5 million cells per cubic millimeter of blood (for women and men, respectively).

Red blood cells differ from the other blood cells because they are anucleate when mature and circulating in the blood. As a result, they are unable to reproduce or repair damage and have a limited life span of 100 to 120 days, after which they begin to fragment and are destroyed in the spleen and other reticuloendothelial tissues of the body.

In various anemias, the red blood cells may appear pale (an indication of decreased hemoglobin content) or may be nucleated (an indication that the bone marrow is turning out cells prematurely). ●

Leukocytes

Leukocytes, or white blood cells, are nucleated cells that are formed in the bone marrow from the same stem cells (*hemocytoblast*) as red blood cells. They are much less numerous than the red blood cells, averaging from 4,800 to 10,800 cells per cubic millimeter. Basically, white blood cells are protective, pathogen-destroying cells that are transported to all parts of the body in the blood or lymph. Important to their protective function is their ability to move in and out of blood vessels, a process called **diapedesis,** and to wander through body tissues by **amoeboid motion** to reach sites of inflammation or tissue destruction. They are classified into two major groups, depending on whether or not they contain conspicuous granules in their cytoplasm.

Granulocytes make up the first group. The granules in their cytoplasm stain differentially with Wright's stain, and they have peculiarly lobed nuclei, which often consist of expanded nuclear regions connected by thin strands of nucleoplasm. There are three types of granulocytes:

Neutrophil: The most abundant of the white blood cells (40% to 70% of the leukocyte population); nucleus consists of 3 to 7 lobes and the pale lilac cytoplasm contains fine cytoplasmic granules, which are generally indistinguishable and take up both the acidic (red) and basic (blue) dyes (*neutrophil* = neutral loving); functions as an active phagocyte. The number of neutrophils increases exponentially during acute infections. (See Plates 58 and 59 in the Histology Atlas.)

Eosinophil: Represents 2% to 4% of the leukocyte population; nucleus is generally figure-8 or bilobed in shape; contains large cytoplasmic granules (elaborate lysosomes) that stain red-orange with the acid dyes in Wright's stain (see Plate 62 in the Histology Atlas). Eosinophils are about the size of neutrophils and play a role in counterattacking parasitic worms. They also lessen allergy attacks by phagocytizing antigen-antibody complexes and inactivating some inflammatory chemicals.

Basophil: Least abundant leukocyte type representing less than 1% of the population; large U- or S-shaped nucleus with two or more indentations. Cytoplasm contains coarse, sparse granules that are stained deep purple by the basic dyes in Wright's stain (see Plate 63 in the Histology Atlas). The granules contain several chemicals, including histamine, a vasodilator which is discharged on exposure to antigens and helps mediate the inflammatory response. Basophils are about the size of neutrophils.

The second group, **agranulocytes,** or **agranular leukocytes,** contains no *visible* cytoplasmic granules. Although found in the bloodstream, they are much more abundant in lymphoid tissues. Their nuclei tend to be closer to the norm, that is, spherical, oval, or kidney shaped. Specific characteristics of the two types of agranulocytes are listed below.

Lymphocyte: The smallest of the leukocytes, approximately the size of a red blood cell (see Plates 58 and 60 in the Histology Atlas). The nucleus stains dark blue to purple, is generally spherical or slightly indented, and accounts for most of the cell mass. Sparse cytoplasm appears as a thin blue rim around the nucleus. Concerned with immunologic responses in the body; one population, the *B lymphocytes,* oversees the production of antibodies that are released to blood. The second population, *T lymphocytes,* plays a regulatory role and destroys grafts, tumors, and virus-infected cells. Represents 25% or more of the WBC population.

Monocyte: The largest of the leukocytes; approximately twice the size of red blood cells (see Plate 61 in the Histology Atlas). Represents 3 to 8% of the leukocyte population. Dark blue nucleus is generally kidney-shaped; abundant cytoplasm stains gray-blue. Once in the tissues, monocytes convert to macrophages, active phagocytes (the "long-term cleanup team"), increasing dramatically in number during chronic infections such as tuberculosis.

Students are often asked to list the leukocytes in order from the most abundant to the least abundant. The following silly phrase may help you with this task: *N*ever *l*et *m*onkeys *e*at *b*ananas (neutrophils, lymphocytes, monocytes, eosinophils, basophils).

Platelets

Platelets are cell fragments of large multinucleate cells (**megakaryocytes**) formed in the bone marrow. They appear as darkly staining, irregularly shaped bodies interspersed among the blood cells (see Plate 58 in the Histology Atlas). The normal platelet count in blood ranges from 150,000 to 400,000 per cubic millimeter. Platelets are instrumental in the clotting process that occurs in plasma when blood vessels are ruptured.

After you have identified these cell types on your slide, observe charts and three-dimensional models of blood cells if these are available. Do not dispose of your slide, as it will be used later for the differential white blood cell count. ■

Hematologic Tests

When someone enters a hospital as a patient, several hematologic tests are routinely done to determine general level of health as well as the presence of pathologic conditions. You will be conducting the most common of these tests in this exercise.

Materials such as cotton balls, lancets, and alcohol swabs are used in nearly all of the following diagnostic tests. These supplies are at the general supply area and should be properly disposed of (glassware to the bleach bucket, lancets in a designated disposal container, and disposable items to the autoclave bag) immediately after use.

Other necessary supplies and equipment are at specific supply areas marked according to the test with which they are used. Since nearly all of the tests require a finger stab, if you will be using your own blood it might be wise to quickly read through the tests to determine in which instances more than one preparation can be done from the same finger stab. For example, the hematocrit capillary tubes and sedimentation rate samples might be prepared at the same time. A little planning will save you the discomfort of a multiple-punctured finger.

An alternative to using blood obtained from the finger stab technique is using heparinized blood samples supplied by your instructor. The purpose of using heparinized tubes is to prevent the blood from clotting. Thus blood collected and stored in such tubes will be suitable for all tests except coagulation time testing.

Total White and Red Blood Cell Counts

A **total WBC count** or **total RBC count** determines the total number of that cell type per unit volume of blood. Total WBC and RBC counts are a routine part of any physical exam. Most clinical agencies use computers to conduct these counts. Since the hand counting technique typically done in college labs is rather outdated, total RBC and WBC counts will not be done here, but the importance of such counts (both normal and abnormal values) is briefly described below.

Total White Blood Cell Count Since white blood cells are an important part of the body's defense system, it is essential to note any abnormalities in them.

Leukocytosis, an abnormally high WBC count, may indicate bacterial or viral infection, metabolic disease, hemorrhage, or poisoning by drugs or chemicals. A decrease in the white cell number below 4000/mm³ (**leukopenia**) may indicate typhoid fever, measles, infectious hepatitis or cirrhosis, tuberculosis, or excessive antibiotic or X-ray therapy. A person with leukopenia lacks the usual protective mechanisms. **Leukemia,** a malignant disorder of the lymphoid tissues characterized by uncontrolled proliferation of abnormal WBCs accompanied by a reduction in the number of RBCs and platelets, is detectable not only by a total WBC count but also by a differential WBC count. ●

Total Red Blood Cell Count Since RBCs are absolutely necessary for oxygen transport, a doctor typically investigates any excessive change in their number immediately.

An increase in the number of RBCs (**polycythemia**) may result from bone marrow cancer or from living at high altitudes where less oxygen is available. A decrease in the number of RBCs results in anemia. (The term **anemia** simply indicates a decreased oxygen-carrying capacity of blood that may result from a decrease in RBC number or size or a decreased hemoglobin content of the RBCs.) A decrease in RBCs may result suddenly from hemorrhage or more gradually from conditions that destroy RBCs or hinder RBC production. ●

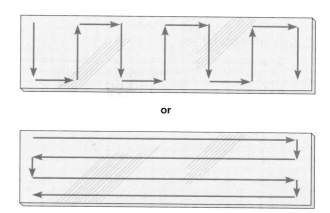

Figure 29.3 Alternative methods of moving the slide for a differential WBC count.

Differential White Blood Cell Count

To make a **differential white blood cell count,** 100 WBCs are counted and classified according to type. Such a count is routine in a physical examination and in diagnosing illness, since any abnormality or significant elevation in percentages of WBC types may indicate a problem or the source of pathology.

Activity 3:
Conducting a Differential WBC Count

1. Use the slide prepared for the identification of the blood cells in Activity 2. Begin at the edge of the smear and move the slide in a systematic manner on the microscope stage—either up and down or from side to side as indicated in Figure 29.3.

2. Record each type of white blood cell you observe by making a count on the chart at the top of page 314 (for example, ⌗⌗II = 7 cells) until you have observed and recorded a total of 100 WBCs. Using the following equation, compute the percentage of each WBC type counted, and record the percentages on the Hematologic Test Data Sheet on page 314.

$$\text{Percent (\%)} = \frac{\text{\# observed}}{\text{Total \# counted (100)}} \times 100$$

3. Select a slide marked "Unknown sample," record the slide number, and use the count chart on p. 314 to conduct a differential count. Record the percentages on the data sheet at the bottom of p. 314.

How does the differential count from the unknown sample slide compare to a normal count?

_____

_____

Count of 100 WBCs	
Cell type	**Number observed** **Student blood smear**
Neutrophils	
Eosinophils	
Basophils	
Lymphocytes	
Monocytes	

Using the text and other references, try to determine the blood pathology on the unknown slide. Defend your answer.

_____

_____

4. How does your differential white blood cell count correlate with the percentages given for each type on page 312?

_____ ■

Hematocrit

The **hematocrit,** or **packed cell volume (PCV),** is routinely determined when anemia is suspected. Centrifuging whole blood spins the formed elements to the bottom of the tube, with plasma forming the top layer (see Figure 29.1). Since the blood cell population is primarily RBCs, the PCV is generally considered equivalent to the RBC volume, and this is the only value reported. However, the relative percentage of WBCs can be differentiated, and both WBC and plasma volume will be reported here. Normal hematocrit values for the male and female, respectively, are 47.0 ± 7 and 42.0 ± 5.

Activity 4:
Determining the Hematocrit

The hematocrit is determined by the micromethod, so only a drop of blood is needed. If possible (and the centrifuge allows), all members of the class should prepare their capillary tubes at the same time so the centrifuge can be run only once.

1. Obtain two heparinized capillary tubes, capillary tube sealer or modeling clay, a lancet, alcohol swabs, and some cotton balls.

2. If you are using your own blood, cleanse a finger, and allow the blood to flow freely. Wipe away the first few drops

---

Hematologic Test Data Sheet

Differential WBC count:

WBC	Student blood smear	Unknown sample #____
% neutrophils	_____	_____
% eosinophils	_____	_____
% basophils	_____	_____
% monocytes	_____	_____
% lymphocytes	_____	_____

Hematocrit (PCV):

RBC _____ % of blood volume

WBC _____ % of blood volume ⎫
⎬ not generally reported
Plasma _____ % of blood ⎭

Hemoglobin (Hb) content:

Hemoglobinometer (type: _____)

_____ g/100 ml blood; _____ % Hb

Tallquist method _____ g/100 ml blood; _____ % Hb

Ratio (PCV to grams Hb per 100 ml blood): _____

Sedimentation rate _____ mm/hr

Coagulation time _____

Blood typing:

ABO group _____   Rh factor _____

Cholesterol concentration _____ mg/dl blood

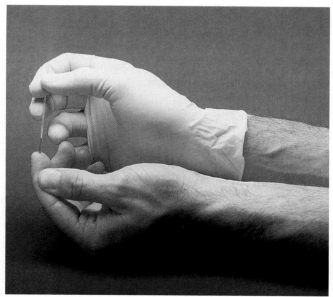

(a)

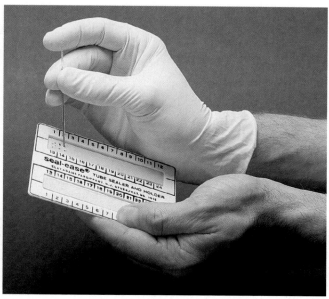

(b)

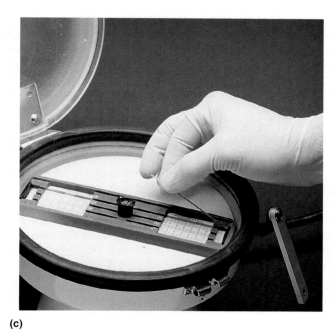

(c)

Figure 29.4 Steps in a hematocrit determination. (a) Load a heparinized capillary tube with blood. (b) Plug the blood-containing end of the tube with clay. (c) Place the tube in a microhematocrit centrifuge. (Centrifuge must be balanced.)

and, holding the red-line-marked end of the capillary tube to the blood drop, allow the tube to fill at least three-fourths full by capillary action (Figure 29.4a). If the blood is not flowing freely, the end of the capillary tube will not be completely submerged in the blood during filling, air will enter, and you will have to prepare another sample.

If you are using instructor-provided blood, simply immerse the red-marked end of the capillary tube in the blood sample and fill it three-quarters full as just described.

3. Plug the blood-containing end by pressing it into the capillary tube sealer or clay (Figure 29.4b). Prepare a second tube in the same manner.

4. Place the prepared tubes opposite one another in the radial grooves of the microhematocrit centrifuge with the sealed ends abutting the rubber gasket at the centrifuge periphery (Figure 29.4c). This loading procedure balances the centrifuge and prevents blood from spraying everywhere by centrifugal force. *Make a note of the numbers of the grooves your tubes are in.* When all the tubes have been loaded, make sure the centrifuge is properly balanced, and secure the centrifuge cover. Turn the centrifuge on, and set the timer for 4 or 5 minutes.

5. Determine the percentage of RBCs, WBCs, and plasma by using the microhematocrit reader. The RBCs are the bottom layer, the plasma is the top layer, and the WBCs are the buff-colored layer between the two. If the reader is not available, use a millimeter ruler to measure the length of the filled capillary tube occupied by each element, and compute its percentage by using the following formula:

$$\frac{\text{Height of the column composed of the element (mm)}}{\text{Height of the original column of whole blood (mm)}} \times 100$$

Record your calculations below and on the data sheet on page 314.

% RBC _____   % WBC _____% plasma _____

Usually WBCs constitute 1% of the total blood volume. How do your blood values compare to this figure and to the normal percentages for RBCs and plasma? (See page 314.)

_____

As a rule, a hematocrit is considered a more accurate test than the total RBC count for determining the RBC composition of the blood. A hematocrit within the normal range generally indicates a normal RBC number, whereas an abnormally high or low hematocrit is cause for concern. ∎

Hemoglobin Concentration

As noted earlier, a person can be anemic even with a normal RBC count. Since hemoglobin (Hb) is the RBC protein responsible for oxygen transport, perhaps the most accurate way of measuring the oxygen-carrying capacity of the blood is to determine its hemoglobin content. Oxygen, which combines reversibly with the heme (iron-containing portion) of the hemoglobin molecule, is picked up by the blood cells in the lungs and unloaded in the tissues. Thus, the more hemoglobin molecules the RBCs contain, the more oxygen they will be able to transport. Normal blood contains 12 to 18 g of hemoglobin per 100 ml of blood. Hemoglobin content in men is slightly higher (13 to 18 g) than in women (12 to 16 g).

Activity 5:
Determining Hemoglobin Concentration

Several techniques have been developed to estimate the hemoglobin content of blood, ranging from the old, rather inaccurate Tallquist method to expensive colorimeters, which are precisely calibrated and yield highly accurate results. Directions for both the Tallquist method and a hemoglobinometer are provided here.

Tallquist Method

1. Obtain a Tallquist hemoglobin scale, test paper, lancets, alcohol swabs, and cotton balls.

2. Use instructor-provided blood or prepare the finger as previously described. (For best results, make sure the alcohol evaporates before puncturing your finger.) Place one good-sized drop of blood on the special absorbent paper provided with the color scale. The blood stain should be larger than the holes on the color scale.

3. As soon as the blood has dried and loses its glossy appearance, match its color, under natural light, with the color standards by moving the specimen under the comparison scale so that the blood stain appears at all the various apertures. (The blood should not be allowed to dry to a brown color, as this will result in an inaccurate reading.) Because the colors on the scale represent 1% variations in hemoglobin content, it may be necessary to estimate the percentage if the color of your blood sample is intermediate between two color standards.

4. On the data sheet, record your results as the percentage of hemoglobin concentration and as grams per 100 ml of blood.

Hemoglobinometer Determination

1. Obtain a hemoglobinometer, hemolysis applicator, alcohol swab, and lens paper, and bring them to your bench. Test the hemoglobinometer light source to make sure it is working; if not, request new batteries before proceeding and test it again.

2. Remove the blood chamber from the slot in the side of the hemoglobinometer and disassemble the blood chamber by separating the glass plates from the metal clip. Notice as you do this that the larger glass plate has an H-shaped depression cut into it that acts as a moat to hold the blood, whereas the smaller glass piece is flat and serves as a coverslip.

3. Clean the glass plates with an alcohol swab, and then wipe them dry with lens paper. Hold the plates by their sides to prevent smearing during the wiping process.

4. Reassemble the blood chamber (remember: larger glass piece on the bottom with the moat up), but leave the moat plate about halfway out to provide adequate exposed surface to charge it with blood.

5. Obtain a drop of blood (from the provided sample or from your fingertip as before), and place it on the depressed area of the moat plate that is closest to you (Figure 29.5a).

6. Using the wooden hemolysis applicator, stir or agitate the blood to rupture (lyse) the RBCs (Figure 29.5b). This usually takes 35 to 45 seconds. Hemolysis is complete when the blood appears transparent rather than cloudy.

7. Push the blood-containing glass plate all the way into the metal clip and then firmly insert the charged blood chamber back into the slot on the side of the instrument (Figure 29.5c).

8. Hold the hemoglobinometer in your left hand with your left thumb resting on the light switch located on the underside of the instrument. Look into the eyepiece and notice that there is a green area divided into two halves (a split field).

9. With the index finger of your right hand, slowly move the slide on the right side of the hemoglobinometer back and forth until the two halves of the green field match (Figure 29.5d).

10. Note and record on the data sheet on page 314 the grams of Hb (hemoglobin)/100 ml of blood indicated on the uppermost scale by the index mark on the slide. Also record % Hb, indicated by one of the lower scales.

11. Disassemble the blood chamber once again, and carefully place its parts (glass plates and clip) into a bleach-containing beaker.

Generally speaking, the relationship between the PCV and grams of hemoglobin per 100 ml of blood is 3:1—for example, a PVC of 35 with 12 g of Hb per 100 ml of blood is a ratio of 3:1. How do your values compare?

Record on the data sheet (page 314) the value obtained from your data. ∎

Sedimentation Rate

The speed at which red blood cells settle to the bottom of a vertical tube when allowed to stand is called the **sedimentation rate.** The normal rate for adults is 0 to 6 mm/hr (averaging 3 mm/hr) and for children is 0 to 8 mm/hr (averaging 4 mm/hr). Sedimentation of RBCs apparently proceeds in three stages: rouleaux formation, rapid settling, and final packing. *Rouleaux formation* (alignment of RBCs like a stack of pennies) does not occur with abnormally shaped red blood

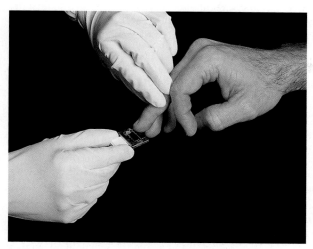

(a) A drop of blood is added to the moat plate of the blood chamber. The blood must flow freely.

(b) The blood sample is hemolyzed with a wooden hemolysis applicator. Complete hemolysis requires 35 to 45 seconds.

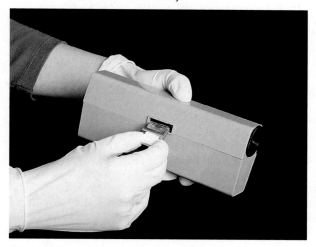

(c) The charged blood chamber is inserted into the slot on the side of the hemoglobinometer.

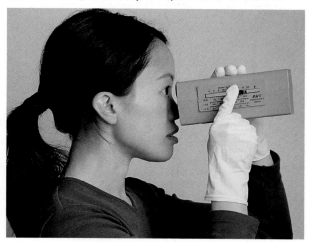

(d) The colors of the green split screen are found by moving the slide with the right index finger. When the two colors match in density, the grams/100 ml and %Hb are read on the scale.

Figure 29.5 **Hemoglobin determination using a hemoglobinometer.**

cells (as in sickle cell anemia); therefore, the sedimentation rate is decreased. The size and number of RBCs affect the packing phase. In anemia the sedimentation rate increases; in polycythemia the rate decreases. The sedimentation rate is greater than normal during menses and pregnancy, and very high sedimentation rates may indicate infectious conditions or tissue destruction occurring somewhere in the body. Although this test is nonspecific, it alerts the diagnostician to the need for further tests to pinpoint the site of pathology. The Landau micromethod, which uses just one drop of blood, is used here. An alternative method is the Westergren ESR method.

Activity 6:
Determining Sedimentation Rate

1. Obtain lancets, cotton balls, alcohol swabs, and Landau Sed-rate pipette and tubing, the Landau rack, a wide-mouthed bottle of 5% sodium citrate, a mechanical suction device, and a millimeter ruler.

2. Use the mechanical suction device to draw up the sodium citrate to the first (most distal) marking encircling the pipette. Prepare the finger for puncture, and produce a free flow of blood. Put the lancet in the designated disposal container.

3. Wipe off the first drop, and then draw the blood into the pipette until the mixture reaches the second encircling line. Keep the pipette tip immersed in the blood to avoid air bubbles.

4. Thoroughly mix the blood with the citrate (an anticoagulant) by drawing the mixture into the bulb and then forcing it back down into the pipette lumen. Repeat this mixing procedure six times, and then adjust the top level of the mixture as close to the zero marking as possible. *If any air bubbles are introduced during the mixing process, discard the sample and begin again.*

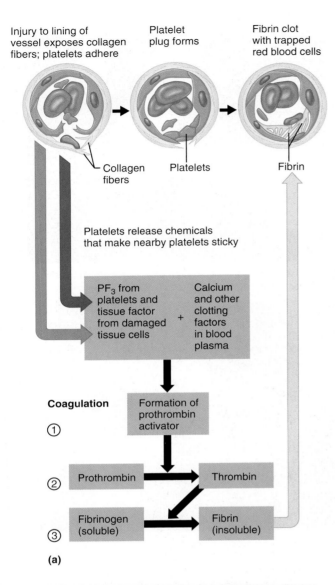

Injury to lining of vessel exposes collagen fibers; platelets adhere

Platelet plug forms

Fibrin clot with trapped red blood cells

Collagen fibers

Platelets

Fibrin

Platelets release chemicals that make nearby platelets sticky

| PF₃ from platelets and tissue factor from damaged tissue cells | + | Calcium and other clotting factors in blood plasma |

Coagulation

① Formation of prothrombin activator

② Prothrombin → Thrombin

③ Fibrinogen (soluble) → Fibrin (insoluble)

(a)

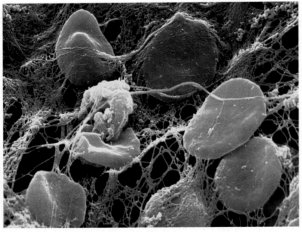

(b)

Figure 29.6 Events of hemostasis and blood clotting. (a) Simple schematic of events. Steps numbered 1–3 represent the major events of coagulation. **(b)** Photomicrograph of RBCs trapped in a fibrin mesh (3000×).

5. Seal the tip of the pipette by holding it tightly against the tip of your index finger, and then carefully remove the suction device from the upper end of the pipette.

6. Stand the pipette in an exactly vertical position on the Landau Sed-rack with its lower end resting on the base of the rack. Record the time, and allow it to stand for exactly 1 hour.

Time _____

7. After 1 hour, measure the number of millimeters of visible clear plasma (which indicates the amount of settling of the RBCs), and record this figure here and on the Hematologic Test Data Sheet on page 314.

Sedimentation rate _____ mm/hr

⚠ 8. Clean the pipette by using the mechanical suction device to draw up each of the cleaning solutions in succession—bleach, distilled water, alcohol, and acetone. Discharge the contents each time before drawing up the next solution. Place the cleaned pipette in the bleach-containing beaker at the general supply area, after first drawing bleach up into the pipette. Put disposable items in the autoclave bag. ■

Bleeding Time

Normally a sharp prick of the finger or earlobe results in bleeding that lasts from 2 to 7 minutes (Ivy method) or 0 to 5 minutes (Duke method), although other factors such as altitude affect the time. How long the bleeding lasts is referred to as **bleeding time** and tests the ability of platelets to stop bleeding in capillaries and small vessels. Absence of some clotting factors may affect bleeding time, but prolonged bleeding time is most often associated with deficient or abnormal platelets.

Coagulation Time

Blood clotting, or **coagulation,** is a protective mechanism that minimizes blood loss when blood vessels are ruptured. This process requires the interaction of many substances normally present in the plasma (clotting factors, or procoagulants) as well as some released by platelets and injured tissues. Basically hemostasis proceeds as follows (Figure 29.6a): The injured tissues and platelets release **tissue factor (TF)** and **PF₃** respectively, which trigger the clotting mechanism, or cascade. Tissue factor and PF₃ interact with other blood protein clotting factors and calcium ions to form **prothrombin activator,** which in turn converts **prothrombin** (present in plasma) to **thrombin.** Thrombin then acts enzymatically to polymerize the soluble **fibrinogen** proteins (present in plasma) into insoluble **fibrin,** which forms a meshwork of strands that traps the RBCs and forms the basis of the clot (Figure 29.6b). Normally, blood removed from the body clots within 2 to 6 minutes.

Activity 7:
Determining Coagulation Time

1.   Obtain a *nonheparinized* capillary tube, a timer (or watch), a lancet, cotton balls, a triangular file, and alcohol swabs.

2.   Clean and prick the finger to produce a free flow of blood. Discard the lancet in the disposal container.

3.   Place one end of the capillary tube in the blood drop, and hold the opposite end at a lower level to collect the sample.

4.   Lay the capillary tube on a paper towel.

Record the time. _____

5.   At 30-second intervals, make a small nick on the tube close to one end with the triangular file, and then carefully break the tube. Slowly separate the ends to see if a gel-like thread of fibrin spans the gap. When this occurs, record below and on the data sheet on page 314 the time for coagulation to occur. Are your results within the normal time range?

_____

6.   Put used supplies in the autoclave bag and broken capillary tubes into the sharps container. ■

Blood Typing

Blood typing is a system of blood classification based on the presence of specific glycoproteins on the outer surface of the RBC plasma membrane. Such proteins are called **antigens,** or **agglutinogens,** and are genetically determined. In many cases, these antigens are accompanied by plasma proteins, **antibodies** or **agglutinins,** that react with RBCs bearing different antigens, causing them to be clumped, agglutinated, and eventually hemolyzed. It is because of this phenomenon that a person's blood must be carefully typed before a whole blood or packed cell transfusion.

Several blood typing systems exist, based on the various possible antigens, but the factors routinely typed for are antigens of the ABO and Rh blood groups which are most commonly involved in transfusion reactions. Other blood factors, such as Kell, Lewis, M, and N, are not routinely typed for unless the individual will require multiple transfusions. The basis of the ABO typing is shown in Table 29.2.

Individuals whose red blood cells carry the Rh antigen are Rh positive (approximately 85% of the U.S. population); those lacking the antigen are Rh negative. Unlike ABO blood groups, neither the blood of the Rh-positive (Rh$^+$) nor Rh-negative (Rh$^-$) individuals carries preformed anti-Rh antibodies. This is understandable in the case of the Rh-positive individual. However, Rh-negative persons who receive transfusions of Rh-positive blood become sensitized by the Rh antigens of the donor RBCs, and their systems begin to produce anti-Rh antibodies. On subsequent exposures to Rh-positive blood, typical transfusion reactions occur, resulting in the clumping and hemolysis of the donor blood cells.

Although the blood of dogs and other mammals does react with some of the human agglutinins (present in the antisera), the reaction is not as pronounced and varies with the animal blood used. Hence, the most accurate and predictable blood typing results are obtained with human blood. The artificial blood kit does not use any body fluids and produces results similar to but not identical to results for human blood.

Activity 8:
Typing for ABO and Rh Blood Groups

Blood may be typed on glass slides or using blood test cards. Both methods are described next.

Typing Blood Using Glass Slides

1.   Obtain two clean microscope slides, a wax marking pencil, anti-A, anti-B, and anti-Rh typing sera, toothpicks, lancets, alcohol swabs, medicine dropper, and the Rh typing box.

2.   Divide slide 1 into halves with the wax marking pencil. Label the lower left-hand corner "anti-A" and the lower right-hand corner "anti-B." Mark the bottom of slide 2 "anti-Rh."

3.   Place one drop of anti-A serum on the *left* side of slide 1. Place one drop of anti-B serum on the *right* side of slide 1. Place one drop of anti-Rh serum in the center of slide 2.

4.   If you are using your own blood, cleanse your finger with an alcohol swab, pierce the finger with a lancet, and wipe away the first drop of blood. Obtain 3 drops of freely flowing blood, placing one drop on each side of slide 1 and a drop on slide 2. Immediately dispose of the lancet in a designated disposal container.

If using instructor-provided animal blood or EDTA-treated red cells, use a medicine dropper to place one drop of blood on each side of slide 1 and a drop of blood on slide 2.

Table 29.2	ABO Blood Typing				
ABO blood type	**Antigens present on RBC membranes**	**Antibodies present in plasma**	**% of U.S. population**		
			White	**Black**	**Asian**
A	A	Anti-B	40	27	28
B	B	Anti-A	11	20	27
AB	A and B	None	4	4	5
O	Neither	Anti-A and anti-B	45	49	40

Blood Typing		
Result	**Observed (+)**	**Not observed (−)**
Presence of clumping with anti-A		
Presence of clumping with anti-B		
Presence of clumping with anti-Rh		

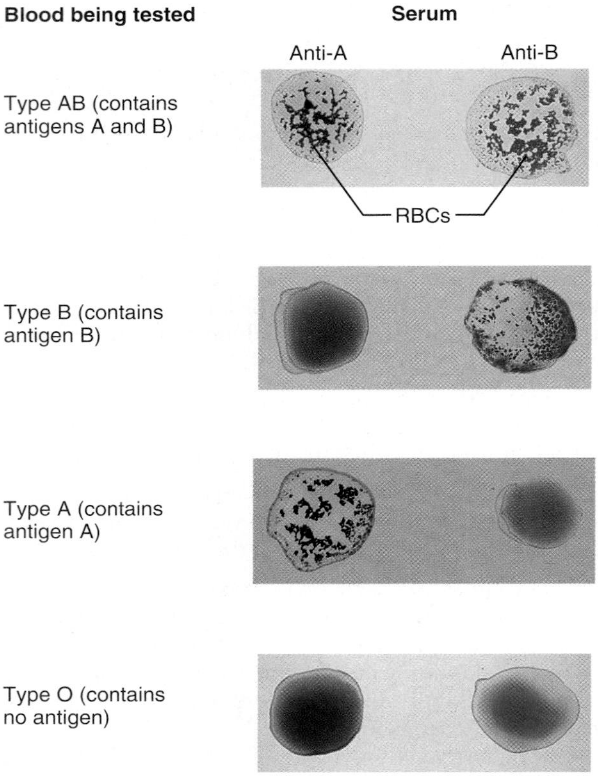

Blood being tested

Serum

Anti-A   Anti-B

Type AB (contains antigens A and B)

—RBCs—

Type B (contains antigen B)

Type A (contains antigen A)

Type O (contains no antigen)

Figure 29.7 Blood typing of ABO blood types. When serum containing anti-A or anti-B antibodies (agglutinins) is added to a blood sample, agglutination will occur between the antibody and the corresponding antigen (agglutinogen A or B). As illustrated, agglutination occurs with both sera in blood group AB, with anti-B serum in blood group B, with anti-A serum in blood group A, and with neither serum in blood group O.

5. Quickly mix each blood-antiserum sample with a ⚠ *fresh* toothpick. Then dispose of the toothpicks and used alcohol swab in the autoclave bag.

6. Place slide 2 on the Rh typing box and rock gently back and forth. (A slightly higher temperature is required for precise Rh typing than for ABO typing.)

7. After 2 minutes, observe all three blood samples for evidence of clumping. The agglutination that occurs in the positive test for the Rh factor is very fine and difficult to perceive; thus if there is any question, observe the slide under the microscope. Record your observations in the chart at left.

8. Interpret your ABO results in light of the information in Figure 29.7. If clumping was observed on slide 2, you are Rh positive. If not, you are Rh negative.

9. Record your blood type on the chart on the bottom of page 314.

10. Put the used slides in the bleach-containing bucket at the general supply area; put disposable supplies in the autoclave bag.

Using Blood Typing Cards

1. Obtain a blood typing card marked A, B, and Rh, dropper bottles of anti-A serum, anti-B serum, and anti-Rh serum, toothpicks, lancets, and alcohol swabs.

2. Place a drop of anti-A serum in the spot marked anti-A, place a drop of anti-B serum on the spot marked anti-B, and place a drop of anti-Rh serum on the spot marked anti-Rh (or anti-D).

3. Carefully add a drop of blood to each of the spots marked "Blood" on the card. If you are using your own blood, refer to direction number 4 in Activity 8: Typing Blood Using Glass Slides. Immediately discard the lancet in the designated disposal container.

4. Using a new toothpick for each test, mix the blood sample with the antibody. Dispose of the toothpicks appropriately.

5. Gently rock the card to allow the blood and antibodies to mix.

6. After 2 minutes, observe the card for evidence of clumping. The Rh clumping is very fine and may be difficult to observe. Record your observations in the chart on the left. Use Figure 29.7 to interpret your results.

7. Record your blood type on the chart at the bottom of page 314, and discard the card in an autoclave bag. ■

Activity 9:
Observing Demonstration Slides

Before continuing on to the cholesterol determination, take the time to look at the slides of *macrocytic hypochromic anemia, microcytic hypochromic anemia, sickle cell anemia, lymphocytic leukemia* (chronic), and *eosinophilia* that have been put on demonstration by your instructor. Record your observations in the appropriate section of the Review Sheets for Exercise 29. You can refer to your notes, the text, and other references later to respond to questions about the blood pathologies represented on the slides. ■

Cholesterol Concentration in Plasma

Atherosclerosis is the disease process in which the body's blood vessels become increasingly occluded by plaques. Because the plaques narrow the arteries, they can contribute to hypertensive heart disease. They also serve as focal points for the formation of blood clots (thrombi), which may break away and block smaller vessels farther downstream in the circulatory pathway and cause heart attacks or strokes.

Ever since medical clinicians discovered that cholesterol is a major component of the smooth muscle plaques formed during atherosclerosis, it has had a bad press. Today, virtually no physical examination of an adult is considered complete until cholesterol levels are assessed along with other lifestyle risk factors. A normal value for plasma cholesterol in adults ranges from 130 to 200 mg per 100 ml plasma; you will use blood to make such a determination.

Although the total plasma cholesterol concentration is valuable information, it may be misleading, particularly if a person's high-density lipoprotein (HDL) level is high and low-density lipoprotein (LDL) level is relatively low. Cholesterol, being water insoluble, is transported in the blood complexed to lipoproteins. In general, cholesterol bound into HDLs is destined to be degraded by the liver and then eliminated from the body, whereas that forming part of the LDLs is "traveling" to the body's tissue cells. When LDL levels are excessive, cholesterol is deposited in the blood vessel walls; hence, LDLs are considered to carry the "bad" cholesterol.

Activity 10:
Measuring Plasma Cholesterol Concentration

1. Go to the appropriate supply area, and obtain a cholesterol test card and color scale, lancet, and alcohol swab.

2. Clean your fingertip with the alcohol swab, allow it to dry, then prick it with a lancet. Place a drop of blood on the test area of the card. Put the lancet in the designated disposal container.

3. After 3 minutes, remove the blood sample strip from the card and discard in the autoclave bag.

4. Analyze the underlying test spot, using the included color scale. Record the cholesterol level below and on the chart at the bottom of page 314.

Cholesterol level _____ mg/dl

⚠ 5. Before leaving the laboratory, use the spray bottle of bleach solution and saturate a paper towel to thoroughly wash down your laboratory bench. ▪

Anatomy of the Heart

Objectives

1. To describe the location of the heart.
2. To name and locate the major anatomical areas and structures of the heart when provided with an appropriate model, diagram, or dissected sheep heart, and to explain the function of each.
3. To trace the pathway of blood through the heart.
4. To explain why the heart is called a double pump, and to compare the pulmonary and systemic circuits.
5. To explain the operation of the atrioventricular and semilunar valves.
6. To name and follow the functional blood supply of the heart.
7. To describe the histology of cardiac muscle, and to note the importance of its intercalated discs and the spiral arrangement of its cells.

Materials

❑ X ray of the human thorax for observation of the position of the heart in situ; X-ray viewing box
❑ Three-dimensional heart model and torso model or laboratory chart showing heart anatomy
❑ Red and blue pencils
❑ Three-dimensional models of cardiac and skeletal muscle
❑ Compound microscope
❑ Prepared slides of cardiac muscle (longitudinal section)
❑ Preserved sheep heart, pericardial sacs intact (if possible)
❑ Dissecting instruments and tray
❑ Pointed glass rods for probes (or Mall probes)
❑ Disposable gloves
❑ Container for disposal of organic debris
❑ Laboratory detergent
❑ Spray bottle with 10% household bleach solution
Human Cardiovascular System: The Heart videotape*

AIA See Appendix B, Exercise 30 for links to A.D.A.M.® Interactive Anatomy.

*Available to qualified adopters from Benjamin Cummings.

The major function of the **cardiovascular system** is transportation. Using blood as the transport vehicle, the system carries oxygen, digested foods, cell wastes, electrolytes, and many other substances vital to the body's homeostasis to and from the body cells. The system's propulsive force is the contracting heart, which can be compared to a muscular pump equipped with one-way valves. As the heart contracts, it forces blood into a closed system of large and small plumbing tubes (blood vessels) within which the blood is confined and circulated. This exercise deals with the structure of the heart, or circulatory pump. The anatomy of the blood vessels is considered separately in Exercise 32.

Gross Anatomy of the Human Heart

The **heart,** a cone-shaped organ approximately the size of a fist, is located within the mediastinum, or medial cavity, of the thorax. It is flanked laterally by the lungs, posteriorly by the vertebral column, and anteriorly by the sternum (Figure 30.1). Its more pointed **apex** extends slightly to the left and rests on the diaphragm, approximately at the level of the fifth intercostal space. Its broader **base,** from which the great vessels emerge, lies beneath the second rib and points toward the right shoulder. In situ, the right ventricle of the heart forms most of its anterior surface.

• If an X ray of a human thorax is available, verify the relationships described above; otherwise, Figure 30.1 should suffice.

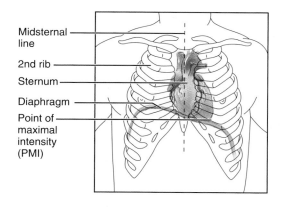

Midsternal line
2nd rib
Sternum
Diaphragm
Point of maximal intensity (PMI)

Figure 30.1 Location of the heart in the thorax.

The heart is enclosed within a double-walled fibroserous sac called the pericardium. The thin **visceral pericardium,** or **epicardium,** is closely applied to the heart muscle. It reflects downward at the base of the heart to form its companion serous membrane, the outer, loosely applied **parietal pericardium,** which is attached at the heart apex to the diaphragm. Serous fluid produced by these membranes allows the heart to beat in a relatively frictionless environment. The serous parietal pericardium, in turn, lines the loosely fitting superficial **fibrous pericardium** composed of dense connective tissue.

H Inflammation of the pericardium, **pericarditis,** causes painful adhesions between the serous pericardial layers. These adhesions interfere with heart movements. ●

The walls of the heart are composed primarily of cardiac muscle—the **myocardium**—which is reinforced internally by a dense fibrous connective tissue network. This network—the *fibrous skeleton of the heart*—is more elaborate and thicker in certain areas, for example, around the valves and at the base of the great vessels leaving the heart.

Figure 30.2 shows two views of the heart—an external anterior view and a frontal section. As its anatomical areas are described in the text, consult the figure.

Heart Chambers

The heart is divided into four chambers: two superior **atria** (singular, *atrium*) and two inferior **ventricles,** each lined by thin serous endothelium called the **endocardium.** The septum that divides the heart longitudinally is referred to as the **interatrial** or **interventricular septum,** depending on which chambers it partitions. Functionally, the atria are receiving chambers and are relatively ineffective as pumps. Blood flows into the atria under low pressure from the veins of the body. The right atrium receives relatively oxygen-poor blood from the body via the **superior** and **inferior venae cavae** and the coronary sinus. Four **pulmonary veins** deliver oxygen-rich blood from the lungs to the left atrium.

The inferior thick-walled ventricles, which form the bulk of the heart, are the discharging chambers. They force blood out of the heart into the large arteries that emerge from its base. The right ventricle pumps blood into the **pulmonary trunk,** which routes blood to the lungs to be oxygenated. The left ventricle discharges blood into the **aorta,** from which all systemic arteries of the body diverge to supply the body tissues. Discussions of the heart's pumping action usually refer to ventricular activity.

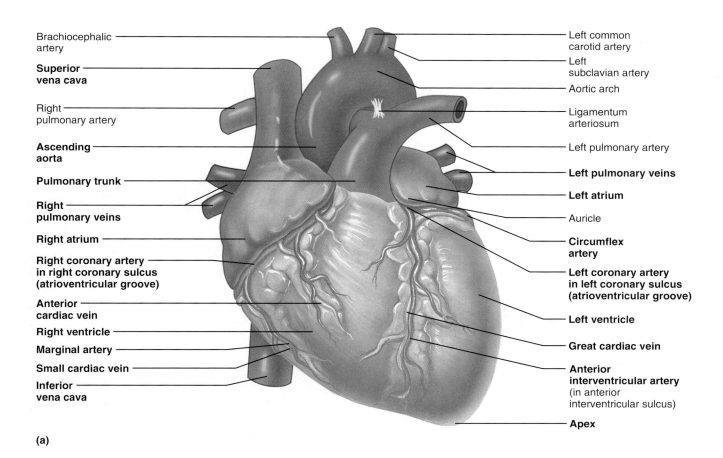

(a)

Figure 30.2   Anatomy of the human heart. (a) External anterior view. *(continues on page 324)*

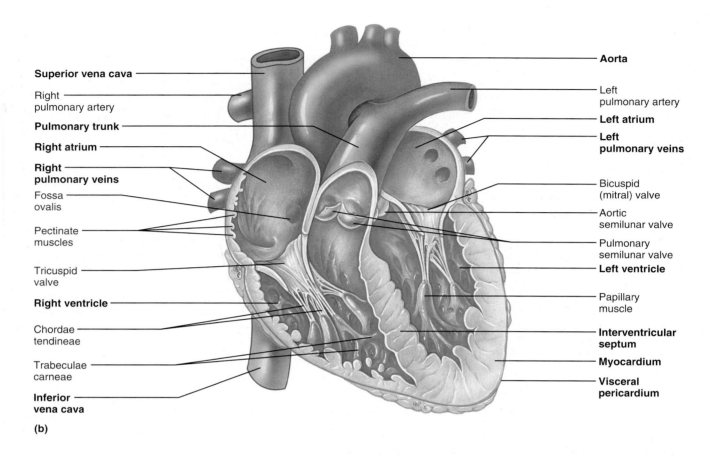

Superior vena cava

Right pulmonary artery

Pulmonary trunk

Right atrium

Right pulmonary veins

Fossa ovalis

Pectinate muscles

Tricuspid valve

Right ventricle

Chordae tendineae

Trabeculae carneae

Inferior vena cava

Aorta

Left pulmonary artery

Left atrium

Left pulmonary veins

Bicuspid (mitral) valve

Aortic semilunar valve

Pulmonary semilunar valve

Left ventricle

Papillary muscle

Interventricular septum

Myocardium

Visceral pericardium

(b)

Figure 30.2 (*continued*) Anatomy of the human heart. (b) Frontal section.

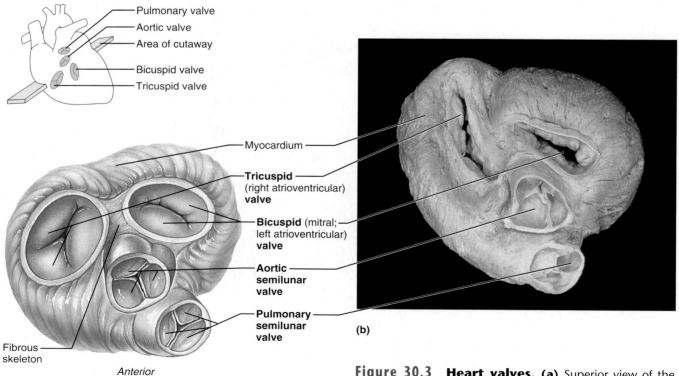

Pulmonary valve
Aortic valve
Area of cutaway
Bicuspid valve
Tricuspid valve

Myocardium

Tricuspid (right atrioventricular) **valve**

Bicuspid (mitral; left atrioventricular) **valve**

Aortic semilunar valve

Pulmonary semilunar valve

Fibrous skeleton

Anterior

(a)

(b)

Figure 30.3 Heart valves. (a) Superior view of the two sets of heart valves (atria removed). **(b)** Photograph of the heart valves, superior view.

Heart Valves

Four valves enforce a one-way blood flow through the heart chambers. The **atrioventricular (AV) valves,** located between the atrial and ventricular chambers on each side, prevent back-flow into the atria when the ventricles are contracting. The left atrioventricular valve, also called the **bicuspid** or **mitral valve,** consists of two cusps, or flaps, of endocardium. The right atrioventricular valve, the **tricuspid valve,** has three cusps (Figure 30.3). Tiny white collagenic cords called the **chordae tendineae** (literally, heart strings) anchor the cusps to the ventricular walls. The chordae tendineae originate from small bundles of cardiac muscle, called **papillary muscles,** that project from the myocardial wall (see Figure 30.2b).

When blood is flowing passively into the atria and then into the ventricles during **diastole** (the period of ventricular filling), the AV valve flaps hang limply into the ventricular chambers and then are carried passively toward the atria by the accumulating blood. When the ventricles contract (**systole**) and compress the blood in their chambers, the intraven-tricular blood pressure rises, causing the valve flaps to be re-flected superiorly, which closes the AV valves. The chordae tendineae, pulled taut by the contracting papillary muscles, anchor the flaps in a closed position that prevents backflow

into the atria during ventricular contraction. If unanchored, the flaps would blow upward into the atria rather like an um-brella being turned inside out by a strong wind.

The second set of valves, the **pulmonary** and **aortic semilunar valves,** each composed of three pocketlike cusps, guards the bases of the two large arteries leaving the ventric-ular chambers. The valve cusps are forced open and flatten against the walls of the artery as the ventricles discharge their blood into the large arteries during systole. However, when the ventricles relax, blood flows backward toward the heart and the cusps fill with blood, closing the semilunar valves and preventing arterial blood from reentering the heart.

Activity 1:
Using the Heart Model to Study Heart Anatomy

When you have located in Figure 30.2 all the structures de-scribed above, observe the human heart model and laboratory charts and reidentify the same structures without referring to the figure. ■

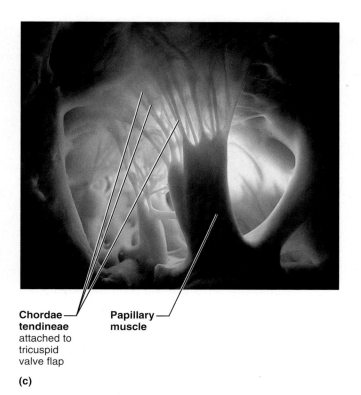

Chordae tendineae attached to tricuspid valve flap
Papillary muscle

(c)

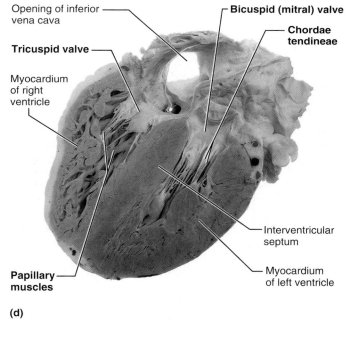

(d)

Figure 30.3 (continued) **(c)** Photograph of the right AV valve. View begins in the right ventricle, looking toward the right atrium. **(d)** Coronal section of the heart.

Pulmonary, Systemic, and Cardiac Circulations

Pulmonary and Systemic Circulations

The heart functions as a double pump. The right side serves as the **pulmonary circulation** pump, shunting the carbon dioxide–rich blood entering its chambers to the lungs to unload carbon dioxide and pick up oxygen, and then back to the left side of the heart (Figure 30.4). The function of this circuit is strictly to provide for gas exchange. The second circuit, which carries oxygen-rich blood from the left heart through the body tissues and back to the right heart, is called the **systemic circulation.** It provides the functional blood supply to all body tissues.

Activity 2:
Tracing the Path of Blood Through the Heart

Use colored pencils to trace the pathway of a red blood cell through the heart by adding arrows to the frontal section diagram (Figure 30.2b). Use red arrows for the oxygen-rich blood and blue arrows for the less oxygen-rich blood. ■

Cardiac Circulation

Even though the heart chambers are almost continually bathed with blood, this contained blood does not nourish the myocardium. The functional blood supply of the heart is provided by the right and left coronary arteries (see Figures 30.2 and 30.5). The **coronary arteries** issue from the base of the aorta just above the aortic semilunar valve and encircle the heart in the **atrioventricular groove** at the junction of the atria and ventricles. They then ramify over the heart's surface, the right coronary artery supplying the posterior surface of the ventricles and the lateral aspect of the right side of the heart, largely through its **posterior interventricular** and **marginal artery** branches. The left coronary artery supplies the anterior ventricular walls and the laterodorsal part of the left side of the heart via its two major branches, the **anterior interventricular artery** and the **circumflex artery.** The coronary arteries and their branches are compressed during systole and fill when the heart is relaxed.

The myocardium is largely drained by the **great, middle,** and **small cardiac veins,** which empty into the **coronary sinus.** The coronary sinus, in turn, empties into the right atrium. In addition, several **anterior cardiac veins** empty directly into the right atrium (Figure 30.5).

Microscopic Anatomy of Cardiac Muscle

Cardiac muscle is found in only one place—the heart. The heart acts as a vascular pump, propelling blood to all tissues of the body; cardiac muscle is thus very important to life. Cardiac muscle is involuntary, ensuring a constant blood supply.

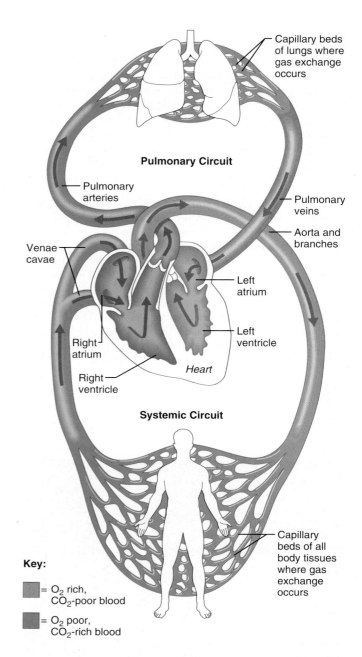

Figure 30.4 The systemic and pulmonary circuits. The heart is a double pump that serves two circulations. The right side of the heart pumps blood through the pulmonary circuit to the lungs and back to the left heart. (For simplicity, the actual number of two pulmonary arteries and four pulmonary veins has been reduced to one each.) The left heart pumps blood via the systemic circuit to all body tissues and back to the right heart. Notice that blood flowing through the pulmonary circuit gains oxygen (O_2) and loses carbon dioxide (CO_2) as depicted by the color change from blue to red. Blood flowing through the systemic circuit loses oxygen and picks up carbon dioxide (red to blue color change).

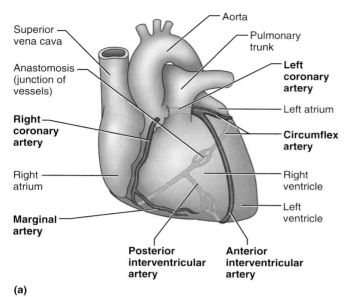

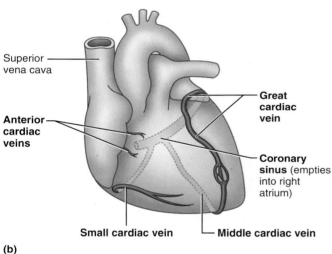

(a)

(b)

Figure 30.5   Cardiac circulation.

The cardiac cells, only sparingly invested in connective tissue, are arranged in spiral or figure-8-shaped bundles (Figure 30.6). When the heart contracts, its internal chambers become smaller (or are temporarily obliterated), forcing the blood into the large arteries leaving the heart.

Activity 3:
Examining Cardiac Muscle Tissue Anatomy

1.   Observe the three-dimensional model of cardiac muscle, examining its branching cells and the areas where the cells interdigitate, the **intercalated discs.** These two structural features provide a continuity to cardiac muscle not seen in other muscle tissues and allow close coordination of heart activity.

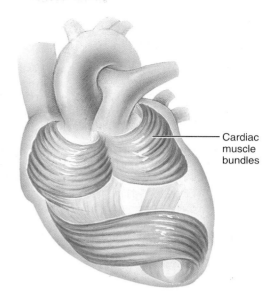

Figure 30.6   Longitudinal view of the heart chambers showing the spiral arrangement of the cardiac muscle fibers.

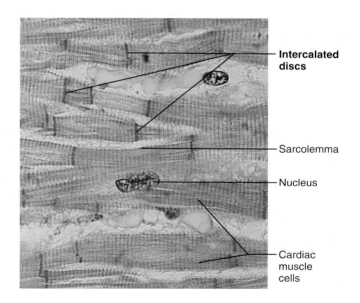

Figure 30.7   Photomicrograph of cardiac muscle (700×).

2.   Compare the model of cardiac muscle to the model of skeletal muscle. Note the similarities and differences between the two kinds of muscle tissue.

3.   Obtain and observe a longitudinal section of cardiac muscle under high power. Identify the nucleus, striations, intercalated discs, and sarcolemma of the individual cells and then compare your observations to the view seen in Figure 30.7. ■

✂ Dissection:
✂ The Sheep Heart

Dissection of a sheep heart is valuable because it is similar in size and structure to the human heart. Also, a dissection experience allows you to view structures in a way not possible with models and diagrams. Refer to Figure 30.8 as you proceed with the dissection.

1.   Obtain a preserved sheep heart, a dissecting tray, dissecting instruments, a glass probe, and gloves. Rinse the sheep heart in cold water to remove excessive preservatives and to flush out any trapped blood clots. Now you are ready to make your observations.

2.   Observe the texture of the pericardium. Also, note its point of attachment to the heart. Where is it attached?

_____

3.   If the serous pericardial sac is still intact, slit open the parietal pericardium and cut it from its attachments. Observe the visceral pericardium (epicardium). Using a sharp scalpel, carefully pull a little of this serous membrane away from the myocardium. How do its position, thickness, and apposition to the heart differ from those of the parietal pericardium?

_____

_____

_____

4.   Examine the external surface of the heart. Notice the accumulation of adipose tissue, which in many cases marks the separation of the chambers and the location of the coronary arteries that nourish the myocardium. Carefully scrape away some of the fat with a scalpel to expose the coronary blood vessels.

5.   Identify the base and apex of the heart, and then identify the two wrinkled **auricles,** earlike flaps of tissue projecting from the atrial chambers. The balance of the heart muscle is ventricular tissue. To identify the left ventricle, compress the ventricular chambers on each side of the longitudinal fissures carrying the coronary blood vessels. The side that feels thicker and more solid is the left ventricle. The right ventricle feels much thinner and somewhat flabby when compressed. This difference reflects the greater demand placed on the left ventricle, which must pump blood through the much longer systemic circulation, a pathway with much higher resistance than the pulmonary circulation served by the right ventricle. Hold the heart in its anatomical position (Figure 30.8a), with the anterior surface uppermost. In this position the left ventricle composes the entire apex and the left side of the heart.

6.   Identify the pulmonary trunk and the aorta extending from the superior aspect of the heart. The pulmonary trunk is more anterior, and you may see its division into the right and left pulmonary arteries if it has not been cut too closely to the heart. The thicker-walled aorta, which branches almost immediately, is located just beneath the pulmonary trunk. The first observable branch of the sheep aorta, the **brachiocephalic artery,** is identifiable unless the aorta has been cut immediately as it leaves the heart. The brachiocephalic artery splits to form the right carotid and subclavian arteries, which supply the right side of the head and right forelimb, respectively.

Carefully clear away some of the fat between the pulmonary trunk and the aorta to expose the **ligamentum arteriosum,** a cordlike remnant of the **ductus arteriosus.** (In the fetus, the ductus arteriosus allows blood to pass directly from the pulmonary trunk to the aorta, thus bypassing the nonfunctional fetal lungs.)

7.   Cut through the wall of the aorta until you see the aortic semilunar valve. Identify the two openings to the coronary arteries just above the valve. Insert a probe into one of these holes to see if you can follow the course of a coronary artery across the heart.

8.   Turn the heart to view its posterior surface. The heart will appear as shown in Figure 30.8b. Notice that the right and left ventricles appear equal-sized in this view. Try to identify the four thin-walled pulmonary veins entering the left atrium. Identify the superior and inferior venae cavae entering the right atrium. Due to the way the heart is trimmed, the pulmonary veins and superior vena cava may be very short or missing. If possible, compare the approximate diameter of the superior vena cava with the diameter of the aorta.

Which is larger? _____

Which has thicker walls?_____

Why do you suppose these differences exist?

_____

_____

_____

9.   Insert a probe into the superior vena cava, through the right atrium, and out the inferior vena cava. Use scissors to cut along the probe so that you can view the interior of the right atrium. Observe the right atrioventricular valve.

How many flaps does it have?_____

Pour some water into the right atrium and allow it to flow into the ventricle. *Slowly and gently* squeeze the right ventricle to watch the closing action of this valve. (If you squeeze too vigorously, you'll get a face full of water!) Drain the water from the heart before continuing.

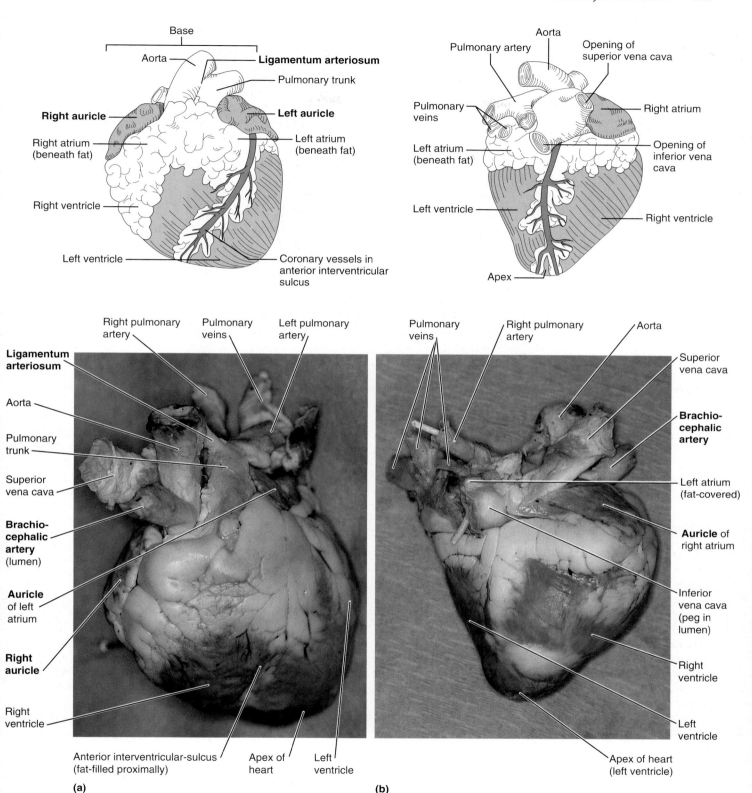

Figure 30.8 Anatomy of the sheep heart. (a) Anterior view.
(b) Posterior view. Diagrammatic views at top; photographs at bottom.

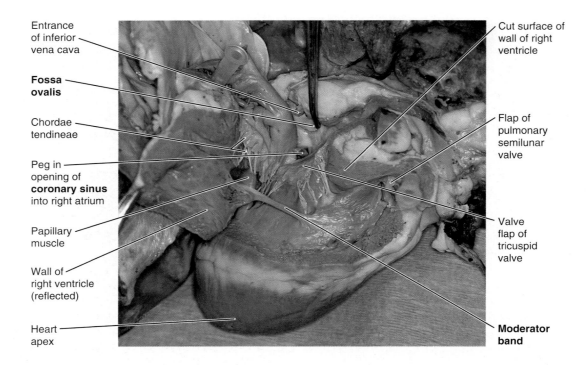

Entrance of inferior vena cava

Fossa ovalis

Chordae tendineae

Peg in opening of **coronary sinus** into right atrium

Papillary muscle

Wall of right ventricle (reflected)

Heart apex

Cut surface of wall of right ventricle

Flap of pulmonary semilunar valve

Valve flap of tricuspid valve

Moderator band

Figure 30.9   Right side of the sheep heart opened and reflected to reveal internal structures.

10. Return to the pulmonary trunk and cut through its anterior wall until you can see the pulmonary semilunar valve (Figure 30.9). Pour some water into the base of the pulmonary trunk to observe the closing action of this valve. How does its action differ from that of the atrioventricular valve?

_____

_____

_____

After observing semilunar valve action, drain the heart once again. Extend the cut through the pulmonary trunk into the right ventricle. Cut down, around, and up through the atrioventricular valve to make the cut continuous with the cut across the right atrium (see Figure 30.9).

11. Reflect the cut edges of the superior vena cava, right atrium, and right ventricle to obtain the view seen in Figure 30.9. Observe the comblike ridges of muscle throughout most of the right atrium. This is called **pectinate muscle** (*pectin* means "comb"). Identify, on the ventral atrial wall,

the large opening of the inferior vena cava and follow it to its external opening with a probe. Notice that the atrial walls in the vicinity of the venae cavae are smooth and lack the roughened appearance (pectinate musculature) of the other regions of the atrial walls. Just below the inferior vena caval opening, identify the opening of the **coronary sinus,** which returns venous blood of the coronary circulation to the right atrium. Nearby, locate an oval depression, the **fossa ovalis,** in the interatrial septum. This depression marks the site of an opening in the fetal heart, the **foramen ovale,** which allows blood to pass from the right to the left atrium, thus bypassing the fetal lungs.

12. Identify the papillary muscles in the right ventricle, and follow their attached chordae tendineae to the flaps of the tricuspid valve. Notice the pitted and ridged appearance (**trabeculae carneae**) of the inner ventricular muscle.

13. Identify the **moderator band** (septomarginal band), a bundle of cardiac muscle fibers connecting the interventricular septum to anterior papillary muscles. It contains a branch of the atrioventricular bundle and helps coordinate contraction of the ventricle.

14. Make a longitudinal incision through the left atrium and continue it into the left ventricle. Notice how much thicker the myocardium of the left ventricle is than that of the right ventricle. Compare the *shape* of the left ventricular cavity to the shape of the right ventricular cavity. (See Figure 30.10.)

_____

_____

_____

Are the papillary muscles and chordae tendineae observed in the right ventricle also present in the left ventricle?

_____

Count the number of cusps in the left atrioventricular valve. How does this compare with the number seen in the right atrioventricular valve?

_____

_____

How do the sheep valves compare with their human counterparts?

_____

15. Reflect the cut edges of the atrial wall, and attempt to locate the entry points of the pulmonary veins into the left atrium. Follow the pulmonary veins, if present, to the heart exterior with a probe. Notice how thin-walled these vessels are.

16. Dispose of the organic debris in the designated container, clean the dissecting tray and instruments with detergent and water, and wash the lab bench with bleach solution before leaving the laboratory. ■

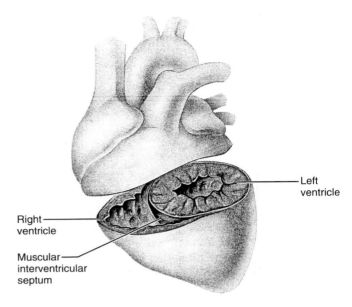

Left ventricle

Right ventricle

Muscular interventricular septum

Figure 30.10   Anatomical differences in the right and left ventricles. The left ventricle has thicker walls, and its cavity is basically circular; by contrast, the right ventricle cavity is crescent-shaped and wraps around the left ventricle.

Anatomy of the Respiratory System

Body cells require an abundant and continuous supply of oxygen. As the cells use oxygen, they release carbon dioxide, a waste product that the body must get rid of. These oxygen-using cellular processes, collectively referred to as *cellular respiration,* are more appropriately described in conjunction with the topic of cellular metabolism. The major role of the **respiratory system,** our focus in this exercise, is to supply the body with oxygen and dispose of carbon dioxide. To fulfill this role, at least four distinct processes, collectively referred to as **respiration,** must occur:

Pulmonary ventilation: The tidelike movement of air into and out of the lungs so that the gases in the alveoli are continuously changed and refreshed. Also more simply called *ventilation,* or *breathing.*

External respiration: The gas exchange between the blood and the air-filled chambers of the lungs (oxygen loading/carbon dioxide unloading).

Transport of respiratory gases: The transport of respiratory gases between the lungs and tissue cells of the body accomplished by the cardiovascular system, using blood as the transport vehicle.

Internal respiration: Exchange of gases between systemic blood and tissue cells (oxygen unloading and carbon dioxide loading).

Only the first two processes are the exclusive province of the respiratory system, but all four must occur for the respiratory system to "do its job." Hence, the respiratory and circulatory systems are irreversibly linked. If either system fails, cells begin to die from oxygen starvation and accumulation of carbon dioxide. Uncorrected, this situation soon causes death of the entire organism.

Upper Respiratory System Structures

The upper respiratory system structures—the nose, pharynx, and larynx—are shown in Figure 36.1 and described below. As you read through the descriptions, identify each structure in the figure.

Air generally passes into the respiratory tract through the **external nares (nostrils),** and enters the **nasal cavity** (divided by the **nasal septum**). It then flows posteriorly over three pairs of lobelike structures, the **inferior, superior,** and **middle nasal conchae,** which increase the air turbulence. As the air passes through the nasal cavity, it is also warmed, moistened, and filtered by the nasal mucosa. The air that flows directly beneath the superior part of the nasal cavity may chemically stimulate the olfactory receptors located in

Objectives

1. To define the following terms: *respiratory system, pulmonary ventilation, external respiration,* and *internal respiration.*

2. To label the major respiratory system structures on a diagram (or identify them on a model), and to describe the function of each.

3. To recognize the histologic structure of the trachea (cross section) and lung tissue on prepared slides, and to describe the functions the observed structural modifications serve.

Materials

❑ Resin cast of the respiratory tree (if available)

❑ Human torso model

❑ Respiratory organ system model and/or chart of the respiratory system

❑ Larynx model (if available)

❑ Preserved inflatable lung preparation (obtained from a biological supply house) or sheep pluck fresh from the slaughterhouse

❑ Source of compressed air*

❑ 0.6 m (2-foot) length of laboratory rubber tubing

❑ Dissecting tray

❑ Disposable gloves

❑ Disposable autoclave bag

❑ Prepared slides of the following (if available): trachea (cross section), lung tissue, both normal and pathological specimens (for example, sections taken from lung tissues exhibiting bronchitis, pneumonia, emphysema, or lung cancer)

❑ Compound and stereomicroscopes

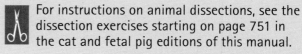

For instructions on animal dissections, see the dissection exercises starting on page 751 in the cat and fetal pig editions of this manual.

AIA See Appendix B, Exercise 36 for links to A.D.A.M.® Interactive Anatomy.

*If a compressed air source is not available, cardboard mouthpieces that fit the cut end of the rubber tubing should be available for student use. Disposable autoclave bags should also be provided for discarding the mouthpiece.

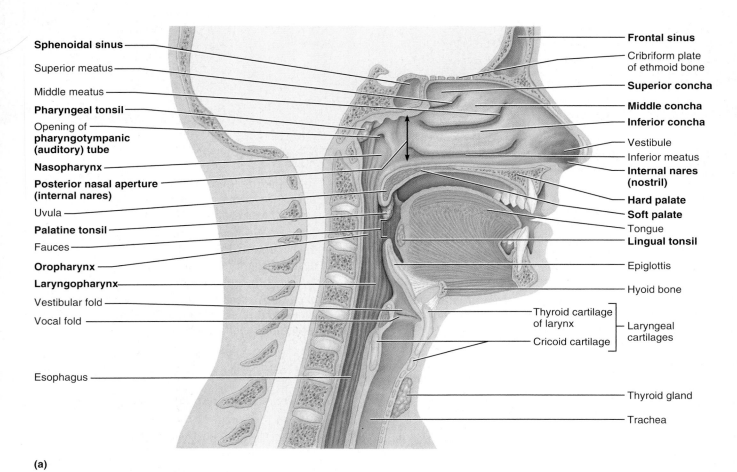

Sphenoidal sinus

Superior meatus

Middle meatus

Pharyngeal tonsil

Opening of pharyngotympanic (auditory) tube

Nasopharynx

Posterior nasal aperture (internal nares)

Uvula

Palatine tonsil

Fauces

Oropharynx

Laryngopharynx

Vestibular fold

Vocal fold

Esophagus

Frontal sinus

Cribriform plate of ethmoid bone

Superior concha

Middle concha

Inferior concha

Vestibule

Inferior meatus

Internal nares (nostril)

Hard palate

Soft palate

Tongue

Lingual tonsil

Epiglottis

Hyoid bone

Thyroid cartilage of larynx

Cricoid cartilage

Laryngeal cartilages

Thyroid gland

Trachea

(a)

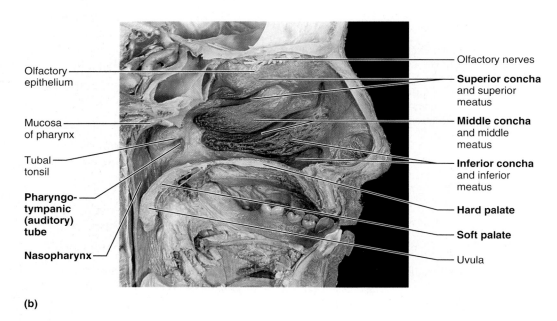

Olfactory epithelium

Mucosa of pharynx

Tubal tonsil

Pharyngo-tympanic (auditory) tube

Nasopharynx

Olfactory nerves

Superior concha and superior meatus

Middle concha and middle meatus

Inferior concha and inferior meatus

Hard palate

Soft palate

Uvula

(b)

Figure 36.1 Structures of the upper respiratory tract (sagittal section).
(a) Diagrammatic view. **(b)** Photograph.

the mucosa of that region. The nasal cavity is surrounded by the **paranasal sinuses** in the frontal, sphenoid, ethmoid, and maxillary bones. These sinuses, named for the bones in which they are located, act as resonance chambers in speech and their mucosae, like that of the nasal cavity, warm and moisten the incoming air.

The nasal passages are separated from the oral cavity below by a partition composed anteriorly of the **hard palate** and posteriorly by the **soft palate.**

The genetic defect called **cleft palate** (failure of the palatine bones and/or the palatine processes of the maxillary bones to fuse medially) causes difficulty in breathing and oral cavity functions such as sucking and, later, mastication and speech. ●

Of course, air may also enter the body via the mouth. From there it passes through the oral cavity to move into the pharynx posteriorly, where the oral and nasal cavities are joined temporarily.

Commonly called the *throat,* the funnel-shaped **pharynx** connects the nasal and oral cavities to the larynx and esophagus inferiorly. It has three named parts (Figure 36.1):

1. The **nasopharynx** lies posterior to the nasal cavity and is continuous with it via the **posterior nasal aperture,** also called the **internal nares.** It lies above the soft palate; hence, it serves only as an air passage. High on its posterior wall is the *pharyngeal tonsil,* masses of lymphoid tissue that help to protect the respiratory passages from invading pathogens. The *pharyngotympanic (auditory) tubes,* which allow middle ear pressure to become equalized to atmospheric pressure, drain into the lateral aspects of the nasopharynx. The *tubule tonsils* surround the openings of these tubes into the nasopharynx.

Because of the continuity of the middle ear and nasopharyngeal mucosae, nasal infections may invade the middle ear cavity and cause **otitis media,** which is difficult to treat. ●

2. The **oropharynx** is continuous posteriorly with the oral cavity. Since it extends from the soft palate to the epiglottis of the larynx inferiorly, it serves as a common conduit for food and air. In its lateral walls are the *palatine tonsils.* The *lingual tonsil* covers the base of the tongue.

3. The **laryngopharynx,** like the oropharynx, accommodates both ingested food and air. It lies directly posterior to the upright epiglottis and extends to the larynx, where the common pathway divides into the respiratory and digestive channels. From the laryngopharynx, air enters the lower respiratory passageways by passing through the larynx (voice box) and into the trachea below.

The **larynx** (Figure 36.2) consists of nine cartilages. The two most prominent are the large shield-shaped **thyroid cartilage,** whose anterior medial laryngeal prominence is commonly referred to as *Adam's apple,* and the inferiorly located, ring-shaped **cricoid cartilage,** whose widest dimension faces posteriorly. All the laryngeal cartilages are composed of hyaline cartilage except the flaplike **epiglottis,** a flexible elastic cartilage located superior to the opening of the larynx. The epiglottis, sometimes referred to as the "guardian of the airways," forms a lid over the larynx when we swallow. This closes off the respiratory passageways to incoming food or drink, which is routed into the posterior esophagus, or food chute.

● Palpate your larynx by placing your hand on the anterior neck surface approximately halfway down its length. Swallow. Can you feel the cartilaginous larynx rising?

If anything other than air enters the larynx, a cough reflex attempts to expel the substance. Note that this reflex operates only when a person is conscious. Therefore, you should never try to feed or pour liquids down the throat of an unconscious person.

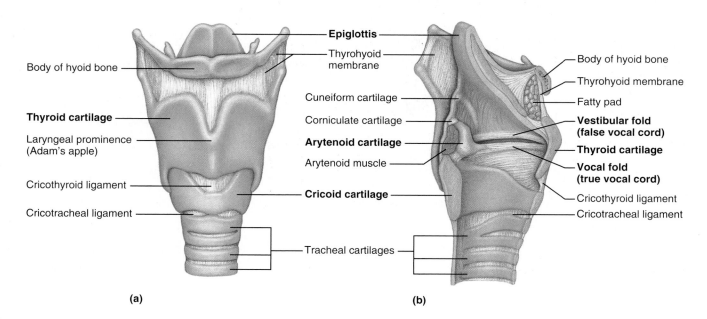

(a)   (b)

Figure 36.2   Structure of the larynx. (a) Anterior view. **(b)** Sagittal section.

The mucous membrane of the larynx is thrown into two pairs of folds—the upper **vestibular folds,** also called the **false vocal cords,** and the lower **vocal folds,** or **true vocal cords,** which vibrate with expelled air for speech. The vocal cords are attached posterolaterally to the small triangular **arytenoid cartilages** by the *vocal ligaments*. The slitlike passageway between the folds is called the *glottis*.

Lower Respiratory System Structures

Air entering the **trachea,** or windpipe, from the larynx travels down its length (about 11.0 cm or 4 inches) to the level of the *sternal angle* (or the disc between the fourth and fifth thoracic vertebrae). There the passageway divides into the right and left **main** *(primary)* **bronchi** (Figure 36.3), which plunge into their respective lungs at an indented area called the **hilus** (see Figure 36.5c). The right main bronchus is wider, shorter, and more vertical than the left, and foreign objects that enter the respiratory passageways are more likely to become lodged in it.

The trachea is lined with a ciliated mucus-secreting, pseudostratified columnar epithelium, as are many of the other respiratory system passageways. The cilia propel mucus (produced by goblet cells) laden with dust particles, bacteria, and other debris away from the lungs and toward the throat, where it can be expectorated or swallowed. The walls of the trachea are reinforced with C-shaped cartilaginous rings, the incomplete portion located posteriorly (see Figure 36.6, page 397). These C-shaped cartilages serve a double function: The incomplete parts allow the esophagus to expand anteriorly when a large food bolus is swallowed. The solid portions reinforce the trachea walls to maintain its open passageway regardless of the pressure changes that occur during breathing.

The primary bronchi further divide into smaller and smaller branches (the secondary, tertiary, on down), finally becoming the **bronchioles,** which have terminal branches called **respiratory bronchioles** (Figure 36.3b). All but the most minute branches have cartilaginous reinforcements in their walls, usually in the form of small plates of hyaline cartilage rather than cartilaginous rings. As the respiratory tubes get smaller and smaller, the relative amount of smooth muscle in their walls increases as the amount of cartilage declines and finally disappears. The complete layer of smooth muscle

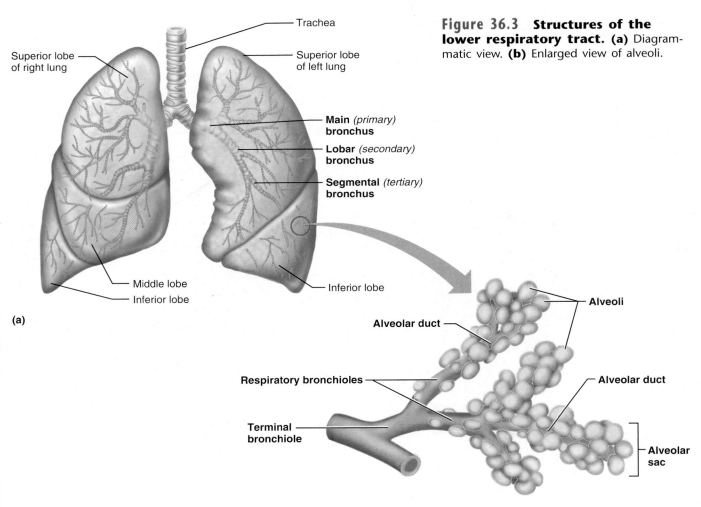

Figure 36.3 Structures of the lower respiratory tract. (a) Diagrammatic view. **(b)** Enlarged view of alveoli.

Trachea

Superior lobe of right lung

Superior lobe of left lung

Main *(primary)* **bronchus**

Lobar *(secondary)* **bronchus**

Segmental *(tertiary)* **bronchus**

Middle lobe

Inferior lobe

Inferior lobe

(a)

Alveoli

Alveolar duct

Alveolar duct

Respiratory bronchioles

Terminal bronchiole

Alveolar sac

(b)

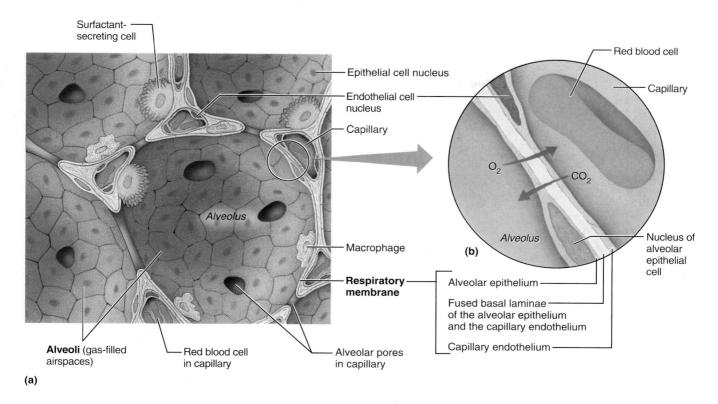

Figure 36.4   Diagrammatic view of the relationship between the alveoli and pulmonary capillaries involved in gas exchange. (a) One alveolus surrounded by capillaries. **(b)** Enlargement of the respiratory membrane.

present in the bronchioles enables them to provide considerable resistance to air flow under certain conditions (asthma, hay fever, etc.). The continuous branching of the respiratory passageways in the lungs is often referred to as the **respiratory tree.** The comparison becomes much more meaningful if you observe a resin cast of the respiratory passages.

• Observe a resin cast of respiratory passages if one is available for observation in the laboratory.

The respiratory bronchioles in turn subdivide into several **alveolar ducts,** which terminate in alveolar sacs that rather resemble clusters of grapes. **Alveoli,** tiny balloonlike expansions along the alveolar sacs and occasionally found protruding from alveolar ducts and respiratory bronchioles, are composed of a single thin layer of squamous epithelium overlying a wispy basal lamina. The external surfaces of the alveoli are densely spiderwebbed with a network of pulmonary capillaries (Figure 36.4). Together, the alveolar and capillary walls and their fused basal laminas form the **respiratory membrane,** also called the **air-blood barrier.**

Because gas exchanges occur by simple diffusion across the respiratory membrane—oxygen passing from the alveolar air to the capillary blood and carbon dioxide leaving the capillary blood to enter the alveolar air—the alveolar sacs, alveolar ducts, and respiratory bronchioles are referred to collectively as **respiratory zone structures.** All other respiratory passageways (from the nasal cavity to the terminal bronchioles) simply serve as access or exit routes to and from these gas exchange chambers and are called **conducting**

zone structures. Because the conducting zone structures have no exchange function, they are also referred to as *anatomical dead space.*

The Lungs and Their Pleural Coverings

The paired lungs are soft, spongy organs that occupy the entire thoracic cavity except for the *mediastinum,* which houses the heart, bronchi, esophagus, and other organs (Figure 36.5). Each lung is connected to the mediastinum by a *root* containing its vascular and bronchial attachments. The structures of the root enter (or leave) the lung via a medial indentation called the *hilus.* All structures distal to the primary bronchi are found within the lung substance. A lung's *apex,* the narrower superior aspect, lies just deep to the clavicle, and its *base,* the inferior concave surface, rests on the diaphragm. Anterior, lateral, and posterior lung surfaces are in close contact with the ribs and, hence, are collectively called the *costal surface.* The medial surface of the left lung exhibits a concavity called the *cardiac notch (impression),* which accommodates the heart where it extends left from the body midline. Fissures divide the lungs into a number of *lobes*—two in the left lung and three in the right. Other than the respiratory passageways and air spaces that make up the bulk of their volume, the lungs are mostly elastic connective tissue, which allows them to recoil passively during expiration.

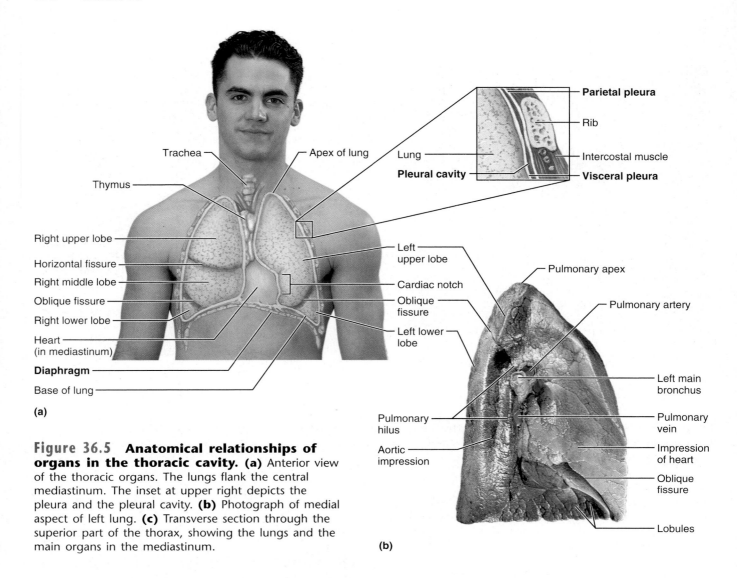

Trachea — Apex of lung

Thymus —

Parietal pleura

Rib

Lung —

Pleural cavity

Intercostal muscle

Visceral pleura

Right upper lobe —

Horizontal fissure —

Right middle lobe —

Oblique fissure —

Right lower lobe —

Heart (in mediastinum) —

Diaphragm —

Base of lung —

Left upper lobe

Cardiac notch

Oblique fissure

Left lower lobe

Pulmonary apex

Pulmonary artery

Left main bronchus

Pulmonary vein

Impression of heart

Oblique fissure

Lobules

Pulmonary hilus

Aortic impression

(a)

(b)

Figure 36.5 Anatomical relationships of organs in the thoracic cavity. (a) Anterior view of the thoracic organs. The lungs flank the central mediastinum. The inset at upper right depicts the pleura and the pleural cavity. **(b)** Photograph of medial aspect of left lung. **(c)** Transverse section through the superior part of the thorax, showing the lungs and the main organs in the mediastinum.

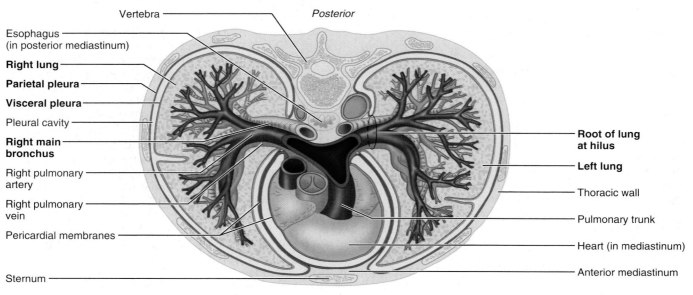

Vertebra — Posterior

Esophagus (in posterior mediastinum) —

Right lung —

Parietal pleura —

Visceral pleura —

Pleural cavity —

Right main bronchus —

Right pulmonary artery —

Right pulmonary vein —

Pericardial membranes —

Sternum —

Root of lung at hilus

Left lung

Thoracic wall

Pulmonary trunk

Heart (in mediastinum)

Anterior mediastinum

Anterior

(c)

Each lung is enclosed in a double-layered sac of serous membrane called the **pleura.** The outer layer, the **parietal pleura,** is attached to the thoracic walls and the **diaphragm;** the inner layer, covering the lung tissue, is the **visceral pleura.** The two pleural layers are separated by the *pleural cavity,* which is more of a potential space than an actual one. The pleural layers produce lubricating serous fluid that causes them to adhere closely to one another, holding the lungs to the thoracic wall and allowing them to move easily against one another during the movements of breathing.

Activity 1:
Identifying Respiratory System Organs

Before proceeding, be sure to locate on the torso model, thoracic cavity structures model, larynx model, or an anatomical chart all the respiratory structures described—both upper and lower respiratory system organs. ■

 For instructions on animal dissections, see the dissection exercises starting on page 751 in the cat and fetal pig editions of this manual.

Activity 2:
Demonstrating Lung Inflation in a Sheep Pluck

A *sheep pluck* includes the larynx, trachea with attached lungs, the heart and pericardium, and portions of the major

blood vessels found in the mediastinum (aorta, pulmonary artery and vein, venae cavae). If a sheep pluck is not available, a good substitute is a preserved inflatable pig lung.

⚠ Don disposable gloves, obtain a dissecting tray and a fresh sheep pluck (or a preserved pluck of another animal), and identify the lower respiratory system organs. Once you have completed your observations, insert a hose from an air compressor (vacuum pump) into the trachea and alternately allow air to flow in and out of the lungs. Notice how the lungs inflate. This observation is educational in a preserved pluck but it is a spectacular sight in a fresh one. Another advantage of using a fresh pluck is that the lung pluck changes color (becomes redder) as hemoglobin in trapped RBCs becomes loaded with oxygen.

If air compressors are not available, the same effect may be obtained by using a length of laboratory rubber tubing to blow into the trachea. Obtain a cardboard mouthpiece and fit it into the cut end of the laboratory tubing before attempting to inflate the lungs.

⚠ Dispose of the mouthpiece and gloves in the autoclave bag immediately after use. ■

Activity 3:
Examining Prepared Slides of Trachea and Lung Tissue

1. Obtain a compound microscope and a slide of a cross section of the tracheal wall. Identify the smooth muscle layer, the hyaline cartilage supporting rings, and the pseudostratified ciliated epithelium. Using Figure 36.6 as a guide, also try to identify a few goblet cells in the epithelium. In the space

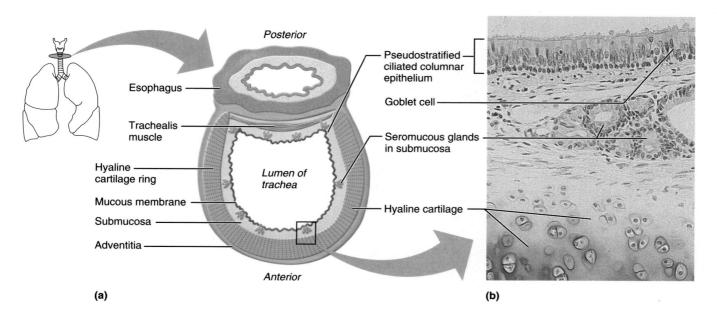

Figure 36.6   Microscopic structure of the trachea. (a) Cross-sectional view of the trachea. **(b)** Photomicrograph of a portion of the tracheal wall (225×). (See also Plate 33 in the Histology Atlas.)

below, draw a section of the tracheal wall, and label all tissue layers.

and the thin squamous epithelium of the alveolar walls (Figure 36.7b). Draw your observations of a small section of the alveolar tissue in the space below and label the alveoli.

2. Obtain a slide of lung tissue for examination. The alveolus is the main structural and functional unit of the lung and is the actual site of gas exchange. Identify a bronchiole (Figure 36.7a)

3. Examine slides of pathological lung tissues, and compare them to the normal lung specimens. Record your observations in the Exercise 36 Review Sheets. ■

Figure 36.7 Microscopic structure of a bronchiole and alveoli. (a) Photomicrograph of a section of a bronchiole. (See also Plate 35 in the Histology Atlas.) **(b)** Photomicrograph and diagrammatic view of alveoli (40×). (See also Plate 32 in the Histology Atlas.)

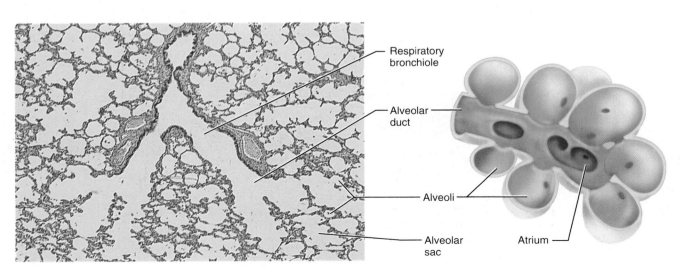

Respiratory System Physiology

Objectives

1. To define the following (and be prepared to provide volume figures if applicable):

inspiration	expiratory reserve volume
expiration	inspiratory reserve volume
tidal volume	minute respiratory volume
vital capacity	

2. To explain the role of muscles and volume changes in the mechanical process of breathing.

3. To demonstrate proper usage of a spirometer.

4. To explain the relative importance of various mechanical and chemical factors in producing respiratory variations.

5. To describe bronchial and vesicular breathing sounds.

6. To explain the importance of the carbonic acid–bicarbonate buffer system in maintaining blood pH.

Materials

- Model lung (bell jar demonstrator)
- Tape measure
- Stethoscope
- Alcohol swabs
- Spirometer
- Disposable cardboard mouthpieces
- Nose clips
- Table (on chalkboard) for recording class data
- Disposable autoclave bag
- Battery jar containing 70% ethanol solution
- Apparatus A or B:

    A: Physiograph, pneumograph, and recording attachments for physiograph

    B: BIOPAC® Apparatus: BIOPAC® MP30 (or MP35) data acquisition unit, PC or Macintosh (Mac) computer with at least 4MB of RAM available above and beyond the operating system needs and any other programs that are running, BIOPAC® Student Lab Software v3.0 or greater, wall transformer, serial cable, BIOPAC® airflow transducer, BIOPAC® calibration syringe, disposable mouthpiece, nose clip, and bacteriological filter.

- Paper bag
- 0.05 *M* NaOH
- Phenol red in a dropper bottle
- 100-ml beakers
- Straws
- Concentrated HCl and NaOH in dropper bottles
- 250- and 50-ml beakers
- Plastic wash bottles containing distilled water
- Graduated cylinder (100 ml)
- Glass stirring rod
- Animal plasma
- pH meter (standardized with buffer of pH 7)
- Buffer solution (pH 7)
- 0.01 *M* HCl
- *Human Respiratory System* videotape*

PhysioEx™ 6.0 Computer Simulation on page P-89

*Available to qualified adopters from Benjamin Cummings.
†The Instructor's Guide provides instructions for use of Power-Lab® equipment.

Mechanics of Respiration

Pulmonary ventilation, or **breathing**, consists of two phases: **inspiration**, during which air is taken into the lungs, and **expiration**, during which air passes out of the lungs. As the inspiratory muscles (external intercostals and diaphragm) contract during inspiration, the size of the thoracic cavity increases. The diaphragm moves from its relaxed dome shape to a flattened position, increasing the superoinferior volume. The external intercostals lift the rib cage, increasing the anteroposterior and lateral dimensions (Figure 37A.1). Because the lungs adhere to the thoracic walls like flypaper because of the presence of serous fluid in the pleural cavity, the intrapulmonary volume (volume within the lungs) also increases, lowering the air (gas) pressure inside the lungs. The gases then expand to fill the available space, creating a partial vacuum that causes air to flow into the lungs—constituting the act of inspiration. During expiration, the inspiratory muscles relax, and the natural tendency of the elastic lung tissue to recoil acts to decrease the intrathoracic and intrapulmonary volumes. As the gas molecules within the lungs are forced closer together, the intrapulmonary

Inspiration

Expiration

Figure 37A.1 Rib cage and diaphragm positions during breathing. (a) At the end of a normal inspiration; chest expanded, diaphragm depressed. **(b)** At the end of a normal expiration; chest depressed, diaphragm elevated.

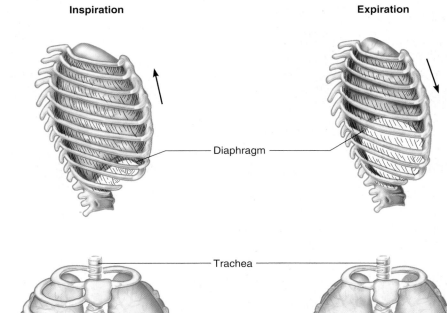

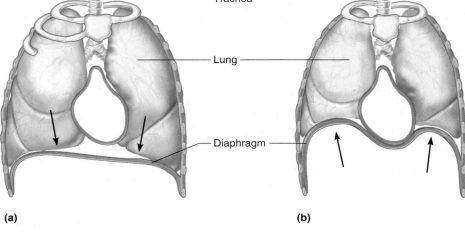

(a)   (b)

pressure rises to a point higher than atmospheric pressure. This causes gases to flow from the lungs to equalize the pressure inside and outside the lungs—the act of expiration.

Activity 1:
Operating the Model Lung

Observe the model lung, which demonstrates the principles involved in gas flows into and out of the lungs. It is a simple apparatus with a bottle "thorax," a rubber membrane "diaphragm," and balloon "lungs."

1.   Go to the demonstration area and work the model lung by moving the rubber diaphragm up and down. The balloons will not fully inflate or deflate, but notice the *relative* changes in balloon (lung) size as the volume of the thoracic cavity is alternately increased and decreased.

2.   Check the appropriate columns in the chart concerning these observations in the Exercise 37A Review Sheet at the back of this book.

3.   Simulate a pneumothorax. Inflate the balloon lungs by pulling down on the diaphragm. Ask your lab partner to let air into the bottle "thorax" by loosening the rubber stopper.

What happens to the balloon lungs?

_____

4.   After observing the operation of the model lung, conduct the following tests on your lab partner. Use the tape measure to determine his or her chest circumference by placing the tape around the chest as high up under the armpits as possible. Record the measurements in inches in the appropriate space for each of the conditions below.

Quiet breathing:

Inspiration _____ Expiration _____

Forced breathing:

Inspiration _____ Expiration _____

Do the results coincide with what you expected on the basis

of what you have learned thus far? _____

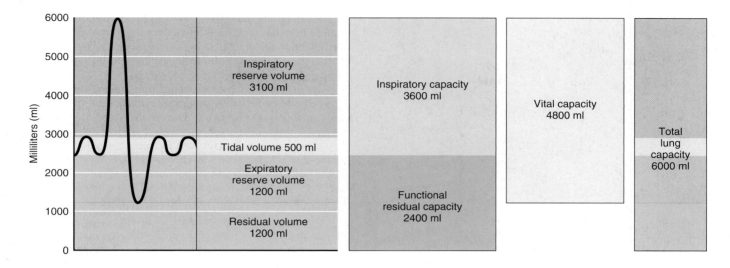

Figure 37A.2   Spirographic record for a healthy young adult male.

How does the structural relationship between the balloon-lungs and bottle-thorax differ from that seen in the human lungs and thorax?

_____

_____

_____ ■

Respiratory Sounds

As air flows in and out of the respiratory tree, it produces two characteristic sounds that can be picked up with a stethoscope (auscultated). The **bronchial sounds** are produced by air rushing through the large respiratory passageways (the trachea and the bronchi). The second sound type, **vesicular breathing sounds,** apparently results from air filling the alveolar sacs and resembles the sound of a rustling or muffled breeze.

Activity 2:
Auscultating Respiratory Sounds

1.   Obtain a stethoscope and clean the earpieces with an alcohol swab. Allow the alcohol to dry before donning the stethoscope.

2.   Place the diaphragm of the stethoscope on the throat of the test subject just below the larynx. Listen for bronchial sounds on inspiration and expiration. Move the stethoscope down toward the bronchi until you can no longer hear sounds.

3.   Place the stethoscope over the following chest areas and listen for vesicular sounds during respiration (heard primarily during inspiration).

•   At various intercostal spaces.

•   At the _triangle of auscultation_ (a small depressed area of

the back where the muscles fail to cover the rib cage; located just medial to the inferior part of the scapula).

•   Under the clavicle. ■

Diseased respiratory tissue, mucus, or pus can produce abnormal chest sounds such as rales (a rasping sound) and wheezing (a whistling sound). ●

Respiratory Volumes and Capacities—Spirometry

A person's size, sex, age, and physical condition produce variations in respiratory volumes. Normal quiet breathing moves about 500 ml of air in and out of the lungs with each breath. As you have seen in the first activity, a person can usually forcibly inhale or exhale much more air than is exchanged in normal quiet breathing. The terms given to the measurable respiratory volumes are defined next. These terms and their normal values for an adult male should be memorized.

Tidal volume (TV): Amount of air inhaled or exhaled with each breath under resting conditions (500 ml).

Inspiratory reserve volume (IRV): Amount of air that can be forcefully inhaled after a normal tidal volume inhalation (3100 ml).

Expiratory reserve volume (ERV): Amount of air that can be forcefully exhaled after a normal tidal volume exhalation (1200 ml).

Vital capacity (VC): Maximum amount of air that can be exhaled after a maximal inspiration (4800 ml).

$$VC = TV + IRV + ERV$$

An idealized tracing of the various respiratory volumes and their relationships to each other is shown in Figure 37A.2.

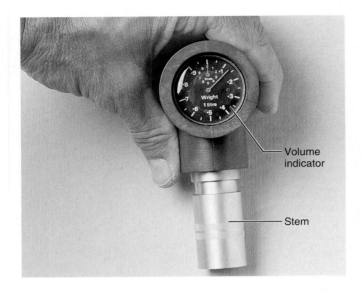

Volume indicator

Stem

Figure 37A.3   The Wright handheld dry spirometer. Reset to zero prior to each test.

Respiratory volumes will be measured with an apparatus called a **spirometer.** There are two major types of spirometers, which give comparable results—the handheld dry, or wheel, spirometers (such as the Wright spirometer illustrated in Figure 37A.3) and "wet" spirometers, such as the Phipps and Bird spirometer and the Collins spirometer (which is available in both recording and nonrecording varieties). The somewhat more sophisticated wet spirometer consists of a plastic or metal *bell* within a rectangular or cylindrical tank that air can be added to or removed from (Figure 37A.4). The outer tank contains water and has a tube running through it to carry air above the water level. The floating bottomless bell is inverted over the water-containing tank and connected to a volume indicator.

In nonrecording spirometers, an indicator moves as air is *exhaled,* and only expired air volumes can be measured directly. By contrast, recording spirometers allow both inspired and expired gas volumes to be measured.

Activity 3:
Measuring Respiratory Volumes

The steps for using a nonrecording spirometer and a wet recording spirometer are given separately below.

Using a Nonrecording Spirometer

1.   Before using the spirometer, count and record the subject's normal respiratory rate. The subject should face away from you as you make the count.

Respirations per minute: _____

Now identify the parts of the spirometer you will be using by comparing it to the illustration in Figure 37A.3 or

37A.4a. Examine the spirometer volume indicator *before beginning* to make sure you know how to read the scale. Work in pairs, with one person acting as the subject while the other records the data of the volume determinations. _Reset the indicator to zero before beginning each trial._

Obtain a disposable cardboard mouthpiece. Insert it in the open end of the valve assembly (attached to the flexible tube) of the wet spirometer or over the fixed stem of the handheld dry spirometer. Before beginning, the subject should practice exhaling through the mouthpiece without exhaling through the nose, or prepare to use the nose clips (clean them first with an alcohol swab). If you are using the handheld spirometer, make sure its dial faces upward so that the volumes can be easily read during the tests.

2.   The subject should stand erect during testing. Conduct the test three times for each required measurement. Record the data where indicated on this page, and then find the average volume figure for that respiratory measurement. After you have completed the trials and computed the averages, enter the average values on the table prepared on the chalkboard for tabulation of class data,* and copy all averaged data onto the Exercise 37A Review Sheet.

3.   Measuring tidal volume (TV). The TV, or volume of air inhaled and exhaled with each normal respiration, is approximately 500 ml. To conduct the test, inhale a normal breath, and then exhale a normal breath of air into the spirometer mouthpiece. (Do not force the expiration!) Record the volume and repeat the test twice.

trial 1: _____ ml   trial 2: _____ ml

trial 3: _____ ml   average TV: _____ ml

4.   Compute the subject's **minute respiratory volume (MRV)** using the following formula:

MRV = TV × respirations/min = _____ ml/min

5.   Measuring expiratory reserve volume (ERV). The ERV is the volume of air that can be forcibly exhaled after a normal expiration. Normally it ranges between 700 and 1200 ml.

Inhale and exhale normally two or three times, then insert the spirometer mouthpiece and exhale forcibly as much of the additional air as you can. Record your results, and repeat the test twice again.

trial 1: _____ ml trial 2: _____ ml

trial 3: _____ ml average ERV: _____ ml

*Note to the Instructor: The format of class data tabulation can be similar to that shown here. However, it would be interesting to divide the class into smokers and nonsmokers and then compare the mean average VC and ERV for each group. Such a comparison might help to determine if smokers are handicapped in any way. It also might be a good opportunity for an informal discussion of the early warning signs of bronchitis and emphysema, which are primarily smokers' diseases.

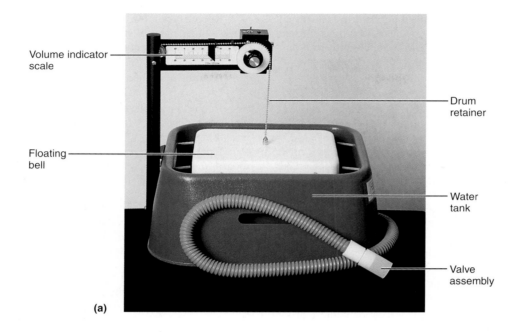

Volume indicator scale

Floating bell

Drum retainer

Water tank

Valve assembly

(a)

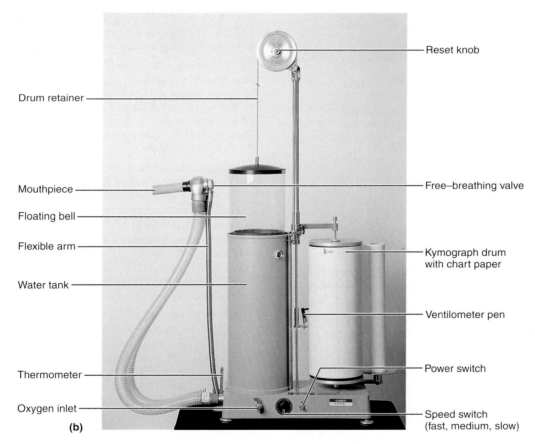

Drum retainer

Mouthpiece

Floating bell

Flexible arm

Water tank

Thermometer

Oxygen inlet

Reset knob

Free–breathing valve

Kymograph drum with chart paper

Ventilometer pen

Power switch

Speed switch (fast, medium, slow)

(b)

Figure 37A.4   Wet spirometers. (a) The Phipps and Bird wet spirometer. **(b)** The Collins-9L wet recording spirometer.

H ERV is dramatically reduced in conditions in which the elasticity of the lungs is decreased by a chronic obstructive pulmonary disease (COPD) such as **emphysema.** Since energy must be used to *deflate* the lungs in such conditions, expiration is physically exhausting to individuals suffering from COPD. ●

6. Measuring vital capacity (VC). The VC, or total exchangeable air of the lungs (the sum of TV + IRV + ERV), normally ranges from 3600 ml to 4800 ml.

Breathe in and out normally two or three times, and then bend forward and exhale all the air possible. Then, as you raise yourself to the upright position, inhale as fully as possible. It is important to *strain* to inhale the maximum amount of air that you can. Quickly insert the mouthpiece, and exhale as forcibly as you can. Record your results and repeat the test twice again.

trial 1: _____ ml   trial 2: _____ ml

trial 3: _____ ml   average VC: _____ ml

7. The inspiratory reserve volume (IRV), or volume of air that can be forcibly inhaled following a normal inspiration, can now be computed using the average values obtained for TV, ERV, and VC and plugging them into the equation:

$$IRV = VC - (TV + ERV)$$

Record your average IRV: _____ ml

The normal IRV is substantial, ranging from 1900 to 3100 ml. How does your computed value compare?

_____

Steps 8–10, which provide common directions for use of both nonrecording and recording spirometers, continue on page 406 after the wet recording spirometer directions.

Using a Recording Spirometer

1. In preparation for recording, familiarize yourself with the spirometer by comparing it to the equipment illustrated in Figure 37A.4b.

2. Examine the chart paper, noting that its horizontal lines represent milliliter units. To apply the chart paper to the recording drum, lift the drum retainer and then remove the kymograph drum. Wrap a sheet of chart paper around the drum, *making sure that the right edge overlaps the left*. Fasten it with tape, and then replace the kymograph drum and lower the drum retainer into its original position in the hole in the top of the drum.

3. Raise and lower the floating bell several times, noting as you do so that the *ventilometer pen* moves up and down on the drum. This pen, which writes in black ink, will be used for recording and should be adjusted so that it records in the approximate middle of the chart paper. This adjustment is made by repositioning the floating bell using the *reset knob* on the metal pulley at the top of the spirometer apparatus. The other pen, the respirometer pen, which records in red ink, will not be used for these tests and should be moved away from the drum's recording surface.

4. Record your normal respiratory rate. Clean the nose clips with an alcohol swab. While you wait for the alcohol to air dry, count and record your normal respiratory rate.

Respirations per minute: _____

5. Recording tidal volume. After the alcohol has air dried, apply the nose clips to your nose. This will enforce mouth breathing.

Open the *free-breathing valve*. Insert a disposable cardboard mouthpiece into the end (valve assembly) of the breathing tube, and then insert the mouthpiece into your mouth. Practice breathing for several breaths to get used to the apparatus. At this time, you are still breathing room air.

Set the spirometer switch to **SLOW** (32 mm/min). Close the free-breathing valve, and breathe in a normal manner for 2 minutes to record your tidal volume—the amount of air inspired or expired with each normal respiratory cycle. This recording should show a regular pattern of inspiration-expiration spikes and should gradually move upward on the chart paper. (A downward slope indicates that there is an air leak somewhere in the system—most likely at the mouthpiece.) Notice that on an apparatus using a counterweighted pen, such as the Collins–9L Ventilometer shown in Fig. 37A.4b, inspirations are recorded by upstrokes and expirations are recorded by downstrokes.*

6. Recording vital capacity. To record your vital capacity, take the deepest possible inspiration you can and then exhale to the greatest extent possible—really *push* the air out. The recording obtained should resemble that shown in Figure 37A.5. Repeat the vital capacity measurement twice again. Then turn off the spirometer and remove the chart paper from the kymograph drum.

7. Determine and record your measured, averaged, and corrected respiratory volumes. Because the pressure and temperature inside the spirometer are influenced by room temperature and differ from those in the body, all measured values are to be multiplied by a **BTPS** (body temperature, atmospheric pressure, and water saturation) **factor.** At room temperature, the BTPS factor is typically 1.1 or very close to that value. Hence, you will multiply your measured values by 1.1 to obtain your corrected respiratory volume values. Copy the averaged and corrected values onto the Exercise 37A Review Sheet.

● Tidal volume (TV). Select a typical resting tidal breath recording. Subtract the millimeter value of the trough (exhalation) from the millimeter value of the peak (inspiration). Record this value below as *measured TV 1*. Select two other TV tracings to determine the TV values for the TV 2 and TV 3 measurements. Then, determine your average TV and multiply it by 1.1 to obtain the BTPS-corrected average TV value.

measured TV 1:_____ ml   average TV: _____ ml

measured TV 2:_____ ml   corrected average TV:

measured TV 3:_____ ml   _____ ml

*If a Collins survey spirometer is used, the situation is exactly opposite: Upstrokes are expirations and downstrokes are inspirations.

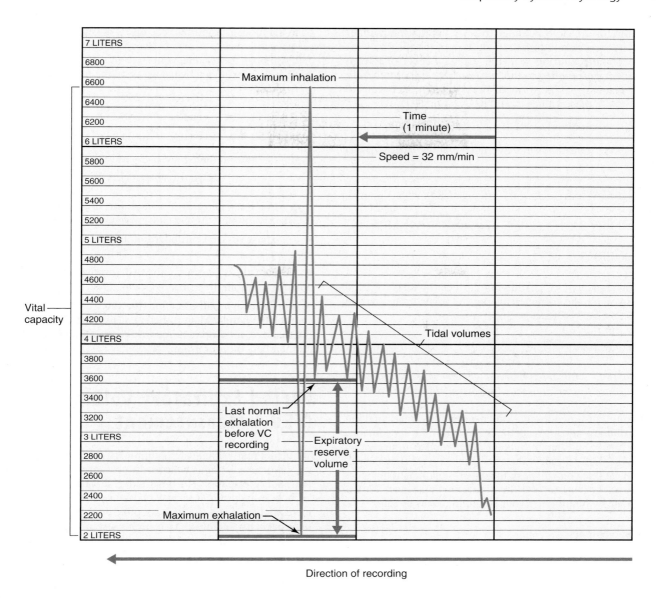

Direction of recording

Figure 37A.5 **A typical spirometry recording of tidal volume, inspiratory capacity, expiratory reserve volume, and vital capacity.** At a drum speed of 32 mm/min, each vertical column of the chart represents a time interval of 1 minute. (Note that downstrokes represent exhalations and upstrokes represent inhalations.)

Also compute your **minute respiratory volume (MRV)** using the following formula:

MRV = TV × respirations/min = _____ ml/min

• Inspiratory capacity (IC). In the first vital capacity recording, find the expiratory trough immediately preceding the maximal inspiratory peak achieved during vital capacity determination. Subtract the milliliter value of that expiration from the value corresponding to the peak of the maximal inspiration that immediately follows. For example, according to Figure 37A.5, these values would be

6600 − 3650 = 2950 ml

Record your computed value and the results of the two subsequent tests on the appropriate lines below. Then calculate

the measured and corrected inspiratory capacity averages and record.

measured IC 1:_____ ml   average IC: _____ ml

measured IC 2:_____ ml   corrected average IC:

measured IC 3:_____ ml   _____ ml

• Inspiratory reserve volume (IRV). Subtract the corrected average tidal volume from the corrected average for the inspiratory capacity and record below.

IRV = corrected average IC − corrected average TV

corrected average IRV _____ ml

• Expiratory reserve volume (ERV). Subtract the number of milliliters corresponding to the trough of the maximal expiration obtained during the vital capacity recording from milliliters corresponding to the last *normal* expiration before the VC maneuver is performed. For example, according to Figure 37A.5, these values would be

$$3650 \text{ ml} - 2050 \text{ ml} = 1600 \text{ ml}$$

Record your measured and averaged values (three trials) below.

measured ERV 1:_____ ml   average ERV: _____ ml

measured ERV 2:_____ ml   corrected average ERV:

measured ERV 3:_____ ml   _____ ml

• Vital capacity (VC). Add your corrected values for ERV and IC to obtain the corrected average VC. Record below and on the Exercise 37A Review Sheet.

corrected average VC: _____ ml

[*Now continue with step 8 (below) whether you are following the procedure for the nonrecording or recording spirometer.*]

8. Figure out how closely your measured average vital capacity volume compares with the *predicted values* for someone your age, sex, and height. Obtain the predicted figure either from Table 37A.1 (male values) or Table 37A.2 (female values). Notice that you will have to convert your height in inches to centimeters (cm) to find the corresponding value. This is easily done by multiplying your height in inches by 2.54.

Computed height: _____ cm

Predicted VC value (obtained from the appropriate table):

_____ ml

Use the following equation to compute your VC as a percentage of the predicted VC value:

$$\% \text{ of predicted VC} = \frac{\text{averaged measured VC}}{\text{predicted value}} \times 100$$

% predicted VC value: _____ %

Figure 37A.2 on page 401 is an idealized tracing of the respiratory volumes described and tested in this exercise. Examine it carefully. How closely do your test results compare to the values in the tracing?

9. Computing residual volume. A respiratory volume that cannot be experimentally demonstrated here is the residual volume (RV). RV is the amount of air remaining in the lungs after a maximal expiratory effort. The presence of residual air (usually about 1200 ml) that cannot be voluntarily flushed

from the lungs is important because it allows gas exchange to go on continuously—even between breaths.

Although the residual volume cannot be measured directly, it can be approximated by using one of the following factors:

For ages 16–34   Factor = 1.250

For ages 35–49   Factor = 1.305

For ages 50–69   Factor = 1.445

Compute your predicted RV using the following equation:

$$RV = VC \times \text{factor}$$

⚠ 10. Recording is finished for this subject. Before continuing with the next member of your group:

• Dispose of used cardboard mouthpieces in the autoclave bag.

• Swish the valve assembly (if removable) in the 70% ethanol solution, then rinse with tap water.

• Put a fresh mouthpiece into the valve assembly (or on the stem of the handheld spirometer). Using the procedures outlined above, measure and record the respiratory volumes for all members of your group. ■

Forced Expiratory Volume (FEV$_T$) Measurement

While not really diagnostic, pulmonary function tests can help the clinician distinguish between obstructive and restrictive pulmonary diseases. (In obstructive disorders, like chronic bronchitis and asthma, airway resistance is increased, whereas in restrictive diseases, such as polio and tuberculosis, total lung capacity declines.) Two highly useful pulmonary function tests used for this purpose are the FVC and the FEV$_T$.

The **FVC** (forced vital capacity) measures the amount of gas expelled when the subject takes the deepest possible breath and then exhales forcefully and rapidly. This volume is reduced in those with restrictive pulmonary disease. The **FEV$_T$** (forced expiratory volume) involves the same basic testing procedure, but it specifically looks at the percentage of the vital capacity that is exhaled during specific time intervals of the FVC test. FEV$_1$, for instance, is the amount exhaled during the first second. Healthy individuals can expire 75% to 85% of their FVC in the first second. The FEV$_1$ is low in those with obstructive disease.

Activity 4:
Measuring the FVC and FEV$_1$

Directions provided here for the FEV$_T$ determination apply only to the recording spirometer.

1. Prepare to make your recording as described for the recording spirometer, steps 1–5 on page 404.

2. At a signal agreed upon by you and your lab partner, take the deepest inspiration possible and hold it for 1 to 2 seconds. As the inspiratory peak levels off, your partner is to change the drum speed to **FAST** (1920 mm/min) so that the distance between the vertical lines on the chart represents a time of 1 second.

Table 37A.1   Predicted Vital Capacities for Males

Age													Height in centimeters												
	146	148	150	152	154	156	158	160	162	164	166	168	170	172	174	176	178	180	182	184	186	188	190	192	194
16	3765	3820	3870	3920	3975	4025	4075	4130	4180	4230	4285	4335	4385	4440	4490	4540	4590	4645	4695	4745	4800	4850	4900	4955	5005
18	3740	3790	3840	3890	3940	3995	4045	4095	4145	4200	4250	4300	4350	4405	4455	4505	4555	4610	4660	4710	4760	4815	4865	4915	4965
20	3710	3760	3810	3860	3910	3960	4015	4065	4115	4165	4215	4265	4320	4370	4420	4470	4520	4570	4625	4675	4725	4775	4825	4875	4930
22	3680	3730	3780	3830	3880	3930	3980	4030	4080	4135	4185	4235	4285	4335	4385	4435	4485	4535	4585	4635	4685	4735	4790	4840	4890
24	3635	3685	3735	3785	3835	3885	3935	3985	4035	4085	4135	4185	4235	4285	4330	4380	4430	4480	4530	4580	4630	4680	4730	4780	4830
26	3605	3655	3705	3755	3805	3855	3905	3955	4000	4050	4100	4150	4200	4250	4300	4350	4395	4445	4495	4545	4595	4645	4695	4740	4790
28	3575	3625	3675	3725	3775	3820	3870	3920	3970	4020	4070	4115	4165	4215	4265	4310	4360	4410	4460	4510	4555	4605	4655	4705	4755
30	3550	3595	3645	3695	3740	3790	3840	3890	3935	3985	4035	4080	4130	4180	4230	4275	4325	4375	4425	4470	4520	4570	4615	4665	4715
32	3520	3565	3615	3665	3710	3760	3810	3855	3905	3950	4000	4050	4095	4145	4195	4240	4290	4340	4385	4435	4485	4530	4580	4625	4675
34	3475	3525	3570	3620	3665	3715	3760	3810	3855	3905	3950	4000	4045	4095	4140	4190	4225	4285	4330	4380	4425	4475	4520	4570	4615
36	3445	3495	3540	3585	3635	3680	3730	3775	3825	3870	3920	3965	4010	4060	4105	4155	4200	4250	4295	4340	4390	4435	4485	4530	4580
38	3415	3465	3510	3555	3605	3650	3695	3745	3790	3840	3885	3930	3980	4025	4070	4120	4165	4210	4260	4305	4350	4400	4445	4495	4540
40	3385	3435	3480	3525	3575	3620	3665	3710	3760	3805	3850	3900	3945	3990	4035	4085	4130	4175	4220	4270	4315	4360	4410	4455	4500
42	3360	3405	3450	3495	3540	3590	3635	3680	3725	3770	3820	3865	3910	3955	4000	4050	4095	4140	4185	4230	4280	4325	4370	4415	4460
44	3315	3360	3405	3450	3495	3540	3585	3630	3675	3725	3770	3815	3860	3905	3950	3995	4040	4085	4130	4175	4220	4270	4315	4360	4405
46	3285	3330	3375	3420	3465	3510	3555	3600	3645	3690	3735	3780	3825	3870	3915	3960	4005	4050	4095	4140	4185	4230	4275	4320	4365
48	3255	3300	3345	3390	3435	3480	3525	3570	3615	3655	3700	3745	3790	3835	3880	3925	3970	4015	4060	4105	4150	4190	4235	4280	4325
50	3210	3255	3300	3345	3390	3430	3475	3520	3565	3610	3650	3695	3740	3785	3830	3870	3915	3960	4005	4050	4090	4135	4180	4225	4270
52	3185	3225	3270	3315	3355	3400	3445	3490	3530	3575	3620	3660	3705	3750	3795	3835	3880	3925	3970	4010	4055	4100	4140	4185	4230
54	3155	3195	3240	3285	3325	3370	3415	3455	3500	3540	3585	3630	3670	3715	3760	3800	3845	3890	3930	3975	4020	4060	4105	4145	4190
56	3125	3165	3210	3255	3295	3340	3380	3425	3465	3510	3550	3595	3640	3680	3725	3765	3810	3850	3895	3940	3980	4025	4065	4110	4150
58	3080	3125	3165	3210	3250	3290	3335	3375	3420	3460	3500	3545	3585	3630	3670	3715	3755	3800	3840	3880	3925	3965	4010	4050	4095
60	3050	3095	3135	3175	3220	3260	3300	3345	3385	3430	3470	3500	3555	3595	3635	3680	3720	3760	3805	3845	3885	3930	3970	4015	4055
62	3020	3060	3110	3150	3190	3230	3270	3310	3350	3390	3440	3480	3520	3560	3600	3640	3680	3730	3770	3810	3850	3890	3930	3970	4020
64	2990	3030	3080	3120	3160	3200	3240	3280	3320	3360	3400	3440	3490	3530	3570	3610	3650	3690	3730	3770	3810	3850	3900	3940	3980
66	2950	2990	3030	3070	3110	3150	3190	3230	3270	3310	3350	3390	3430	3470	3510	3550	3600	3640	3680	3720	3760	3800	3840	3880	3920
68	2920	2960	3000	3040	3080	3120	3160	3200	3240	3280	3320	3360	3400	3440	3480	3520	3560	3600	3640	3680	3720	3760	3800	3840	3880
70	2890	2930	2970	3010	3050	3090	3130	3170	3210	3250	3290	3330	3370	3410	3450	3480	3520	3560	3600	3640	3680	3720	3760	3800	3840
72	2860	2900	2940	2980	3020	3060	3100	3140	3180	3210	3250	3290	3330	3370	3410	3450	3490	3530	3570	3610	3650	3680	3720	3760	3800
74	2820	2860	2900	2930	2970	3010	3050	3090	3130	3170	3200	3240	3280	3320	3360	3400	3440	3470	3510	3550	3590	3630	3670	3710	3740

Courtesy of Warren E. Collins, Inc., Braintree, Mass.

Table 37A.2 Predicted Vital Capacities for Females

| Age | Height in centimeters | | | | | | | | | | | | | | | | | | | | | | | | |
	146	148	150	152	154	156	158	160	162	164	166	168	170	172	174	176	178	180	182	184	186	188	190	192	194
16	2950	2990	3030	3070	3110	3150	3190	3230	3270	3310	3350	3390	3430	3470	3510	3550	3590	3630	3670	3715	3755	3800	3840	3880	3920
17	2935	2975	3015	3055	3095	3135	3175	3215	3255	3295	3335	3375	3415	3455	3495	3535	3575	3615	3655	3695	3740	3780	3820	3860	3900
18	2920	2960	3000	3040	3080	3120	3160	3200	3240	3280	3320	3360	3400	3440	3480	3520	3560	3600	3640	3680	3720	3760	3800	3840	3880
20	2890	2930	2970	3010	3050	3090	3130	3170	3210	3250	3290	3330	3370	3410	3450	3490	3525	3565	3605	3645	3695	3720	3760	3800	3840
22	2860	2900	2940	2980	3020	3060	3095	3135	3175	3215	3255	3290	3330	3370	3410	3450	3490	3530	3570	3610	3650	3685	3725	3765	3800
24	2830	2870	2910	2950	2985	3025	3065	3100	3140	3180	3220	3260	3300	3335	3375	3415	3455	3490	3530	3570	3610	3650	3685	3725	3765
26	2800	2840	2880	2920	2960	3000	3035	3070	3110	3150	3190	3230	3265	3300	3340	3380	3420	3455	3495	3530	3570	3610	3650	3685	3725
28	2775	2810	2850	2890	2930	2965	3000	3040	3070	3115	3155	3190	3230	3270	3305	3345	3380	3420	3460	3495	3535	3570	3610	3650	3685
30	2745	2780	2820	2860	2895	2935	2970	3010	3045	3085	3120	3160	3195	3235	3270	3310	3345	3385	3420	3460	3495	3535	3570	3610	3645
32	2715	2750	2790	2825	2865	2900	2940	2975	3015	3050	3090	3125	3160	3200	3235	3275	3310	3350	3385	3425	3460	3495	3535	3570	3610
34	2685	2725	2760	2795	2835	2870	2910	2945	2980	3020	3055	3090	3130	3165	3200	3240	3275	3310	3350	3385	3425	3460	3495	3535	3570
36	2655	2695	2730	2765	2805	2840	2875	2910	2950	2985	3020	3060	3095	3130	3165	3205	3240	3275	3310	3350	3385	3420	3460	3495	3530
38	2630	2665	2700	2735	2770	2810	2845	2880	2915	2950	2990	3025	3060	3095	3130	3170	3205	3240	3275	3310	3350	3385	3420	3455	3490
40	2600	2635	2670	2705	2740	2775	2810	2850	2885	2920	2955	2990	3025	3060	3095	3135	3170	3205	3240	3275	3310	3345	3380	3420	3455
42	2570	2605	2640	2675	2710	2745	2780	2815	2850	2885	2920	2955	2990	3025	3060	3100	3135	3170	3205	3240	3275	3310	3345	3380	3415
44	2540	2575	2610	2645	2680	2715	2750	2785	2820	2855	2890	2925	2960	2995	3030	3060	3095	3130	3165	3200	3235	3270	3305	3340	3375
46	2510	2545	2580	2615	2650	2685	2715	2750	2785	2820	2855	2890	2925	2960	2995	3030	3060	3095	3130	3165	3200	3235	3270	3305	3340
48	2480	2515	2550	2585	2620	2650	2685	2715	2750	2785	2820	2855	2890	2925	2960	2995	3030	3060	3095	3130	3160	3195	3230	3265	3300
50	2455	2485	2520	2555	2590	2625	2655	2690	2720	2755	2785	2820	2855	2890	2925	2955	2990	3025	3060	3090	3125	3155	3190	3225	3260
52	2425	2455	2490	2525	2555	2590	2625	2655	2690	2720	2755	2790	2820	2855	2890	2925	2955	2990	3020	3055	3090	3125	3155	3190	3220
54	2395	2425	2460	2495	2530	2560	2590	2625	2655	2690	2720	2755	2790	2820	2855	2885	2920	2950	2985	3020	3050	3085	3115	3150	3180
56	2365	2400	2430	2460	2495	2525	2560	2590	2625	2655	2690	2720	2755	2790	2820	2855	2885	2920	2950	2980	3015	3045	3080	3110	3145
58	2335	2370	2400	2430	2460	2495	2525	2560	2590	2625	2655	2690	2720	2750	2785	2815	2850	2880	2920	2945	2975	3010	3040	3075	3105
60	2305	2340	2370	2400	2430	2460	2495	2525	2560	2590	2625	2655	2685	2720	2750	2780	2810	2845	2875	2915	2940	2970	3000	3035	3065
62	2280	2310	2340	2370	2405	2435	2465	2495	2525	2560	2590	2620	2655	2685	2715	2745	2775	2810	2840	2870	2900	2935	2965	2995	3025
64	2250	2280	2310	2340	2370	2400	2430	2465	2495	2525	2555	2585	2620	2650	2680	2710	2740	2770	2805	2835	2865	2895	2925	2955	2990
66	2220	2250	2280	2310	2340	2370	2400	2430	2460	2495	2525	2555	2585	2615	2645	2675	2705	2735	2765	2800	2825	2860	2890	2920	2950
68	2190	2220	2250	2280	2310	2340	2370	2400	2430	2460	2490	2520	2550	2580	2610	2640	2670	2700	2730	2760	2795	2820	2850	2880	2910
70	2160	2190	2220	2250	2280	2310	2340	2370	2400	2425	2455	2485	2515	2545	2575	2605	2635	2665	2695	2725	2755	2780	2810	2840	2870
72	2130	2160	2190	2220	2250	2280	2310	2335	2365	2395	2425	2455	2480	2510	2540	2570	2600	2630	2660	2685	2715	2745	2775	2805	2830
74	2100	2130	2160	2190	2220	2245	2275	2305	2335	2360	2390	2420	2450	2475	2505	2535	2565	2590	2620	2650	2680	2710	2740	2765	2795

Courtesy of Warren E. Collins, Inc., Braintree, Mass.

3. Once the drum speed is changed, exhale as much air as rapidly and forcibly as possible.

4. When the tracing plateaus (bottoms out), stop recording and determine your FVC. Subtract the milliliter reading in the expiration trough (the bottom plateau) from the preceding inhalation peak (the top plateau). Record this value.

FVC: _____ ml

5. Prepare to calculate the FEV_1. Draw a vertical line intersecting with the spirogram tracing at the precise point that exhalation began. Identify this line as *line 1*. From line 1, measure 32 mm horizontally to the left, and draw a second vertical line. Label this as *line 2*. The distance between the two lines represents 1 second, and the volume exhaled in the first second is read where line 2 intersects the spirogram tracing. Subtract that milliliter value from the milliliter value of the inhalation peak (at the intersection of line 1), to determine the volume of gas expired in the first second. According to the values given in Figure 37A.6, that figure would be 3400 ml (6800 ml − 3400 ml). Record your measured value below.

Milliliters of gas expired in second 1: _____ ml

6. To compute the FEV_1 use the following equation:

$$FEV_1 = \frac{\text{volume expired in second 1}}{\text{FVC volume}} \times 100\%$$

Record your calculated value below and on the Exercise 37A Review Sheet.

FEV_1: _____ % of FVC ■

Using the Pneumograph to Determine Factors Influencing Rate and Depth of Respiration*

The neural centers that control respiratory rhythm and maintain a rate of 12 to 18 respirations/min are located in the medulla and pons. On occasion, input from the stretch receptors in the lungs (via the vagus nerve to the medulla) modifies the respiratory rate, as in cases of extreme overinflation of the lungs (Hering-Breuer reflex).

H Death occurs when medullary centers are completely suppressed, as from an overdose of sleeping pills or gross overindulgence in alcohol, and respiration ceases completely. ●

Although the nervous system centers initiate the basic rhythm of breathing, there is no question that physical phenomena such as talking, yawning, coughing, and exercise can modify the rate and depth of respiration. So, too, can chemi-

cal factors such as changes in oxygen or carbon dioxide concentrations in the blood or fluctuations in blood pH. Changes in carbon dioxide blood levels seem to act directly on the medulla control centers, whereas changes in pH and oxygen concentrations are monitored by chemoreceptor regions in the aortic and carotid bodies, which in turn send input to the medulla. The experimental sequence in this section is designed to test the relative importance of various physical and chemical factors in the process of respiration.

The **pneumograph,** an apparatus that records variations in breathing patterns, is the best means of observing respiratory variations resulting from physical and chemical factors. The chest pneumograph is a coiled rubber hose that is attached around the thorax. As the subject breathes, chest movements produce pressure changes within the pneumograph that are transmitted to a recorder. BIOPAC® uses an airflow transducer to record breathing movements.

The instructor will demonstrate the method of setting up the recording equipment and discuss the interpretation of the results. Work in pairs so that one person can mark the record to identify the test for later interpretation. Ideally, the student being tested should face away from the recording apparatus to prevent voluntary modification of the record.

Activity 5:
Visualizing Respiratory Variations
Using the Physiograph- Pneumograph Apparatus

1. Attach the pneumograph tubing firmly, but not restrictively, around the thoracic cage at the level of the sixth rib, leaving room for chest expansion during testing. If the subject is female, position the tubing above the breasts to prevent slippage during testing. Set the pneumograph speed at 1 or 2, and the time signal at 10-second intervals. Record quiet breathing for 1 minute with the subject in a sitting position.

Record breaths per minute: _____

2. Make a vital capacity tracing: Record a maximal inhalation followed by a maximal exhalation. This should correlate to the vital capacity measurement obtained earlier and will provide a baseline for comparison during the rest of the pneumograph testing. Stop recording, and mark the graph appropriately to indicate: tidal volume, expiratory reserve volume, inspiratory reserve volume, and vital capacity (the total of the three measurements). Also mark, with arrows, the direction the recording stylus moves during inspiration and during expiration.

Measure in mm the height of the vital capacity recording. Divide the vital capacity measurement average recorded on the Exercise 37A Review Sheet by the millimeter figure to obtain the volume (in milliliters of air) represented by 1 mm on the recording. For example, if your vital capacity reading is 4000 ml and the vital capacity tracing occupies a vertical distance of 40 mm on the pneumograph recording, then a vertical distance of 1 mm equals 100 ml of air.

*****Note to the Instructor:** This exercise may also be done without using the recording apparatus by simply having the students count the respiratory rate visually.

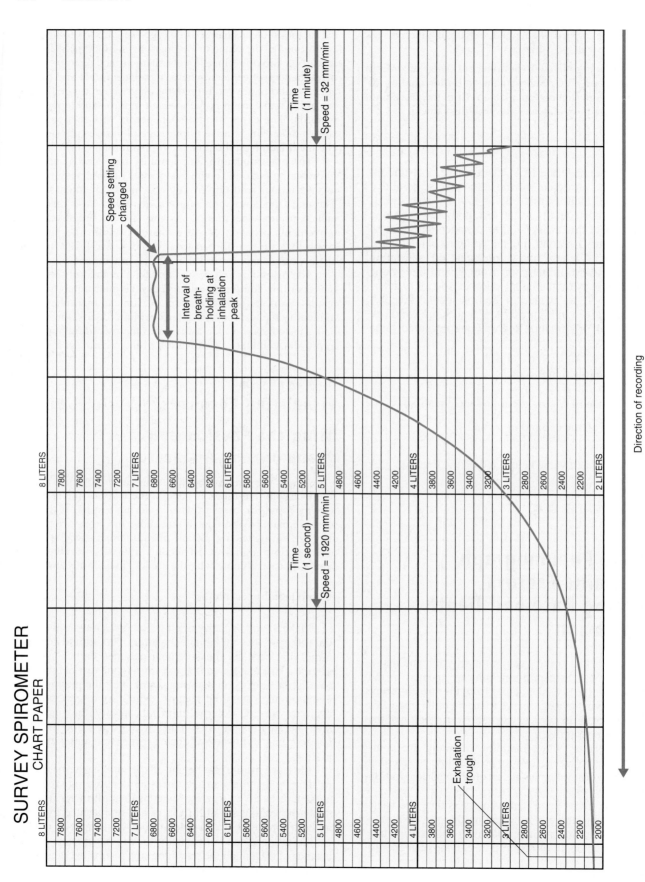

Figure 37A.6 A recording of the forced vital capacity (FVC) and forced expiratory volume (FEV) or timed vital capacity test.

Record your computed value: _____ ml air/mm

3. Record the subject's breathing as he or she performs activities from the list below. Make sure the record is marked accurately to identify each test conducted. Record your results on the Exercise 37A Review Sheet.

talking   swallowing water

yawning   coughing

laughing   lying down

standing   doing a math problem

running in place   (concentrating)

4. Without recording, have the subject breathe normally for 2 minutes, then inhale deeply and hold his or her breath for as long as he or she can.

Time the breath-holding interval: _____ sec

As the subject exhales, turn on the recording apparatus and record the recovery period (time to return to normal breathing—usually slightly over 1 minute):

Time of recovery period: _____ sec

Did the subject have the urge to inspire *or* expire during breath holding?

_____

Without recording, repeat the above experiment, but this time exhale completely and forcefully *after* taking the deep breath. What was observed this time?

_____

_____

Explain the results. (Hint: The vagus nerve is the sensory nerve of the lungs and plays a role here.)

_____

_____

_____

5. Have the subject hyperventilate (breathe deeply and forcefully at the rate of 1 breath/4 sec) for about 30 seconds.* Record both during and after hyperventilation. How does the pattern obtained during hyperventilation compare with that

*A sensation of dizziness may develop. (As the carbon dioxide is washed out of the blood by overventilation, the blood pH increases, leading to a decrease in blood pressure and reduced cerebral circulation.) The subject may experience a lack of desire to breathe after forced breathing is stopped. If the period of breathing cessation—apnea—is extended, cyanosis of the lips may occur.

recorded during the vital capacity tracing?

_____

Is the respiratory rate after hyperventilation faster *or* slower than during normal quiet breathing?

_____

6. Repeat the above test, but do not record until after hyperventilating. After hyperventilation, the subject is to hold his or her breath as long as he or she can. Can the breath be held for a longer or shorter time after hyperventilating?

_____

7. Without recording, have the subject breathe into a paper bag for 3 minutes, then record his or her breathing movements.

⚠ *During the bag-breathing exercise the subject's partner should watch the subject carefully for any untoward reactions.*

Is the breathing rate faster *or* slower than that recorded during normal quiet breathing?

_____

After hyperventilating? _____

8. Run in place for 2 minutes, and then have your partner determine the length of time that you can hold your breath.

Length of breath-holding: _____ sec

9. To prove that respiration has a marked effect on circulation, conduct the following test. Have your lab partner record the rate and relative force of your radial pulse before you begin.

Rate: _____ beats/min   Relative force: _____

Inspire forcibly. Immediately close your mouth and nose to retain the inhaled air, and then make a forceful and prolonged expiration. Your lab partner should observe and record the condition of the blood vessels of your neck and face, and again immediately palpate the radial pulse.

Observations: _____

_____

Radial pulse: _____ beats/min   Relative force: _____

Explain the changes observed. _____

_____

_____

⚠ Dispose of the paper bag in the autoclave bag. Keep

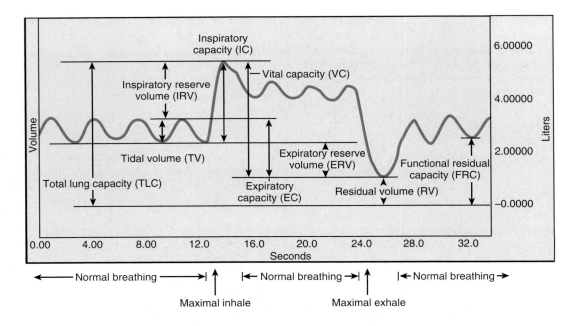

Figure 37A.7 **Example of a computer-generated spirogram.**

the pneumograph records to interpret results and hand them in if requested by the instructor. Observation of the test results should enable you to determine which chemical factor, carbon dioxide or oxygen, has the greatest effect on modifying the respiratory rate and depth. ■

Measuring Respiratory Volumes Using BIOPAC®

In this activity, you will measure **respiratory volumes** using the BIOPAC® airflow transducer. An example of these volumes is demonstrated in the computer-generated spirogram in Figure 37A.7. Since it is not possible to measure **residual volume (RV)** using the airflow transducer, assume that it is 1.0 liter for each subject, which is a reasonable estimation. It is also important to estimate the **predicted vital capacity** of the subject for comparison to the measured value. A rough estimate of the vital capacity in liters (VC) of a subject can be calculated using the following formulas based on height in centimeters (H) and age in years (A).

Male VC   = (0.052)H − (0.022)A − 3.60

Female VC = (0.041)H − (0.018)A − 2.69

Because there are many other factors besides height and age that influence vital capacity, it should be assumed that measured values 20% lesser or greater than the calculated predicted value are considered normal.

Setting up the Equipment

1.   Connect the BIOPAC® unit to the computer and turn the computer **ON.**

2.   Make sure the BIOPAC® MP30 (or MP 35) unit is **OFF.**

3.   Plug in the equipment as shown in Figure 37A.8.

  •   Airflow transducer—CH 1

4.   Turn the BIOPAC® MP30 (or MP35) unit **ON.**

5.   Place a *clean* bacteriological filter onto the end of the BIOPAC® calibration syringe as shown in Figure 37A.9. Since the subject will be blowing through a filter, it is necessary to use a filter for calibration also.

6.   Insert the calibration syringe and filter assembly into the airflow transducer on the side labeled **Inlet.**

7.   Start the BIOPAC® Student Lab program on the computer by double-clicking the icon on the desktop or by following your instructor's guidance.

8.   Select lesson **L12-Lung-1** from the menu, and click **OK.**

9.   Type in a filename that will save this subject's data on the computer hard drive. You may want to use subject last name followed by Lung-1 (for example, SmithLung-1), then click **OK.**

Calibrating the Equipment

There are two precautions that must be followed:

•   The airflow transducer is sensitive to gravity, so it must be held directly parallel to the ground during calibration and recording.

•   Do not hold onto the airflow transducer when it is attached to the calibration syringe and filter assembly—the syringe tip is likely to break. See Figure 37A.10 for the proper handling of the calibration assembly.

1.   Make sure the plunger is pulled all the way out. While the assembly is held in a steady position parallel to the ground, click **Calibrate** and then **OK** after you have read the alert box. This part of the calibration will terminate automatically with an alert box ensuring that you have read the on-screen instructions and those indicated in step 2, below.

2.   The final part of the calibration will involve simulating five breathing cycles using the calibration syringe. A single cycle consists of:

Figure 37A.8 **Setting up the BIOPAC® MP30 (or MP35) unit.** Plug the airflow transducer into Channel 1.

- Pushing the plunger in (taking one second for this stroke).
- Waiting for two seconds.
- Pulling the plunger out (taking one second for this stroke).
- Waiting two seconds.

Remember, the airflow transducer must be held directly parallel to the ground during calibration and recording.

4. When ready to perform this second stage of the calibration, click **Yes.** After you have completed five cycles, click **End Calibration.**

5. Observe the data, which should look similar to that in Figure 37A.11.

- If the data look very different, click **Redo Calibration** and repeat the steps above.

- If the data look similar, gently remove the calibration syringe, leaving the air filter attached to the transducer. Proceed to the next section.

Recording the Data

Follow these procedures very precisely because the airflow transducer is very sensitive. Hints to obtaining the best data:

- Always insert air filter on, and breathe through, the transducer side labeled **Inlet.**

- Keep the airflow transducer upright at all times.

- The subject should not look at the computer screen during the recording of data.

- The subject must keep a nose clip on throughout the experiment.

1. Insert a clean mouthpiece into the air filter that is already attached to the airflow transducer. *Be sure that the filter is attached to the **Inlet** side of the airflow transducer.*

2. Write the name of the subject on the mouthpiece and air filter. For safety purposes, each subject must use their own air filter and mouthpiece.

3. The subject should now place the nose clip on the nose (or hold the nose very tightly with finger pinch), wrap the lips

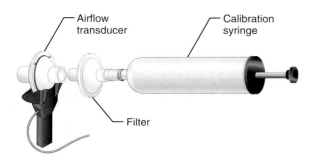

Figure 37A.9 Placement of the calibration syringe and filter assembly onto the airflow transducer for calibration.

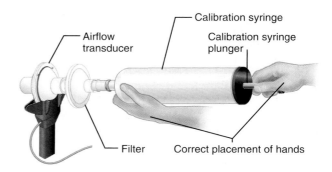

Figure 37A.10 Proper handling of the calibration assembly.

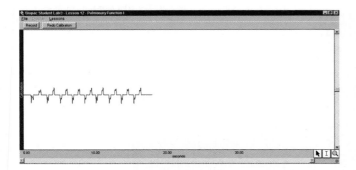

Figure 37A.11   Example of calibration data.

tightly around the mouthpiece, and begin breathing normally through the airflow transducer, as shown in Figure 37A.12.

4.   When prepared, the subject will complete the following unbroken series with nose plugged and lips tightly sealed around the mouthpiece:

•   Take three normal breaths (1 breath = inhale + exhale).

•   Inhale as much air as possible, then exhale back to normal breathing.

•   Take three normal breaths.

•   Exhale as much air as possible, then inhale back to normal breathing.

•   Take three normal breaths.

5.   When the subject is prepared to proceed, click **Record** on the first normal inhalation and proceed. When the subject finishes the last exhalation at the end of the series, click **Stop**.

6.   Observe the data, which should look similar to that in Figure 37A.13.

•   If the data look very different, click **Redo** and repeat the steps above. Be certain that the lips are sealed around the mouthpiece, the nose is completely plugged, and the transducer is upright.

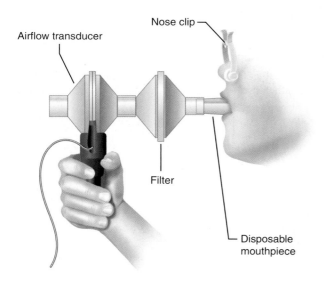

Figure 37A.12   Proper equipment setup for recording data.

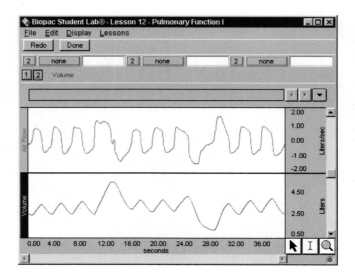

Figure 37A.13   Example of pulmonary data.

•   If the data look similar, proceed to step 7.

7.   When finished, click **Done.** A pop-up window will appear.

•   Click **Yes** if you are done and want to stop recording.

•   To record from another subject select **Record from another Subject** and return to step 1 under **Recording the Data.** Note that you will not need to redo the calibration procedure for the second subject.

•   If continuing to the **Data Analysis** section, select **Analyze current data file** and proceed to step 2 of the Data Analysis section.

Data Analysis

1.   If just starting the BIOPAC® program to perform data analysis, enter **Review Saved Data** mode and choose the file with the subject's Lung data (for example, SmithLung-1).

2.   Observe how the channel numbers are designated: CH 1—Airflow; CH 2—Volume.

3.   To set up the display for optimal viewing, hide CH 1—Airflow. To do this, hold down the control key (PC) or option key (Mac) while using the cursor to click on channel box 1 (the small box with a 1 in the upper left of the screen).

4.   To analyze the data, set up the first pair of channel/measurement boxes at the top of the screen by selecting the following channel and measurement type from the drop-down menu:

Channel	Measurement
CH 2	p-p

5.   Use the arrow cursor and click on the I-beam cursor box on the lower right side of the screen to activate the "area selection" function. Using the activated I-beam cursor, highlight the region containing the first three breaths as shown in Figure 37A.14.

6. Observe that the computer automatically calculates the **p-p** for the selected area. This measurement, calculated from the data by the computer, represents the difference in value between the highest and lowest values in the selected area.

7. For the first three breaths that are highlighted, the **p-p** measurement represents the **tidal volume** (in liters). Record this value in the chart below.

Pulmonary Measurements	
Volumes	**Measurement (liters)**
Tidal volume (TV)	
Inspiratory reserve volume (IRV)	
Expiratory reserve volume (ERV)	
Vital capacity (VC)	
Residual volume (RV)	1.00 (assumed)

8. Use the I-beam cursor to measure the **IRV.** Highlight from the peak of maximum inhalation to the peak of the last normal inhalation just before it (see Figure 37A.7 for an example of IRV). Observe and record the **p-p** value in the chart (to the nearest 1/100 liter).

9. Use the I-beam cursor to measure the **ERV.** Highlight from the trough of maximum exhalation to the trough of the last normal exhalation just before it (see Figure 37A.7 for an example of ERV). Observe and record the **p-p** value in the chart (to the nearest 1/100 liter).

10. Lastly, use the I-beam cursor to measure the **VC.** Highlight from the trough of maximum exhalation to the peak of maximum inhalation (see Figure 37A.7 for an example of VC). Observe and record the **p-p** value in the chart (to the nearest 1/100 liter).

11. When finished, **Exit** the program.

Calculated Pulmonary Capacities		
Capacity	**Formula**	**Calculation (liters)**
Inspiratory capacity (IC)	= TV + IRV	
Expiratory capacity (EC)	= TV + ERV	
Functional residual capacity (FRC)	= ERV + RV	
Total lung capacity (TLC)	= TV + RV + IRV + ERV	

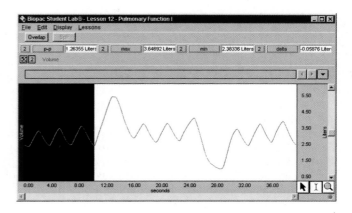

Figure 37A.14 Highlighting data for the first three breaths.

Using the measured data, calculate the following capacities: Use the formula in the introduction of this activity (page 412) to calculate the predicted vital capacity of the subject based on height and age.

Predicted VC: _____ liters

How does the measured vital capacity compare to the predicted vital capacity?

_____

_____

_____

Describe why height and weight might correspond with a subject's VC.

_____

_____

_____

What other factors might influence the VC of a subject?

_____

_____

_____

Role of the Respiratory System in Acid-Base Balance of Blood

As you have already learned, pulmonary ventilation is necessary for continuous oxygenation of the blood and removal of carbon dioxide (a waste product of cellular respiration) from the blood. Blood pH must be relatively constant for the cells of the body to function optimally. The carbonic acid–bicarbonate buffer system of the blood is extremely important because it helps stabilize arterial blood pH at 7.4 ± 0.02.

When carbon dioxide diffuses into the blood from the tissue cells, much of it enters the red blood cells, where it combines with water to form carbonic acid (Figure 37A.15):

$$H_2O + CO_2 \xrightarrow[\text{enzyme present in RBC}]{\text{Carbonic anhydrase}} H_2CO_3$$

Some carbonic acid is also formed in the plasma, but that reaction is very slow because of the lack of the carbonic anhydrase enzyme. Shortly after it forms, carbonic acid dissociates to release bicarbonate (HCO_3^-) and hydrogen (H^+) ions. The hydrogen ions that remain in the cells are neutralized, or buffered, when they combine with hemoglobin molecules. If they were not neutralized, the intracellular pH would become very acidic as H^+ ions accumulated. The bicarbonate ions diffuse out of the red blood cells into the plasma, where they become part of the carbonic acid–bicarbonate buffer system. As HCO_3^- follows its concentration gradient into the plasma, an electrical imbalance develops in the RBCs that draws Cl^-

into them from the plasma. This exchange phenomenon is called the *chloride shift*.

Acids (more precisely, H^+) released into the blood by the body cells tend to lower the pH of the blood and to cause it to become acidic. On the other hand, basic substances that enter the blood tend to cause the blood to become more alkaline and the pH to rise. Both of these tendencies are resisted in large part by the carbonic acid–bicarbonate buffer system. If the H^+ concentration in the blood begins to increase, the H^+ ions combine with bicarbonate ions to form carbonic acid (a weak acid that does not tend to dissociate at physiological or acid pH) and are thus removed.

$$H^+ + HCO_3^- \rightarrow H_2CO_3$$

Likewise, as blood H^+ concentration drops below what is desirable and blood pH rises, H_2CO_3 dissociates to release bicarbonate ions and H^+ ions to the blood. The released H^+ lowers the pH again. The bicarbonate ions, being *weak* bases, are poorly functional under alkaline conditions and have little effect on blood pH unless and until blood pH drops toward acid levels.

$$H_2CO_3 \rightarrow H^+ + HCO_3^-$$

In the case of excessively slow or shallow breathing (hypoventilation) or fast deep breathing (hyperventilation), the amount of carbonic acid in the blood can be greatly modified—increasing dramatically during hypoventilation and decreasing substantially during hyperventilation. In either situation, if the buffering ability of the blood is inadequate, respiratory acidosis or alkalosis can result. Therefore, maintaining the normal rate and depth of breathing is important for proper control of blood pH.

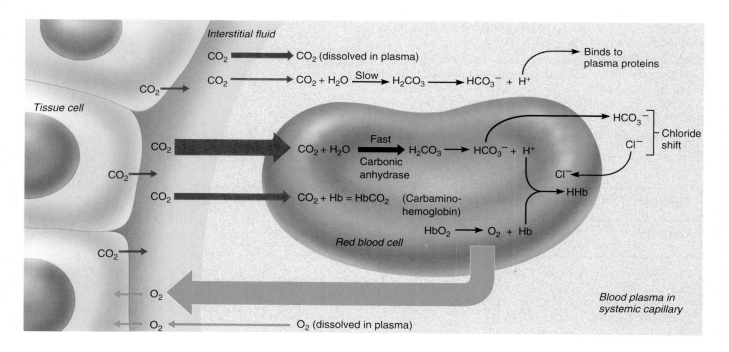

Figure 37A.15 **Oxygen release and carbon dioxide loading at the tissues.**

Activity 6:
Demonstrating the Reaction Between Carbon Dioxide (in Exhaled Air) and Water

1. Fill a beaker with 100 ml of distilled water.

2. Add 5 ml of 0.05 M NaOH and five drops of phenol red. Phenol red is a pH indicator that turns yellow in acidic solutions.

3. Blow through a straw into the solution.

What do you observe?

_____

_____

What chemical reaction is taking place in the beaker?

_____

_____

4. Discard the straw in the autoclave bag. ■

Activity 7:
Observing the Operation of Standard Buffers

1. To observe the ability of a buffer system to stabilize the pH of a solution, obtain five 250-ml beakers and a wash bottle containing distilled water. Set up the following experimental samples:

Beaker 1:
(150 ml distilled water)   pH _____

Beaker 2:
(150 ml distilled water and
1 drop concentrated HCl)   pH _____

Beaker 3:
(150 ml distilled water and
1 drop concentrated NaOH)   pH _____

Beaker 4:
(150 ml standard buffer solution
[pH 7] and 1 drop concentrated HCl)   pH _____

Beaker 5:
(150 ml standard buffer solution
[pH 7] and 1 drop concentrated NaOH)   pH _____

2. Using a pH meter standardized with a buffer solution of pH 7, determine the pH of the contents of each beaker and record above. After *each and every* pH recording, the pH meter switch should be turned to **STANDBY,** and the electrodes rinsed thoroughly with a stream of distilled water from the wash bottle.

3. Add 3 more drops of concentrated HCl to beaker 4, stir, and record the pH: _____

4. Add 3 more drops of concentrated NaOH to beaker 5, stir, and record the pH: _____

How successful was the buffer solution in resisting pH changes when a strong acid (HCl) or a strong base (NaOH) was added?

_____ ■

Activity 8:
Exploring the Operation of the Carbonic Acid–Bicarbonate Buffer System

To observe the ability of the carbonic acid–bicarbonate buffer system of blood to resist pH changes, perform the following simple experiment.

1. Obtain two small beakers (50 ml), animal plasma, graduated cylinder, glass stirring rod, and a dropper bottle of 0.01 M HCl. Using the pH meter standardized with the buffer solution of pH 7.0, measure the pH of the animal plasma. Use only enough plasma to allow immersion of the electrodes and measure the volume used carefully.

pH of the animal plasma: _____

2. Add 2 drops of the 0.01 M HCl solution to the plasma; stir and measure the pH again.

pH of plasma plus 2 drops of HCl: _____

3. Turn the pH meter switch to **STANDBY,** rinse the electrodes, and then immerse them in a quantity of distilled water (pH 7) exactly equal to the amount of animal plasma used. Measure the pH of the distilled water.

pH of distilled water: _____

4. Add 2 drops of 0.01 M HCl, swirl, and measure the pH again.

pH of distilled water plus the two drops of HCl: _____

Is the plasma a good buffer? _____

What component of the plasma carbonic acid–bicarbonate buffer system was acting to counteract a change in pH when HCl was added?

_____ ■

The Microscope

Care and Structure of the Compound Microscope

1. Label all indicated parts of the microscope.

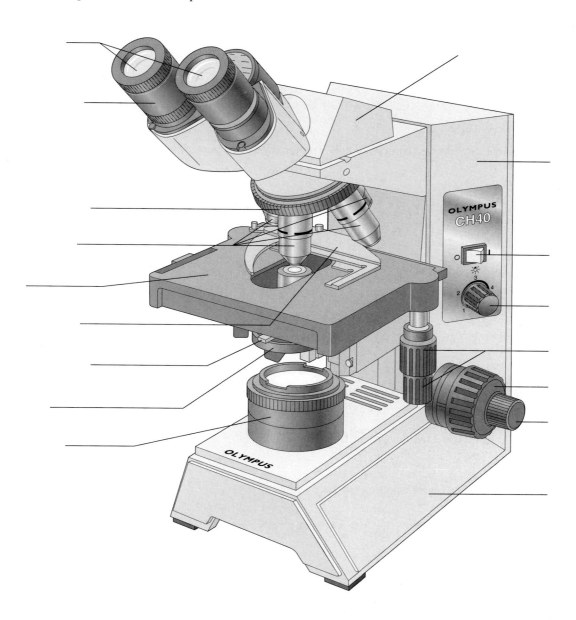

2. The following statements are true or false. If true, write *T* on the answer blank. If false, correct the statement by writing on the blank the proper word or phrase to replace the one that is underlined.

_____ 1. The microscope lens may be cleaned with any soft tissue.

_____ 2. The coarse adjustment knob may be used in focusing with all objective lenses.

_____ 3. The microscope should be stored with the oil immersion lens in position over the stage.

_____ 4. When beginning to focus, the lowest power lens should be used.

_____ 5. When focusing, always focus toward the specimen.

_____ 6. A coverslip should always be used with wet mounts and the high-power and oil lenses.

_____ 7. The greater the amount of light delivered to the objective lens, the less the resolution.

3. Match the microscope structures given in column B with the statements in column A that identify or describe them.

Column A

_____ 1. platform on which the slide rests for viewing

_____ 2. lens located at the superior end of the body tube

_____ 3. secure(s) the slide to the stage

_____ 4. delivers a concentrated beam of light to the specimen

_____ 5. used for precise focusing once initial focusing has been done

_____ 6. carries the objective lenses; rotates so that the different objective lenses can be brought into position over the specimen

_____ 7. used to increase the amount of light passing through the specimen

Column B

a. coarse adjustment knob

b. condenser

c. fine adjustment knob

d. iris diaphragm

e. mechanical stage or spring clips

f. movable nosepiece

g. objective lenses

h. ocular

i. stage

4. Explain the proper technique for transporting the microscope.

_____

_____

5. Define the following terms.

real image: _____

_____

virtual image: _____

_____

Total magnification: _____

_____

Resolution: _____

Viewing Objects Through the Microscope

6. Complete, or respond to, the following statements:

_____ 1. The distance from the bottom of the objective lens in use to the specimen is called the _____.

_____ 2. The resolution of the human eye is approximately _____ μm.

_____ 3. The area of the specimen seen when looking through the microscope is the _____.

_____ 4. If a microscope has a 10× ocular and the total magnification at a particular time is 950×, the objective lens in use at that time is _____ ×.

_____ 5. Why should the light be dimmed when looking at living (nearly transparent) cells?

_____ 6. If, after focusing in low power, only the fine adjustment need be used to focus the specimen at the higher powers, the microscope is said to be _____.

_____ 7. If, when using a 10× ocular and a 15× objective, the field size is 1.5 mm, the approximate field size with a 30× objective is _____ mm.

_____ 8. If the size of the high-power field is 1.2 mm, an object that occupies approximately a third of that field has an estimated diameter of _____ mm.

_____ 9. Assume there is an object on the left side of the field that you want to bring to the center (that is, toward the apparent right). In what direction would you move your slide?

_____ 10. If the object is in the top of the field and you want to move it downward to the center, you would move the slide _____.

7. You have been asked to prepare a slide with the letter *k* on it (as shown below). In the circle below, draw the *k* as seen in the low-power field.

k

8. The numbers for the field sizes below are too large to represent the typical compound microscope lens system, but the relationships depicted are accurate. Figure out the magnification of fields 1 and 3, and the field size of 2. (*Hint:* Use your ruler.)

5 mm   _____ mm   0.5 mm

1. →◯←   2. →◯←   3. →∘←

_____×   100×   _____×

9. Say you are observing an object in the low-power field. When you switch to high-power, it is no longer in your field of view.

Why might this occur? _____

What should be done initially to prevent this from happening? _____

_____

10. Do the following factors increase or decrease as one moves to higher magnifications with the microscope?

resolution: _____   amount of light needed: _____

working distance: _____   depth of field: _____

11. A student has the high-dry lens in position and appears to be intently observing the specimen. The instructor, noting a working distance of about 1 cm, knows the student isn't actually seeing the specimen.

How so? _____

12. If you are observing a slide of tissue two cell layers thick, how can you determine which layer is superior?

_____

_____

_____

13. Describe the proper procedure for preparing a wet mount.

_____

_____

_____

14. Give two reasons why the light should be dimmed when viewing living or unstained material.

_____

_____

15. Indicate the probable cause of the following situations arising during use of a microscope.

a. Only half of the field is illuminated: _____

_____

b. Field does not change as mechanical stage is moved: _____

_____

16. Under what circumstances is the stereomicroscope used to study biological specimens? _____

_____

The Cell: Transport Mechanisms and Permeability—Wet Lab

Choose all answers that apply to questions 1 and 2, and place their letters on the response blanks to the right.

1. Molecular motion _____

   a. reflects the kinetic energy of molecules.
   b. reflects the potential energy of molecules.
   c. is ordered and predictable.
   d. is random and erratic.

2. Velocity of molecular movement _____

   a. is higher in larger molecules.
   b. is lower in larger molecules.
   c. increases with increasing temperature.
   d. decreases with increasing temperature.
   e. reflects kinetic energy.

3. The following refer to Activity 4, the laboratory experiment using dialysis sacs to study diffusion through nonliving membranes:

   Sac 1: 40% glucose suspended in distilled water

         Did glucose pass out of the sac? _____

         Test used to determine presence of glucose: _____

         Did the sac weight change? _____

         If so, explain the reason for its weight change. _____

         _____

   Sac 2: 40% glucose suspended in 40% glucose

         Was there net movement of glucose in either direction? _____

         Explanation: _____

         Did the sac weight change? _____ Explanation: _____

         _____

   Sac 3: 10% NaCl in distilled water

         Was there net movement of NaCl out of the sac? _____

         Test used to determine the presence of NaCl: _____

         Direction of net osmosis: _____

Sac 4: Sucrose and Congo red dye in distilled water

Was there net movement of dye out of the sac? _____

Was the net movement of sucrose out of the sac? _____

Test used to determine sucrose movement from the sac to the beaker and rationale for use of this test:

_____

Direction of net osmosis: _____

4. What single characteristic of the differentially permeable membranes *used in the laboratory* determines the substances that

can pass through them? _____

In addition to this characteristic, what other factors influence the passage of substances through living membranes?

_____

_____

5. A semipermeable sac containing 4% NaCl, 9% glucose, and 10% albumin is suspended in a solution with the following composition: 10% NaCl, 10% glucose, and 40% albumin. Assume that the sac is permeable to all substances except albumin. State whether each of the following will (a) move into the sac, (b) move out of the sac, or (c) not move.

glucose: _____   albumin: _____

water: _____   NaCl: _____

6. The diagrams below represent three microscope fields containing red blood cells. Arrows show the direction of net osmosis.

Which field contains a hypertonic solution? _____ The cells in this field are said to be _____.

Which field contains an isotonic bathing solution? _____ Which field contains a hypotonic solution? _____ What is

happening to the cells in this field? _____

_____

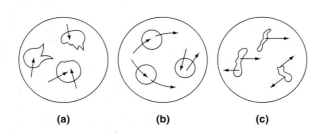

(a)   (b)   (c)

7. Assume you are conducting the experiment illustrated in the next figure. Both hydrochloric acid (HCl) with a molecular weight of about 36.5 and ammonium hydroxide (NH_4OH) with a molecular weight of 35 are volatile and easily enter the gaseous state. When they meet, the following reaction will occur:

$$HCl + NH_4OH \rightarrow H_2O + NH_4Cl$$

Ammonium chloride (NH_4Cl) will be deposited on the glass tubing as a smoky precipitate where the two gases meet. Predict which gas will diffuse more quickly and indicate to which end of the tube the smoky precipitate will be closer.

a. The faster diffusing gas is _____.

b. The precipitate forms closer to the _____ end.

Rubber stopper   Cotton wad with HCl   Cotton wad with NH_4OH

Support

8. What determines whether a transport process is active or passive? _____

_____

9. Characterize membrane transport as fully as possible by choosing all the phrases that apply and inserting their letters on the answer blanks.

Passive processes: _____   Active processes: _____

a. account for the movement of fats and respiratory gases through the plasma membrane
b. explain solute pumping, phagocytosis, and pinocytosis
c. include osmosis, simple diffusion, and filtration
d. may occur against concentration and/or electrical gradients
e. use hydrostatic pressure or molecular energy as the driving force
f. move ions, amino acids, and some sugars across the plasma membrane

10. For the osmometer demonstration (Activity 5), explain why the level of the water column rose during the laboratory session.

_____

_____

_____

_____

_____

11. Define the following terms.

diffusion: _____

_____

_____

osmosis: _____

_____

_____

simple diffusion: _____

_____

_____

filtration: _____

_____

_____

active transport: _____

_____

_____

phagocytosis: _____

_____

_____

fluid-phase endocytosis: _____

_____

_____

Classification of Tissues

Tissue Structure and Function—General Review

1. Define *tissue*. _____

_____

2. Use the key choices to identify the major tissue types described below.

   Key: a. connective tissue   b. epithelium   c. muscle   d. nervous tissue

   _____   1. lines body cavities and covers the body's external surface

   _____   2. pumps blood, flushes urine out of the body, allows one to swing a bat

   _____   3. transmits electrochemical impulses

   _____   4. anchors, packages, and supports body organs

   _____   5. cells may absorb, secrete, and filter

   _____   6. most involved in regulating and controlling body functions

   _____   7. major function is to contract

   _____   8. synthesizes hormones

   _____   9. the most durable tissue type

   _____ 10. abundant nonliving extracellular matrix

   _____ 11. most widespread tissue in the body

   _____ 12. forms nerves and the brain

Epithelial Tissue

3. Describe five general characteristics of epithelial tissue. _____

_____

_____

_____

4. On what basis are epithelial tissues classified? _____

5. List the six major functions of epithelium in the body, and give examples of each. _____

Function 1: _____ Example: _____

Function 2: _____ Example: _____

Function 3: _____ Example: _____

Function 4: _____ Example: _____

Function 5: _____ Example: _____

Function 6: _____ Example: _____

6. How is the function of epithelium reflected in its arrangement? _____

_____

7. Where is ciliated epithelium found? _____

_____

What role does it play? _____

_____

8. Transitional epithelium is actually stratified squamous epithelium, but there is something special about it.

How does it differ structurally from other stratified squamous epithelia? _____

_____

How does this reflect its function in the body? _____

_____

9. How do the endocrine and exocrine glands differ in structure and function? _____

_____

_____

10. Respond to the following with the key choices.

Key: a. pseudostratified ciliated columnar   c. simple cuboidal   e. stratified squamous
        b. simple columnar   d. simple squamous   f. transitional

_____ 1. lining of the esophagus

_____ 2. lining of the stomach

_____ 3. alveolar sacs of lungs

_____ 4. tubules of the kidney

_____ 5. epidermis of the skin

_____ 6. lining of bladder; peculiar cells that have the ability to slide over each other

_____ 7. forms the thin serous membranes; a single layer of flattened cells

Connective Tissue

11. What are three general characteristics of connective tissues? _____

_____

_____

_____

_____

12. What functions are performed by connective tissue? _____

_____

13. How are the functions of connective tissue reflected in its structure? _____

_____

_____

14. Using the key, choose the best response to identify the connective tissues described below.

_____ 1. attaches bones to bones and muscles to bones   *Key:*   a. adipose connective tissue
                         b. areolar connective tissue

_____ 2. acts as a storage depot for fat   c. dense fibrous connective tissue
                         d. elastic cartilage

_____ 3. the dermis of the skin   e. fibrocartilage
                         f. hematopoietic tissue

_____ 4. makes up the intervertebral discs   g. hyaline cartilage
                         h. osseous tissue

_____ 5. forms the hip bone

_____ 6. composes basement membranes; a soft packaging tissue with a jellylike matrix

_____ 7. forms the larynx, the costal cartilages of the ribs, and the embryonic skeleton

_____ 8. provides a flexible framework for the external ear

_____ 9. firm, structurally amorphous matrix heavily invaded with fibers; appears glassy and smooth

_____ 10. matrix hard owing to calcium salts; provides levers for muscles to act on

_____ 11. insulates against heat loss

15. Why do adipose cells remind people of a ring with a single jewel? _____

_____

Muscle Tissue

16. The three types of muscle tissue exhibit similarities as well as differences. Check the appropriate space in the chart to indicate which muscle types exhibit each characteristic.

Characteristic	Skeletal	Cardiac	Smooth
Voluntarily controlled			
Involuntarily controlled			
Striated			
Has a single nucleus in each cell			
Has several nuclei per cell			
Found attached to bones			
Allows you to direct your eyeballs			
Found in the walls of the stomach, uterus, and arteries			
Contains spindle-shaped cells			
Contains branching cylindrical cells			
Contains long, nonbranching cylindrical cells			
Has intercalated discs			
Concerned with locomotion of the body as a whole			
Changes the internal volume of an organ as it contracts			
Tissue of the heart			

Nervous Tissue

17. What two physiological characteristics are highly developed in neurons (nerve cells)? _____

_____

18. In what ways are neurons similar to other cells? _____

_____

How are they different? _____

19. Sketch a neuron, recalling in your diagram the most important aspects of its structure. Below the diagram, describe how its particular structure relates to its function in the body.

_____

_____

For Review

20. Label the following tissue types here and on the next pages, and identify all visible major structures—cell types, matrix (ground substance and fibers), fat vacuole, basement membrane—if present.

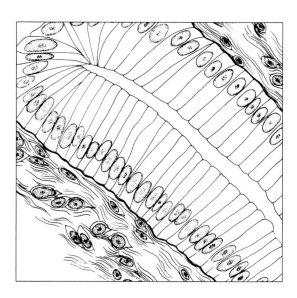

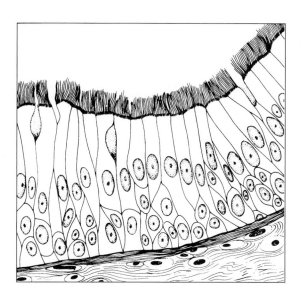

(a) _____   **(b)** _____

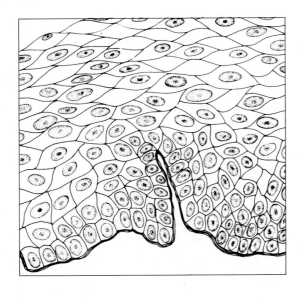

(c) _____

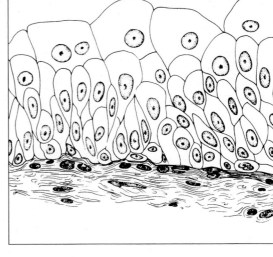
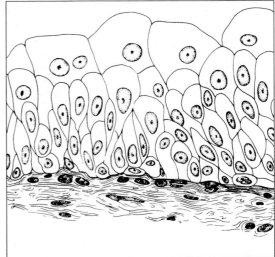

(d) _____

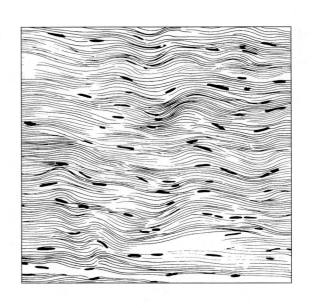

(e) _____

(f) _____

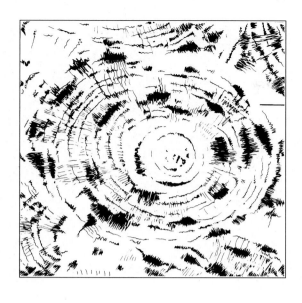

(g) _____

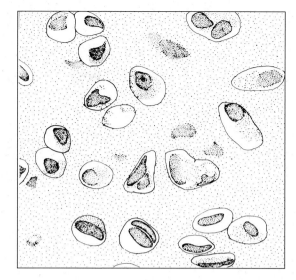

(h) _____

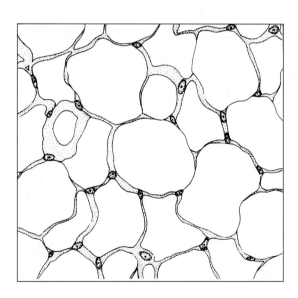

(i) _____

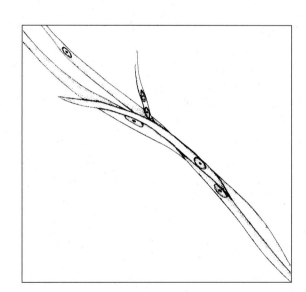

(j) _____

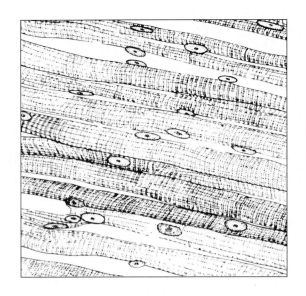

(k) _____

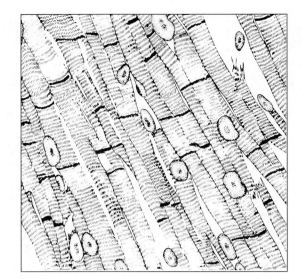

(l) _____

Blood

Composition of Blood

1. What is the blood volume of an average-size adult male? _____ liters   An average adult female? _____ liters

2. What determines whether blood is bright red or a dull brick-red? _____

_____

3. Use the key to identify the cell type(s) or blood elements that fit the following descriptive statements.

Key: a. red blood cell   d. basophil   g. lymphocyte
       b. megakaryocyte   e. monocyte   h. formed elements
       c. eosinophil   f. neutrophil   i. plasma

_____ 1. most numerous leukocyte

_____, _____, and

_____ 2. granulocytes

_____ 3. also called an erythrocyte; anucleate formed element

_____, _____ 4. actively phagocytic leukocytes

_____, _____ 5. agranulocytes

_____ 6. ancestral cell of platelets

_____ 7. (a) through (g) are all examples of these

_____ 8. number rises during parasite infections

_____ 9. releases histamine; promotes inflammation

_____ 10. many formed in lymphoid tissue

_____ 11. transports oxygen

_____ 12. primarily water, noncellular; the fluid matrix of blood

_____ 13. increases in number during prolonged infections

_____, _____, _____,

_____, _____ 14. also called white blood cells

4. List four classes of nutrients normally found in plasma. _____ ,

_____ , _____ , and _____

Name two gases. _____ and _____

Name three ions. _____ , _____ , and _____

5. Describe the consistency and color of the plasma you observed in the laboratory. _____

_____

6. What is the average life span of a red blood cell? How does its anucleate condition affect this life span?

_____

_____

_____

7. From memory, describe the structural characteristics of each of the following blood cell types as accurately as possible, and note the percentage of each in the total white blood cell population.

eosinophils: _____

_____

neutrophils: _____

_____

lymphocytes: _____

_____

basophils: _____

_____

monocytes: _____

_____

8. Correctly identify the blood pathologies described in column A by matching them with selections from column B:

	Column A	Column B
_____ 1.	abnormal increase in the number of WBCs	a. anemia
_____ 2.	abnormal increase in the number of RBCs	b. leukocytosis
_____ 3.	condition of too few RBCs or of RBCs with hemoglobin deficiencies	c. leukopenia
_____ 4.	abnormal decrease in the number of WBCs	d. polycythemia

Anatomy of the Respiratory System

Upper and Lower Respiratory System Structures

1. Complete the labeling of the diagram of the upper respiratory structures (sagittal section).

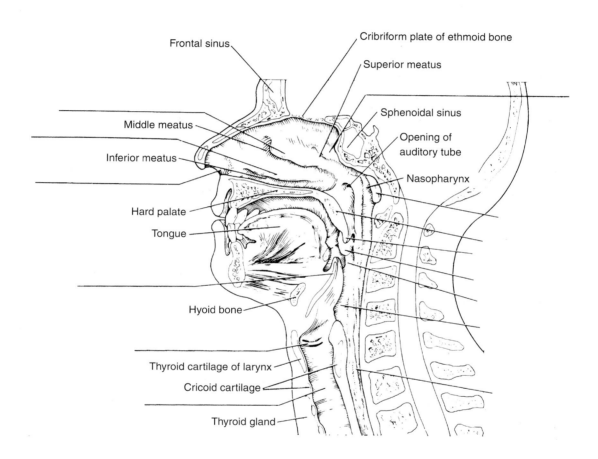

Frontal sinus

Cribriform plate of ethmoid bone

Superior meatus

Middle meatus

Sphenoidal sinus

Inferior meatus

Opening of auditory tube

Hard palate

Nasopharynx

Tongue

Hyoid bone

Thyroid cartilage of larynx

Cricoid cartilage

Thyroid gland

2. Two pairs of vocal folds are found in the larynx. Which pair are the true vocal cords (superior or inferior)?

_____

3. Name the specific cartilages in the larynx that correspond to the following descriptions.

forms the Adam's apple: _____   shaped like a signet ring: _____

a "lid" for the larynx: _____   vocal cord attachment: _____

4. What is the significance of the fact that the human trachea is reinforced with cartilaginous rings?

_____

Of the fact that the rings are incomplete posteriorly? _____

_____

5. What is the function of the pleural membranes? _____

_____

_____

6. Name two functions of the nasal cavity mucosa. _____

and _____

7. The following questions refer to the primary bronchi.

Which is longer?_____   Larger in diameter?_____   More horizontal?_____

The more common site that traps a foreign object that has entered the respiratory passageways? _____

8. Appropriately label all structures provided with leader lines on the diagrams below.

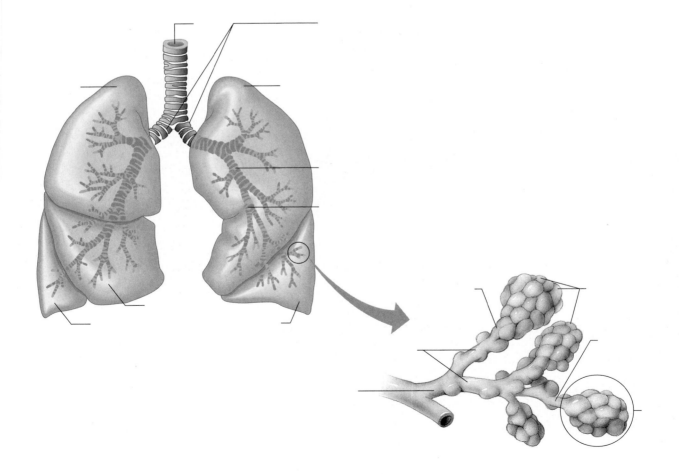

9. Trace a molecule of oxygen from the external nares to the pulmonary capillaries of the lungs: External nares →

_____

_____

_____

10. Match the terms in column B to the descriptions in column A.

Column A

_____ 1. connects the larynx to the primary bronchi

_____ 2. site of tonsils

_____ 3. food passageway posterior to the trachea

_____ 4. covers the glottis during swallowing of food

_____ 5. contains the vocal cords

_____ 6. nerve that activates the diaphragm during inspiration

_____ 7. pleural layer lining the walls of the thorax

_____ 8. site from which oxygen enters the pulmonary blood

_____ 9. connects the middle ear to the nasopharynx

_____ 10. opening between the vocal folds

_____ 11. increases air turbulence in the nasal cavity

_____ 12. separates the oral cavity from the nasal cavity

Column B

a. alveolus

b. bronchiole

c. concha

d. epiglottis

e. esophagus

f. glottis

g. larynx

h. opening of auditory tube

i. palate

j. parietal pleura

k. pharynx

l. phrenic nerve

m. primary bronchi

n. trachea

o. vagus nerve

p. visceral pleura

11. What portions of the respiratory system are referred to as anatomical dead space? _____

_____

_____

Why? _____

12. Define the following terms.

external respiration: _____

_____

internal respiration: _____

_____

cellular respiration: _____

_____

13. On the diagram below identify alveolar epithelium, capillary endothelium, alveoli, and red blood cells. Bracket the respiratory membrane.

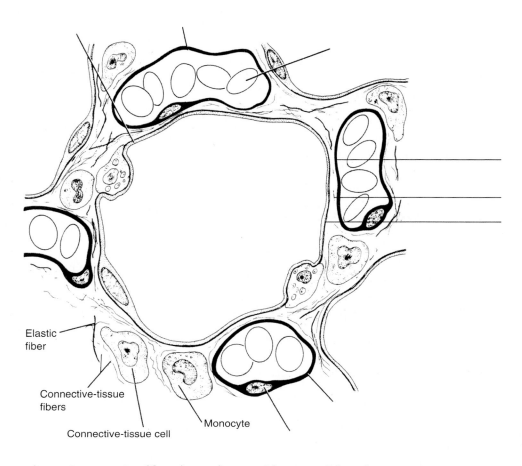

Elastic
fiber

Connective-tissue
fibers

Connective-tissue cell

Monocyte

Demonstrating Lung Inflation in a Sheep Pluck

14. Does the lung inflate part by part or as a whole, like a balloon? _____

15. What happened when the pressure was released? _____

16. What type of tissue ensures this phenomenon? _____

Examining Prepared Slides of Lung and Tracheal Tissue

17. The tracheal epithelium is ciliated and has goblet cells. What is the function of each of these modifications?

Cilia? _____

Goblet cells? _____

18. The tracheal epithelium is said to be pseudostratified. Why? _____

_____

_____

19. What structural characteristics of the alveoli make them an ideal site for the diffusion of gases?

_____

Why does oxygen move from the alveoli into the pulmonary capillary blood? _____

_____

_____

20. If you observed pathological lung sections, record your observations. Also record how the tissue differed from normal lung tissue. Complete the table below using your answers.

Slide type	Observations	Comparison to normal lung tissue

NAME ______________________ LAB TIME/DATE ______________________

REVIEW SHEET
exercise
37A

Respiratory System Physiology

Mechanics of Respiration

1. For each of the following cases, check the column appropriate to your observations on the operation of the model lung.

	Diaphragm pushed up		Diaphragm pulled down	
Change	**Increased**	**Decreased**	**Increased**	**Decreased**
In internal volume of the bell jar (thoracic cage)				
In internal pressure				
In the size of the balloons (lungs)				
In direction of air flow	Into lungs	Out of lungs	Into lungs	Out of lungs

2. Base your answers to the following on your observations in question 1.

Under what internal conditions does air tend to flow into the lungs? ______________________

____

Under what internal conditions does air tend to flow out of the lungs? Explain why this is so. ______________________

____

3. Activation of the diaphragm and the external intercostal muscles begins the inspiratory process. What effect does contraction of these muscles have on thoracic volume, and how is this accomplished? ______________________

____

____

____

4. What was the approximate increase in diameter of chest circumference during a quiet inspiration? ____________ inches

During forced inspiration? ____________ inches.

What temporary physiological advantage is created by the substantial increase in chest circumference during forced

inspiration? _____

_____

_____

5. The presence of a partial vacuum between the pleural membranes is integral to normal breathing movements. What would happen if an opening were made into the chest cavity, as with a puncture wound?

_____

How is this condition treated medically? _____

Respiratory Sounds

6. Which of the respiratory sounds is heard during both inspiration and expiration? _____

Which is heard primarily during inspiration? _____

7. Where did you best hear the vesicular respiratory sounds? _____

Respiratory Volumes and Capacities—Spirometry

8. Write the respiratory volume term and the normal value that is described by the following statements.

Volume of air present in the lungs after a forceful expiration: _____

Volume of air that can be expired forcibly after a normal expiration: _____

Volume of air that is breathed in and out during a normal respiration: _____

Volume of air that can be inspired forcibly after a normal inspiration: _____

Volume of air corresponding to TV + IRV + ERV: _____

9. Record experimental respiratory volumes as determined in the laboratory. (Corrected values are for the recording spirometer only.)

Average TV: _____ ml

Corrected value for TV: _____ ml

Average IRV: _____ ml

Corrected value for IRV: _____ ml

MRV: _____ ml/min

Average ERV: _____ ml

Corrected value for ERV: _____ ml

Average VC: _____ ml

Corrected value for VC: _____ ml

% predicted VC: _____ %

FEV_1: _____ % FVC

10. Would your vital-capacity measurement differ if you performed the test while standing? _____ While lying down?

_____ Explain. _____

_____

11. Which respiratory ailments can respiratory volume tests be used to detect?

_____

_____

12. Using an appropriate reference, complete the chart below.

		O_2	CO_2	N_2
% of composition of air	Inspired			
	Expired			

Use of the Pneumograph to Determine Factors Influencing Rate and Depth of Respiration

13. Where are the neural control centers of respiratory rhythm? _____ and _____

14. Based on the pneumograph reading of respiratory variation, what was the rate of quiet breathing?

Initial testing _____ breaths/min

Record observations of how the initial pneumograph or respiratory belt transducer recording was modified during the various testing procedures described below. Indicate the respiratory rate, and include comments on the relative depth of the respiratory peaks observed.

Test performed	Observations
Talking	
Yawning	
Laughing	
Standing	
Concentrating	
Swallowing water	
Coughing	
Lying down	
Running in place	

15. Record student data below.

Breath-holding interval after a deep inhalation: _____ sec   length of recovery period: _____ sec

Breath-holding interval after a forceful expiration: _____ sec   length of recovery period: _____ sec

After breathing quietly and taking a deep breath (which you held), was your urge to inspire *or* expire? _____

After exhaling and then holding one's breath, was the desire for inspiration *or* expiration? _____

Explain these results. (Hint: What reflex is involved here?) _____

_____

_____

16. Observations after hyperventilation: _____

_____

17. Length of breath holding after hyperventilation: _____ sec

Why does hyperventilation produce apnea or a reduced respiratory rate? _____

_____

_____

18. Observations for rebreathing breathed air: _____

_____

Why does rebreathing breathed air produce an increased respiratory rate? _____

_____

19. What was the effect of running in place (exercise) on the duration of breath holding? _____

Explain this effect. _____

_____

20. Record student data from the test illustrating the effect of respiration on circulation.

Radial pulse before beginning test: _____ /min   Radial pulse after testing: _____ /min

Relative pulse force before beginning test: _____   Relative force of radial pulse after testing: _____

Condition of neck and facial veins after testing: _____

Explain these data. _____

_____

21. Do the following factors generally increase (indicate with I) or decrease (indicate with D) the respiratory rate and depth?

increase in blood CO_2: _____   increase in blood pH: _____

decrease in blood O_2: _____   decrease in blood pH: _____

Did it appear that CO_2 or O_2 had a more marked effect on modifying the respiratory rate? _____

22. Where are sensory receptors sensitive to changes in blood pressure located? _____

_____

23. Where are sensory receptors sensitive to changes in O_2 levels in the blood located? _____

_____

24. What is the primary factor that initiates breathing in a newborn infant? _____

_____

25. Blood CO_2 levels and blood pH are related. When blood CO_2 levels increase, does the pH increase or decrease?

_____ Explain why. _____

_____

_____

Role of the Respiratory System in Acid-Base Balance of Blood

26. Define *buffer.* _____

27. How successful was the laboratory buffer (pH 7) in resisting changes in pH when the acid was added? _____

_____

When the base was added? _____

How successful was the buffer in resisting changes in pH when the additional aliquots (3 more drops) of the acid and base

were added to the original samples? _____

28. What buffer system operates in blood plasma? _____

Which member of the buffer system resists a *drop* in pH? _____

Which resists a *rise* in pH? _____

29. Explain how the carbonic acid–bicarbonate buffer system of the blood operates. _____

_____

_____

_____

_____

_____

30. What happened when the carbon dioxide in exhaled air mixed with water? _____

_____

_____

What role does exhalation of carbon dioxide play in maintaining relatively constant blood pH? _____

_____

_____

Measuring Respiratory Volumes Using BIOPAC®

31. Which, if any, of the measurable respiratory volumes would likely be exaggerated in a person who is cardiovascularly fit, such as a runner or a swimmer?

_____

_____

_____

Which, if any, of the measurable respiratory volumes would likely be exaggerated in a person who has smoked a lot for over twenty years?

_____

_____

_____

Dissection and Identification of Cat Muscles

The skeletal muscles of all mammals are named in a similar fashion. However, some muscles that are separate in lower animals are fused in humans, and some muscles present in lower animals are lacking in humans. This exercise involves dissection of the cat musculature to enhance your knowledge of the human muscular system. Since the aim is to become familiar with the muscles of the human body, you should pay particular attention to the similarities between cat and human muscles. However, pertinent differences will be pointed out as they are encountered.

If you have a lab coat, it might be a good idea to wear it (or even an old baggy T-shirt) over your clothes when dissecting to prevent staining your clothes with embalming fluid. Also, it will help you to prevent missteps during dissection if you read through this entire exercise before coming to the lab.

Activity 1:
Preparing the Cat for Dissection

The preserved laboratory animals purchased for dissection have been embalmed with a solution that prevents deterioration of the tissues. The animals are generally delivered in plastic bags that contain a small amount of the embalming fluid. _Do not dispose of this fluid_ when you remove the cat; the fluid prevents the cat from drying out. It is very important to keep the cat's tissues moist because you will probably use the same cat from now until the end of the course. The embalming fluid may cause your eyes to smart and may dry your skin, but these small irritants are preferable to working with a cat that has become hard and odoriferous due to bacterial action.

1.   Don disposable gloves and then obtain a cat, dissecting tray, dissecting instruments, and a name tag. Using a pencil, mark the name tag with the names of the members of your group and set it aside. The name tag will be attached to the plastic bag at the end of the dissection so that you may identify your animal in subsequent laboratories.

2.   To begin removing the skin, place the cat ventral side down on the dissecting tray. Cutting away from yourself with a newly-bladed scalpel, make a short, shallow incision in the midline of the neck, just to penetrate the skin. From this point on, use scissors. Continue to cut the length of the back to the sacrolumbar region, stopping at the tail (Figure D1.1).

See Exercise 15 of this manual for a discussion of the anatomy of the human muscular system.

Objectives

1. To name and locate muscles on a dissected cat.
2. To recognize similarities and differences between human and cat musculature.

Materials

❑ Disposable gloves or protective skin cream
❑ Preserved and injected cat (one for every two to four students)
❑ Dissecting instruments and tray
❑ Name tag and large plastic bag
❑ Paper towels
❑ Embalming fluid
❑ Organic debris container

3.   From the dorsal surface of the tail region, continue the incision around the tail, encircling the anus and genital organs. The skin will not be removed from this region.

4.   Beginning again at the dorsal tail region, make an incision through the skin down each hind leg nearly to the ankle.* Continue the cuts completely around the ankles.

5.   Return to the neck. Cut the skin around the circumference of the neck.

6.   Cut down each foreleg to the wrist.* Completely cut through the skin around the wrists.

7.   Now free the skin from the loose connective tissue (superficial fascia) that binds it to the underlying structures. With one hand, grasp the skin on one side of the midline dorsal incision. Then, using your fingers or a blunt probe, break through the "cottony" connective tissue fibers to release the skin from the muscle beneath. Work toward the ventral surface and then toward the neck. As you pull the skin from the body, you should see small, white, cordlike structures extending from the skin to the muscles at fairly regular intervals. These are the cutaneous nerves that serve the skin.

*Check with your instructor. He or she may want you to skin only the right or left side of the cat.

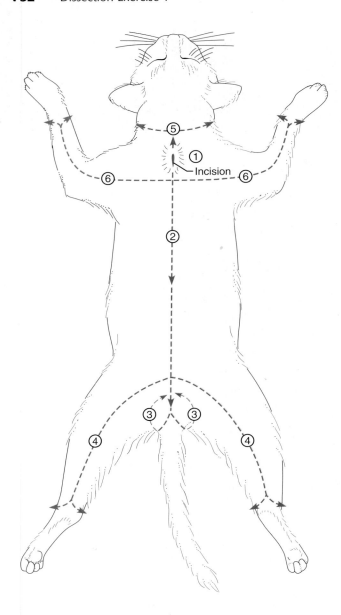

Figure D1.1 Incisions to be made in skinning a cat. Numbers indicate sequence.

You will also see (particularly as you approach the ventral surface) that a thin layer of muscle fibers remains adhered to the skin. This is the **cutaneous maximus** muscle, which enables the cat to move its skin rather like our facial muscles allow us to express emotion. Where the cutaneous maximus fibers cling to those of the deeper muscles, they should be carefully cut free. Along the ventral surface of the trunk, notice the two lines of nipples associated with the mammary glands. These are more prominant in females, especially if they are pregnant or recently lactating.

8.   You will notice as you start to free the skin in the neck that it is more difficult to remove. Take extra care and time in this area. The large flat **platysma** muscle in the ventral neck region (a skin muscle like the cutaneous maximus) will remain attached to the skin. The skin will not be removed from the head since the cat's muscles are not sufficiently similar to human head muscles to merit study.

9.   Complete the skinning process by freeing the skin from the forelimbs, the lower torso, and the hindlimbs in the same manner. The skin may be more difficult to remove as you approach the paws so additional time may be needed in these areas to avoid damaging the underlying muscles and tendons. *Do not discard the skin.*

10.   Inspect your skinned cat. Notice that it is difficult to see any cleavage lines between the muscles because of the overlying connective tissue, which is white or yellow. If time allows, carefully remove as much of the fat and fascia from the surface of the muscles as possible, using forceps or your fingers. The muscles, when exposed, look grainy or threadlike and are light brown. If this clearing process is done carefully and thoroughly, you will be ready to begin your identification of the superficial muscles.

11.   If the muscle dissection exercises are to be done at a later laboratory session, follow the cleanup instructions noted in the box below. *Prepare your cat for storage in this way every time the cat is used.* ■

Preparing the Dissection Animal for Storage

Before leaving the lab, prepare your animal for storage as follows:

1. To prevent the internal organs from drying out, dampen a layer of folded paper towels with embalming fluid, and wrap them snugly around the animal's torso. (Do not use *water-soaked* paper towels as this will encourage the growth of mold.) Make sure the dissected areas are completely enveloped.

2. Return the animal's skin flaps to their normal position over the ventral cavity body organs.

3. Place the animal in a plastic storage bag adding more embalming fluid if necessary, press out excess air, securely close the bag with a rubber band or twine.

4. Make sure your name tag is securely attached, and place the animal in the designated storage container.

5. Clean all dissecting equipment with soapy water, rinse and dry it for return to the storage area. Wash down the lab bench and properly dispose of organic debris and your gloves before leaving the laboratory.

Activity 2:
Dissecting Neck and Trunk Muscles

The proper dissection of muscles involves careful separation of one muscle from another and transection of superficial muscles in order to study those lying deeper. In general, when directions are given to transect a muscle, it first should be completely freed from all adhering connective tissue and *then* cut through the belly (fleshiest part) of the muscle about halfway between its origin and insertion points. *Use caution when working around points of muscle origin or insertion, and do not remove the fascia associated with such attachments.*

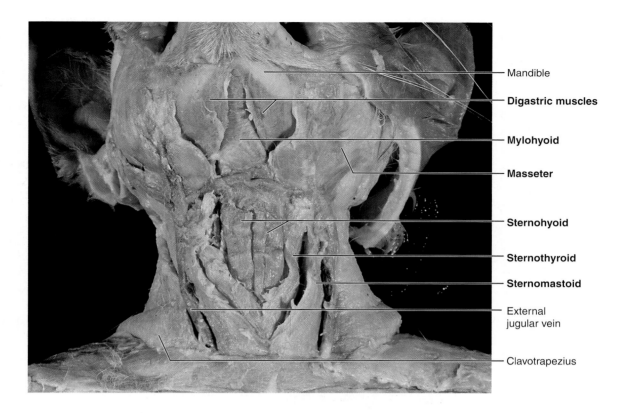

Figure D1.2   Superficial muscles of the anterior neck of the cat.
The sternomastoids are pulled slightly laterally to reveal the deeper sternothyroid muscles.

As a rule, all the fibers of one muscle are held together by a connective tissue sheath (epimysium) and run in the same general direction. Before you begin dissection, observe your skinned cat. If you look carefully, you can see changes in the direction of the muscle fibers, which will help you to locate the muscle borders. Pulling in slightly different directions on two adjacent muscles will usually expose subtle white lines created by the connective tissue surrounding the muscles and allow you to find the normal cleavage line between them. Once cleavage lines are identified, *use a blunt probe* to break the connective tissue between muscles and to separate them. If the muscles separate as clean, distinct bundles, your procedure is probably correct. If they appear ragged or chewed up, you are probably tearing a muscle apart rather than separating it from adjacent muscles. Only the muscles that are most easily identified and separated out will be identified in this exercise because of time considerations.

Anterior Neck Muscles

1.   Using Figure D1.2 as a guide, examine the anterior neck surface of the cat and identify the following superficial neck muscles. (The *platysma* belongs in this group but was probably removed during the skinning process.) The **sternomastoid** muscle and the more lateral and deeper **cleidomastoid** muscle (not visible in Figure D1.2) are joined in humans to form the sternocleidomastoid. The large external jugular veins, which drain the head, should be obvious crossing the anterior aspect of these muscles. The **mylohyoid** muscle parallels

the bottom aspect of the chin, and the **digastric** muscles form a V over the mylohyoid muscle. Although it is not one of the neck muscles, you can now identify the fleshy **masseter** muscle, which flanks the digastric muscle laterally. Finally, the **sternohyoid** is a narrow muscle between the mylohyoid (superiorly) and the inferior sternomastoid.

2.   The deeper muscles of the anterior neck of the cat are small and straplike and hardly worth the effort of dissection. However, one of these deeper muscles can be seen with a minimum of extra effort. Transect the sternomastoid and sternohyoid muscles approximately at midbelly. Reflect the cut ends to reveal the bandlike **sternothyroid** muscle, which runs along the anterior surface of the throat just deep and lateral to the sternohyoid muscle. The cleidomastoid muscle, which lies deep to the sternomastoid, is also more easily identified now.

Superficial Chest Muscles

In the cat, the chest or pectoral muscles adduct the arm, just as they do in humans. However, humans have only two pectoral muscles, and cats have four—the pectoralis major, pectoralis minor, xiphihumeralis, and pectoantebrachialis (Figure D1.3). However, because of their relatively great degree of fusion, the cat's pectoral muscles appear to be a single muscle. The pectoral muscles are rather difficult to dissect and identify, as they do not separate from one another easily.

The **pectoralis major** is 5 to 8 cm (2 to 3 inches) wide and can be seen arising on the manubrium, just inferior to the

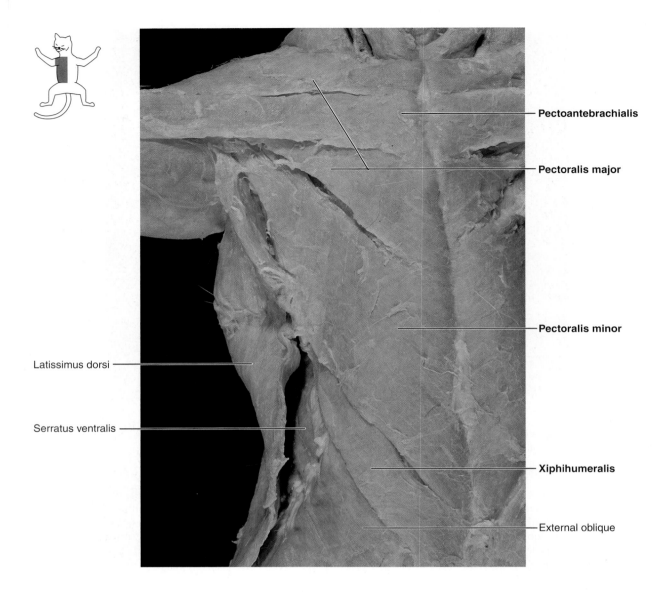

Pectoantebrachialis

Pectoralis major

Pectoralis minor

Latissimus dorsi

Serratus ventralis

Xiphihumeralis

External oblique

Figure D1.3 Superficial thorax muscles, ventral view. Latissimus dorsi is reflected away from the thorax. (Compare to human thorax muscles, anterior view, Figure 15.5.)

sternomastoid muscle of the neck, and running to the humerus. Its fibers run at right angles to the longitudinal axis of the cat's body.

The **pectoralis minor** lies beneath the pectoralis major and extends posterior to it on the abdominal surface. It originates on the sternum and inserts on the humerus. Its fibers run obliquely to the long axis of the body, which helps to distinguish it from the pectoralis major. Contrary to what its name implies, the pectoralis minor is a larger and thicker muscle than the pectoralis major.

The **xiphihumeralis** can be distinguished from the posterior edge of the pectoralis minor only by virtue of the fact that its origin is lower—on the xiphoid process of the sternum.

Its fibers run parallel to and are fused with those of the pectoralis minor.

The **pectoantebrachialis** is a thin, straplike muscle, about 1.3 cm (½ inch) wide, lying over the pectoralis major. Notice that the pectoralis major is visible both anterior and posterior to the borders of the pectoantebrachialis. It originates from the manubrium, passes laterally over the pectoralis major, and merges with the muscles of the forelimb approximately halfway down the humerus. It has no homologue in humans.

Identify, free, and trace out the origin and insertion of the cat's chest muscles. Refer to Figure D1.3 as you work.

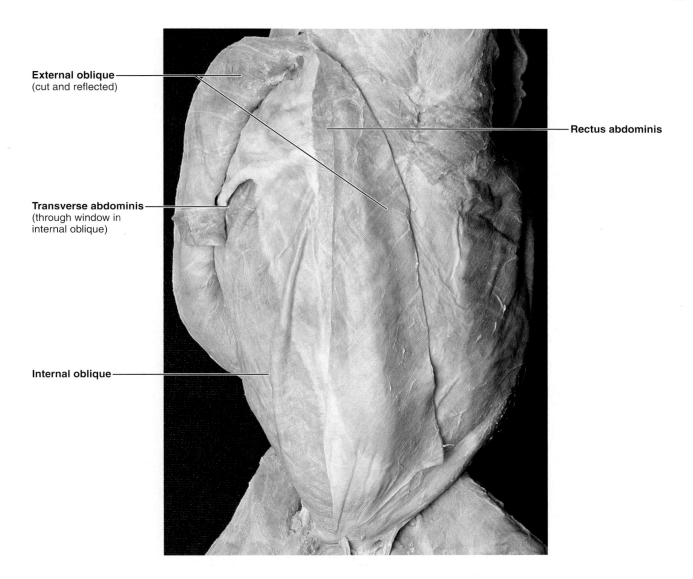

External oblique
(cut and reflected)

Transverse abdominis
(through window in
internal oblique)

Internal oblique

Rectus abdominis

Figure D1.4   **Muscles of the abdominal wall of the cat.**

Muscles of the Abdominal Wall

The superficial trunk muscles include those of the abdominal wall (Figure D1.4). Cat musculature in this area is quite similar in function to that of humans.

1.   Complete the dissection of the more superficial anterior trunk muscles of the cat by identifying the origins and insertions of the muscles of the abdominal wall. Work carefully here. These muscles are very thin, and it is easy to miss their boundaries. Begin with the **rectus abdominis,** a long band of muscle approximately 2.5 cm (1 inch) wide running immediately lateral to the midline of the body on the abdominal surface. Humans have four transverse *tendinous intersections* in the rectus abdominis (see Figure 15.7a), but they are absent or difficult to identify in the cat. Identify the **linea alba,** the longitudinal band of connective tissue which separates the rectus abdominis muscles. Note the relationship of the rectus abdominis to the other abdominal muscles and their fascia.

2.   The **external oblique** is a sheet of muscle immediately beside (and running beneath) the rectus abdominis (see Figure D1.4). Carefully free and then transect the external oblique to reveal the anterior attachment of the rectus abdominis and the deeper **internal oblique.** Reflect the external oblique; observe the deeper muscle. Notice which way the fibers run.

How does the fiber direction of the internal oblique compare to that of the external oblique?

_____

_____

3.   Free and then transect the internal oblique muscle to reveal the fibers of the **transversus abdominis,** whose fibers run transversely across the abdomen.

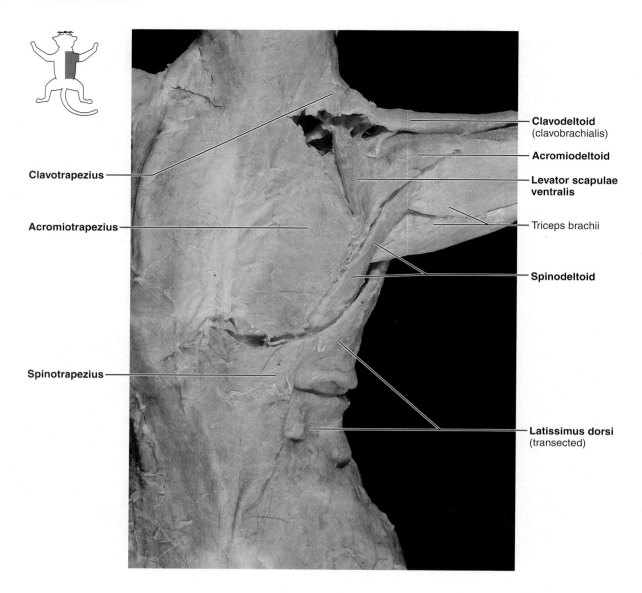

Clavotrapezius

Acromiotrapezius

Spinotrapezius

Clavodeltoid
(clavobrachialis)

Acromiodeltoid

Levator scapulae
ventralis

Triceps brachii

Spinodeltoid

Latissimus dorsi
(transected)

Figure D1.5 Superficial muscles of the anterodorsal aspect of the right shoulder, trunk, and neck of the cat. (Compare to human thorax muscles, posterior view, Figure 15.8a.)

Superficial Muscles of the Shoulder and the Dorsal Trunk and Neck

Refer to Figure D1.5 as you dissect the superficial muscles of the dorsal surface of the trunk.

1. Turn your cat on its ventral surface, and start your observations with the **trapezius group.** Humans have a single large *trapezius muscle*, but the cat has three separate muscles—the clavotrapezius, acromiotrapezius, and spinotrapezius—that together perform a similar function. The prefix in each case (clavo-, acromio-, and spino-) reveals the muscle's site of insertion. The **clavotrapezius,** the most anterior muscle of the group, is homologous to that part of the human trapezius that inserts into the clavicle. Slip a probe under this muscle and follow it to its apparent origin.

Where does the clavotrapezius appear to originate?

_____

Is this similar to its origin in humans?_____

The fibers of the clavotrapezius are continuous posteriorly with those of the clavicular part of the cat's deltoid muscle (clavodeltoid), and the two muscles work together to extend the humerus. Release the clavotrapezius muscle from adjoining muscles. The **acromiotrapezius** is a large, thin, nearly square muscle easily identified by its aponeurosis, which passes over the vertebral border of the scapula. It originates from the cervical and T_1 vertebrae and inserts into the scapular spine. The triangular **spinotrapezius** runs from the thoracic vertebrae to the scapular spine. This is the most posterior of the trapezius muscles in the cat. Now that you know where they are located, pull on the three trapezius muscles to mimic their action.

Do the trapezius muscles appear to have the same functions in cats as in humans?

_____

2. The **levator scapulae ventralis,** a flat, straplike muscle, can be located in the triangle created by the division of the fibers of the clavotrapezius and acromiotrapezius. Its anterior fibers run underneath the clavotrapezius from its origin at the base of the skull (occipital bone), and it inserts on the vertebral border of the scapula. In the cat it helps to hold the upper edges of the scapulae together and draws them toward the head.

What is the function of the levator scapulae in humans?

_____

_____

_____

3. The **deltoid group:** Like the trapezius, the human *deltoid muscle* is represented by three separate muscles in the cat—the clavodeltoid, acromiodeltoid, and spinodeltoid. The **clavodeltoid** (also called the *clavobrachialis*), the most superficial muscle of the shoulder, is a continuation of the clavotrapezius below the clavicle, which is this muscle's point of origin (see Figure D1.5). Follow its course down the forelimb to the point where it merges along a white line with the pectoantebrachialis. Separate it from the pectoantebrachialis, and then transect it and pull it back.

Where does the clavodeltoid insert?_____

What do you think the function of this muscle is?

_____

_____

The **acromiodeltoid** lies posterior to the clavodeltoid and runs over the top of the shoulder. This small triangular muscle originates on the acromion of the scapula. It inserts into the spinodeltoid (a muscle of similar size) posterior to it. The **spinodeltoid** is covered with fascia near the anterior end of the scapula. Its tendon extends under the acromiodeltoid muscle and inserts on the humerus. Notice that its fibers run obliquely to those of the acromiodeltoid. Like the human deltoid muscle, the acromiodeltoid and clavodeltoid muscles in the cat raise and rotate the humerus.

4. The **latissimus dorsi** is a large, thick, flat muscle covering most of the lateral surface of the posterior trunk. Its anterior edge is covered by the spinotrapezius and may appear ragged because it has been cut off from the cutaneous maximus muscle attached to the skin. As in humans, it inserts into the humerus. But before inserting, its fibers merge with the fibers of many other muscles, among them the xiphihumeralis of the pectoralis group.

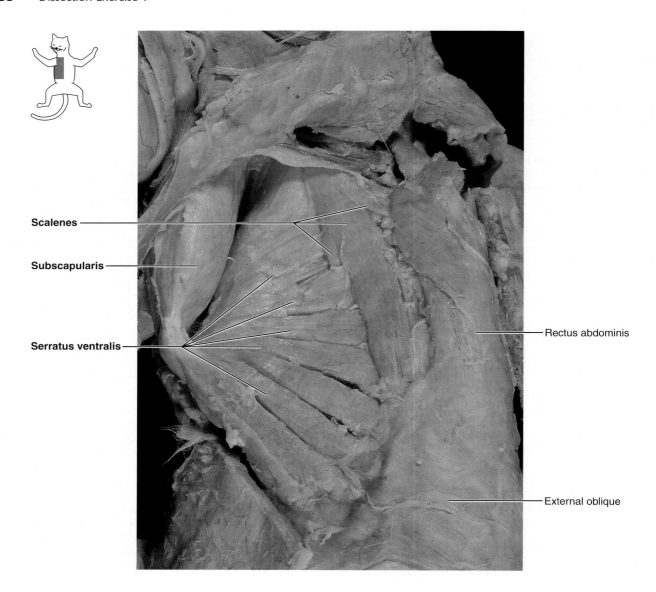

Figure D1.6   Deep muscles of the right inferolateral thorax of the cat.

Deep Muscles of the Dorsal Trunk and Neck

1.   In preparation for indentifying deep muscles of the dorsal trunk, transect the latissimus dorsi, the muscles of the pectoralis group, and the spinotrapezius and reflect them back. Be careful not to damage the large brachial nerve plexus, which lies in the axillary space beneath the pectoralis group.

2.   The **serratus ventralis,** homologous to the *serratus anterior* of humans, arises deep to the pectoral muscles and covers the lateral surface of the rib cage. It is easily identified by its fingerlike muscular origins, which arise on the first 9 or 10 ribs. It inserts into the scapula. The anterior portion of the serratus ventralis, which arises from the cervical vertebrae, is homologous to the *levator scapulae* in humans; both pull the scapula toward the sternum. Trace this muscle to its insertion.

In general, in the cat, this muscle acts to pull the scapula posteriorly and downward (Figure D1.6).

3.   Reflect the upper limb to reveal the **subscapularis,** which occupies most of the ventral surface of the scapula. Humans have a homologous muscle.

4.   Locate the anterior, posterior, and middle **scalene** muscles on the lateral surface of the cat's neck and trunk. The most prominent and longest of these muscles is the middle scalene, which lies between the anterior and posterior members. The scalenes originate on the ribs and run cephalad over the serratus ventralis to insert in common on the cervical vertebrae. These muscles draw the ribs anteriorly and bend the neck downward; thus they are homologous to the human scalene muscles, which elevate the ribs and flex the neck. (Notice that the difference is only one of position. Humans walk erect, but cats are quadrupeds.)

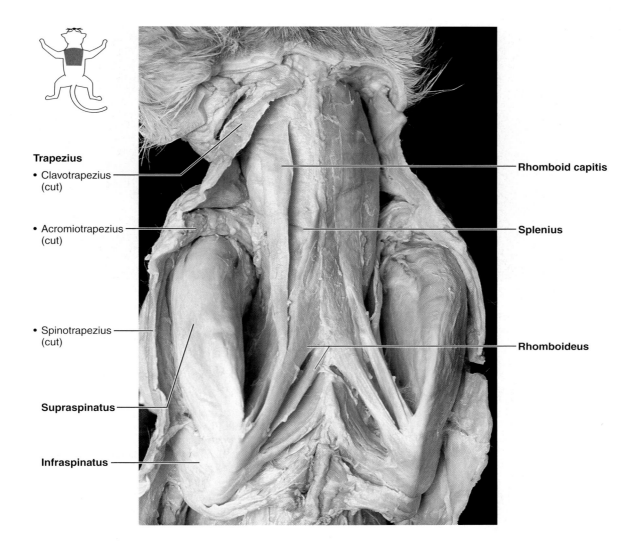

Trapezius
- Clavotrapezius (cut)
- Acromiotrapezius (cut)
- Spinotrapezius (cut)

Supraspinatus

Infraspinatus

Rhomboid capitis

Splenius

Rhomboideus

Figure D1.7   Deep muscles of the superior aspect of the dorsal thorax of the cat.

5.   Reflect the flaps of the transected latissimus dorsi, spinodeltoid, acromiodeltoid, and levator scapulae ventralis. The **splenius** is a large flat muscle occupying most of the side of the neck close to the vertebrae (Figure D1.7). As in humans, it originates on the ligamentum nuchae at the back of the neck and inserts into the occipital bone. It functions to raise the head.

6.   To view the rhomboid muscles, lay the cat on its side and hold its forelegs together to spread the scapulae apart. The rhomboid muscles lie between the scapulae and beneath the acromiotrapezius. All the rhomboid muscles originate on the vertebrae and insert on the scapula. They function to hold the dorsal part of the scapula to the cat's back.

There are three rhomboids in the cat. The ribbonlike **rhomboid capitis,** the most anterolateral muscle of the group, has no counterpart in the human body. The **rhomboid minor,** located posterior to the rhomboid capitis, is much larger. The fibers of the rhomboid minor run transversely to those of the rhomboid capitis. The most posterior muscle of the group, the **rhomboid major,** is so closely fused to the rhomboid minor that many consider them to be one muscle—the **rhomboideus,** which is homologous to human *rhomboid muscles.*

7.   The **supraspinatus** and **infraspinatus** muscles are similar to the same muscles in humans. The supraspinatus can be found under the acromiotrapezius, and the infraspinatus is deep to the spinotrapezius. Both originate on the lateral scapular surface and insert on the humerus. ∎

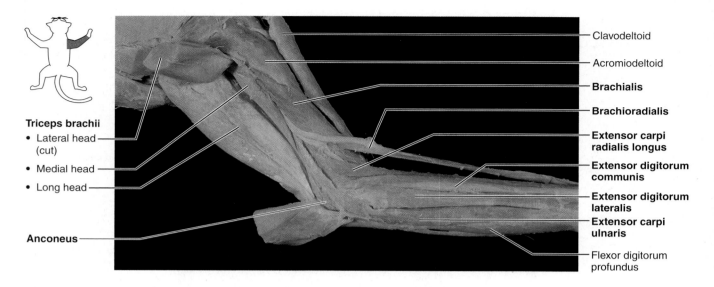

Figure D1.8 **Lateral surface of the right forelimb of the cat.**
The lateral head of the triceps brachii has been transected and reflected.

Activity 3:
Dissecting Forelimb Muscles

Cat forelimb muscles fall into the same three categories as human upper limb muscles, but in this section the muscles of the entire forelimb are considered together. Refer to Figure D1.8 as you study these muscles.

Muscles of the Lateral Surface

1.   The triceps muscle (**triceps brachii**) of the cat is easily identified if the cat is placed on its side. It is a large fleshy muscle covering the posterior aspect and much of the side of the humerus. As in humans, this muscle arises from three heads, which originate from the humerus and scapula and insert jointly into the olecranon process of the ulna. Remove the fascia from the superior region of the lateral arm surface to identify the lateral and long heads of the triceps. The long head is approximately twice as long as the lateral head and lies medial to it on the posterior arm surface. The medial head can be exposed by transecting the lateral head and pulling it aside. Now pull on the triceps muscle.

How does the function of the triceps muscle compare in cats and in humans?

_____

_____

Anterior and distal to the medial head of the triceps is the tiny **anconeus** muscle, sometimes called the fourth head of the triceps muscle. Notice its darker color and the way it wraps the tip of the elbow.

2.   The **brachialis** can be located anterior to the lateral head of the triceps muscle. Identify its origin on the humerus, and trace its course as it crosses the elbow and inserts on the ulna. It flexes the cat's foreleg.

Identification of the forearm muscles is difficult because of the tough fascia sheath that encases them, but give it a try.

3.   Remove as much of the connective tissue as possible and cut through the ligaments that secure the tendons at the wrist (transverse carpal ligaments) so that you will be able to follow the muscles to their insertions. Begin your identification of the forearm muscles at the lateral surface of the forearm. The muscles of this region are very much alike in appearance and are difficult to identify accurately unless a definite order is followed. Thus you will begin with the most anterior muscles and proceed to the posterior aspect. Remember to check carefully the tendons of insertion to verify your muscle identifications.

4.   The ribbonlike muscle on the lateral surface of the humerus is the **brachioradialis.** Observe how it passes down the forearm to insert on the styloid process of the radius. (If your removal of the fascia was not very careful, this muscle may have been removed.)

5.   The **extensor carpi radialis longus** has a broad origin and is larger than the brachioradialis. It extends down the anterior surface of the radius (see Figure D1.8). Transect this muscle to view the **extensor carpi radialis brevis,** which is partially covered by and sometimes fused with the extensor carpi radialis longus. Both muscles have origins, insertions, and actions similar to their human counterparts.

6.   You can see the entire **extensor digitorum communis** along the lateral surface of the forearm. Trace it to its four tendons, which insert on the second to fifth digits. This muscle extends these digits. The **extensor digitorum lateralis** (absent in humans) also extends the digits. This muscle lies immediately posterior to the extensor digitorum communis.

7.   Follow the **extensor carpi ulnaris** from the lateral epicondyle of the humerus to the ulnar side of the fifth metacarpal. Often this muscle has a shiny tendon, which helps in its identification.

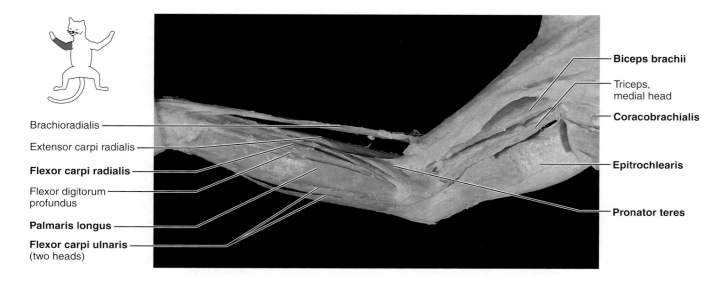

Brachioradialis

Extensor carpi radialis

Flexor carpi radialis

Flexor digitorum profundus

Palmaris longus

Flexor carpi ulnaris (two heads)

Biceps brachii

Triceps, medial head

Coracobrachialis

Epitrochlearis

Pronator teres

Figure D1.9 **Medial surface of the right forelimb of the cat.**

Muscles of the Medial Surface

1. The **biceps brachii** (Figure D1.9) is a large spindle-shaped muscle medial to the brachialis on the anterior surface of the humerus. Pull back the cut ends of the pectoral muscles to get a good view of the biceps. This muscle is much more prominent in humans, but its origin, insertion, and action are very similar in cats and in humans. Follow the muscle to its origin.

Does the biceps have two heads in the cat? _____

2. The broad, flat, exceedingly thin muscle on the postero-medial surface of the arm is the **epitrochlearis.** Its tendon originates from the fascia of the latissimus dorsi, and the muscle inserts into the olecranon process of the ulna. This muscle extends the forearm of the cat; it is not found in humans.

3. The **coracobrachialis** of the cat is insignificant (approximately 1.3 cm, or ½ inch, long) and can be seen as a very small muscle crossing the ventral aspect of the shoulder joint. It runs beneath the biceps brachii to insert on the humerus and has the same function as the human coracobrachialis.

4. Referring again to Figure D1.9, turn the cat so that the ventral forearm muscles (mostly flexors and pronators) can be observed. As in humans, most of these muscles arise from the medial epicondyle of the humerus. The **pronator teres** runs from the medial epicondyle of the humerus and declines in size as it approaches its insertion on the radius. Do not bother to trace it to its insertion.

5. Like its human counterpart, the **flexor carpi radialis** runs from the medial epicondyle of the humerus to insert into the second and third metacarpals.

6. The large flat muscle in the center of the medial surface is the **palmaris longus.** Its origin on the medial epicondyle of the humerus abuts that of the pronator teres and is shared with the flexor carpi radialis. The palmaris longus extends

down the forearm to terminate in four tendons on the digits. Comparatively speaking, this muscle is much larger in cats than in humans.

The **flexor carpi ulnaris** arises from a two-headed origin (medial epicondyle of the humerus and olecranon of the ulna). Its two bellies pass downward to the wrist, where they are united by a single tendon that inserts into the carpals of the wrist. As in humans, this muscle flexes the wrist. ■

Activity 4:
Dissecting Hindlimb Muscles

Remove the fat and fascia from all thigh surfaces, but do not cut through or remove the **fascia lata** (or iliotibial band), which is a tough white aponeurosis covering the anterolateral surface of the thigh from the hip to the leg. If the cat is a male, the cordlike sperm duct will be embedded in the fat near the pubic symphysis. Carefully clear around, but not in, this region.

Posterolateral Hindlimb Muscles

1. Turn the cat on its ventral surface and identify the following superficial muscles of the hip and thigh, referring to Figure D1.10. (The deeper hip muscles of the cat will not be identified.) Viewing the lateral aspect of the hindlimb, you will identify these muscles in sequence from the anterior to the posterior aspects of the hip and thigh. Most anterior is the **sartorius.** Approximately 4 cm (1½ inches) wide, it extends around the lateral aspect of the thigh to the anterior surface, where the major portion of it lies. Free it from the adjacent muscles and pass a blunt probe under it to trace its origin and insertion. Homologous to the sartorius muscle in humans, it adducts and rotates the thigh, but in addition, the cat sartorius acts as a knee extensor. Transect this muscle.

2. The **tensor fasciae latae** is posterior to the sartorius. It is wide at its superior end, where it originates on the iliac crest, and narrows as it approaches its insertion into the fascia lata,

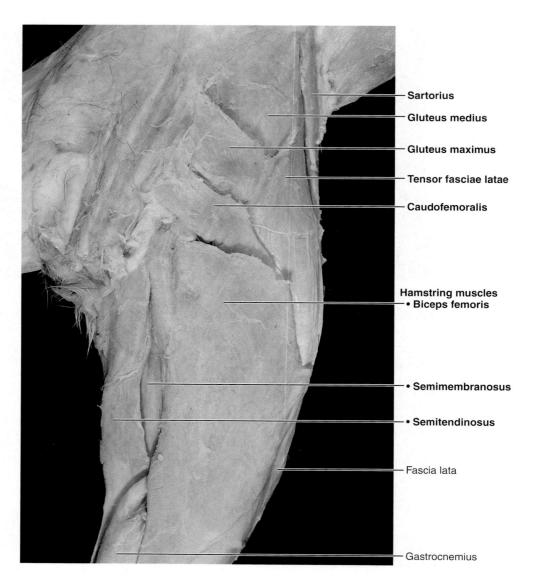

— Sartorius

— Gluteus medius

— Gluteus maximus

— Tensor fasciae latae

— Caudofemoralis

Hamstring muscles
• Biceps femoris

• Semimembranosus

• Semitendinosus

— Fascia lata

— Gastrocnemius

Figure D1.10   Muscles of the right posterolateral thigh in the cat; superficial view.

which runs to the proximal tibial region. Transect its superior end and pull it back to expose the **gluteus medius** lying beneath it. This is the largest of the gluteus muscles in the cat. It originates on the ilium and inserts on the greater trochanter of the femur. The gluteus medius overlays and obscures the gluteus minimus, pyriformis, and gemellus muscles (which will not be identified here).

3.   The **gluteus maximus** is a small triangular hip muscle posterior to the superior end of the tensor fasciae latae and paralleling it. In humans the gluteus maximus is a large fleshy muscle forming most of the buttock mass. In the cat it is only about 1.3 cm (½ inch) wide and 5 cm (2 inches) long, and is smaller than the gluteus medius. The gluteus maximus covers part of the gluteus medius as it extends from the sacral region and the end of the femur. It abducts the thigh.

4.   Posterior to the gluteus maximus, identify the triangular **caudofemoralis,** which originates on the caudal vertebrae and inserts into the patella via an aponeurosis. There is no homologue to this muscle in humans; in cats it abducts the thigh and flexes the vertebral column.

5.   The **hamstring muscles** of the hindlimb include the biceps femoris, the semitendinosus, and the semimembranosus muscles. The **biceps femoris** is a large, powerful muscle that covers about three-fourths of the posterolateral surface of the thigh. It is 4 cm (1½ inches) to 5 cm (2 inches) wide throughout its length. Trace it from its origin on the ischial tuberosity to its insertion on the tibia. Part of the **semitendinosus** can be seen beneath the posterior border of the biceps femoris. Transect and reflect the biceps muscle to reveal the whole length of the semitendinosus and the large sciatic nerve positioned under the biceps. Contrary to what its name implies ("half-tendon"), this muscle is muscular and fleshy except at its

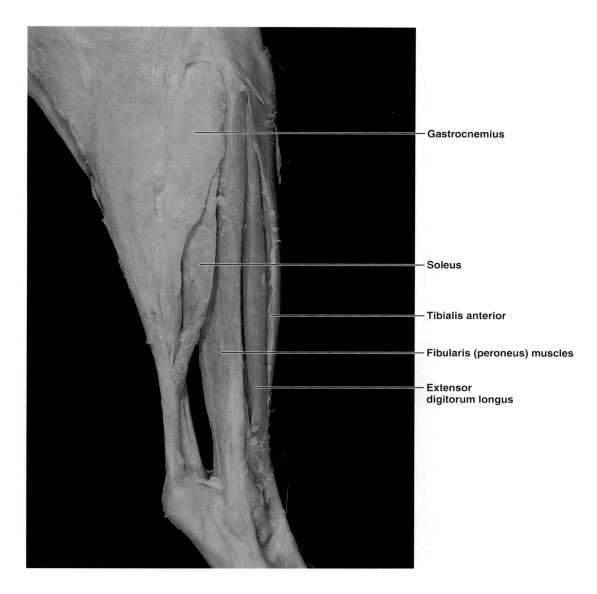

Gastrocnemius

Soleus

Tibialis anterior

Fibularis (peroneus) muscles

Extensor digitorum longus

Figure D1.11   Superficial muscles of the posterolateral aspect of the right shank (leg).

insertion. It is uniformly about 2 cm (¾ inch) wide as it runs down the thigh from the ischial tuberosity to the medial side of the ulna. It acts to bend the knee. The **semimembranosus,** a large muscle lying medial to the semitendinosus and largely obscured by it, is best seen in an anterior view of the thigh (see Figure D1.12b). If desired, however, the semitendinosus can be transected to view it from the posterior aspect. The semimembranosus is larger and broader than the semitendinosus. Like the other hamstrings, it originates on the ischial tuberosity and inserts on the medial epicondyle of the femur and the medial tibial surface.

How does the semimembranosus compare with its human homologue?

_____

_____

6.   Remove the heavy fascia covering the lateral surface of the shank. Moving from the posterior to the anterior aspect, identify the following muscles on the posterolateral shank (leg) (Figure D1.11). First reflect the lower portion of the biceps femoris to see the origin of the **triceps surae,** the large composite muscle of the calf. Humans also have a triceps surae. The **gastrocnemius,** part of the triceps surae, is the largest muscle on the shank. As in humans, it has two heads and inserts via the calcaneal (Achilles) tendon into the calcaneus. Run a probe beneath this muscle and then transect it to reveal the **soleus,** which is deep to the gastrocnemius.

7.   Another important group of muscles in the leg is the **fibularis (peroneus) muscles**, which collectively appear as a slender, evenly shaped superficial muscle lying anterior to the triceps surae. Originating on the fibula and inserting on the digits and metatarsals, the fibularis muscles flex the foot.

8.   The **extensor digitorum longus** lies anterior to the fibularis muscles. Its origin, insertion, and action in cats are similar

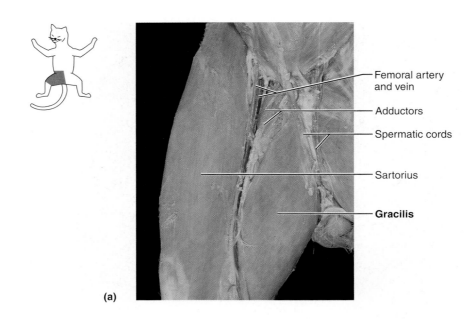

(a)

- Femoral artery and vein
- Adductors
- Spermatic cords
- Sartorius
- **Gracilis**

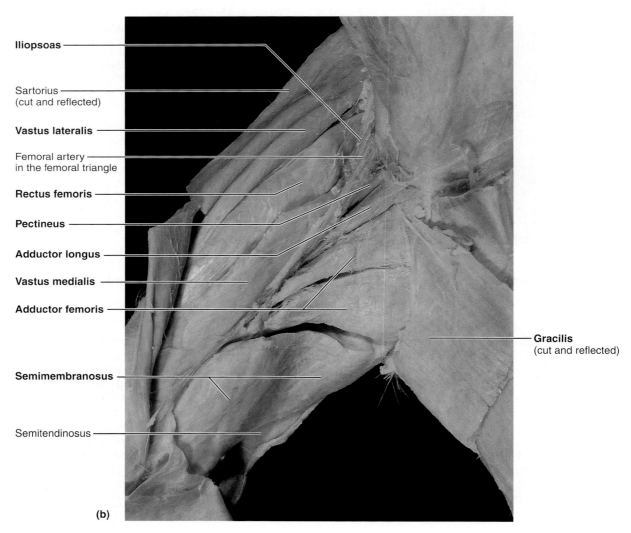

Iliopsoas

Sartorius
(cut and reflected)

Vastus lateralis

Femoral artery
in the femoral triangle

Rectus femoris

Pectineus

Adductor longus

Vastus medialis

Adductor femoris

Semimembranosus

Semitendinosus

Gracilis
(cut and reflected)

(b)

Figure D1.12 **Superficial muscles of the anteromedial thigh.** **(a)** Gracilis and sartorius are intact in this superficial view of the right thigh. **(b)** The gracilis and sartorius are transected and reflected to show deeper muscles.

to the homologous human muscle. The **tibialis anterior** is anterior to the extensor digitorum longus. The tibialis anterior is roughly triangular in cross section and heavier at its proximal end. Locate its origin on the proximal fibula and tibia and its insertion on the first metatarsal. You can see the sharp edge of the tibia at the anterior border of this muscle. As in humans, it is a foot flexor.

Anteromedial Hindlimb Muscles

1. Turn the cat onto its dorsal surface to identify the muscles of the anteromedial hindlimb (Figure D1.12). Note once again the straplike sartorius at the surface of the thigh, which you have already identified and transected. It originates on the ilium and inserts on the medial region of the tibia.

2. Reflect the cut ends of the sartorius to identify the **quadriceps** muscles. The most medial muscle of this group, the **vastus medialis,** lies just beneath the sartorius. Resting close to the femur, it arises from the ilium and inserts into the patellar ligament. The small spindle-shaped muscle anterior and lateral to the vastus medialis is the **rectus femoris.** In cats this muscle originates entirely from the femur.

What is the origin of the rectus femoris in humans?

_____

_____

Free the rectus femoris from the most lateral muscle of this group, the large, fleshy **vastus lateralis,** which lies deep to the tensor fasciae latae. The vastus lateralis arises from the lateral femoral surface and inserts, along with the other vasti muscles, into the patellar ligament. Transect this muscle to identify the deep **vastus intermedius,** the smallest of the vasti muscles. It lies medial to the vastus lateralis and merges superiorly with the vastus medialis. (The vastus intermedius is not shown in the figure.)

3. The **gracilis** is a broad thin muscle that covers the posterior portion of the medial aspect of the thigh (see Figure D1.12a). It originates on the pubic symphysis and inserts on the medial proximal tibial surface. In cats the gracilis adducts the leg and draws it posteriorly.

How does this compare with the human gracilis?

_____

_____

4. Free and transect the gracilis to view the adductor muscles deep to it. The **adductor femoris** is a large muscle that lies beneath the gracilis and abuts the semimembranosus medially. Its origin is the pubic ramus and the ischium, and its fibers pass downward to insert on most of the length of the femoral shaft. The adductor femoris is homologous to the human *adductor magnus, brevis,* and *longus.* Its function is to extend the thigh after it has been drawn forward, and to adduct the thigh. A small muscle about 2.5 cm (1 inch) long—the **adductor longus**—touches the superior margin of the adductor femoris. It originates on the pubic bone and inserts on the proximal surface of the femur.

5. Before continuing your dissection, locate the **femoral triangle** (Scarpa's triangle), an important area bordered by the proximal edge of the sartorius and the adductor muscles. It is usually possible to identify the femoral artery (injected with red latex) and the femoral vein (injected with blue latex), which span the triangle (see Figure D1.12a). (You will identify these vessels again in your study of the circulatory system.) If your instructor wishes you to identify the pectineus and iliopsoas, remove these vessels and go on to steps 6 and 7.

6. Examine the superolateral margin of the adductor longus to locate the small **pectineus.** It is normally covered by the gracilis (which you have cut and reflected). The pectineus, which originates on the pubis and inserts on the proximal end of the femur, is similar in all ways to its human homologue.

7. Just lateral to the pectineus you can see a small portion of the **iliopsoas,** a long and cylindrical muscle. Its origin is on the transverse processes of T_1 through T_{12} and the lumbar vertebrae, and it passes posteriorly toward the body wall to insert on the medial aspect of the proximal femur. The iliopsoas flexes and laterally rotates the thigh. It corresponds to the human iliopsoas and psoas minor.

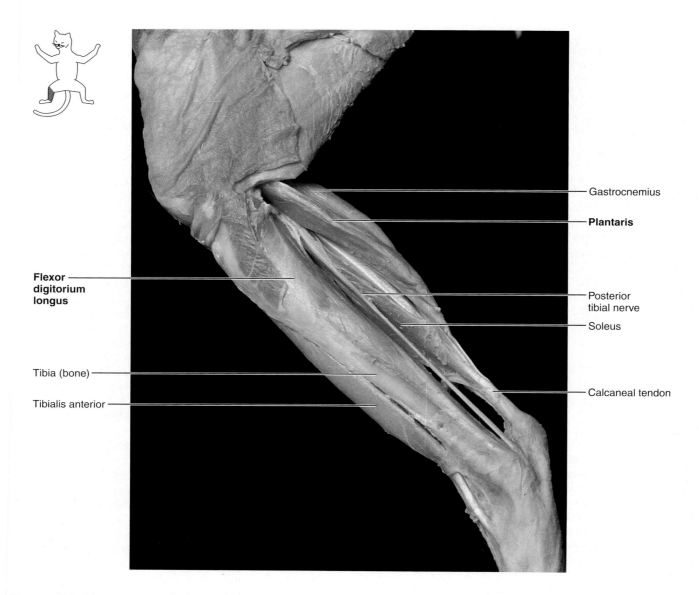

Gastrocnemius

Plantaris

Flexor digitorium longus

Posterior tibial nerve

Soleus

Tibia (bone)

Tibialis anterior

Calcaneal tendon

Figure D1.13   Superficial muscles of the right anteromedial shank (leg) of the cat.

8.   Reidentify the gastrocnemius of the shank and then the **plantaris,** which is fused with the lateral head of the gastrocnemius (Figure D1.13). It originates from the lateral aspect of the femur and patella, and its tendon passes around the calcaneus to insert on the second phalanx. Working with the triceps surae, it flexes the digits and extends the foot.

9.   Anterior to the plantaris is the **flexor digitorum longus,** a long, tapering muscle with two heads. It originates on the lateral surfaces of the proximal fibula and tibia and inserts via four tendons into the terminal phalanges. As in humans, it flexes the toes.

10.   The **tibialis posterior** is a long, flat muscle lateral and deep to the flexor digitorum longus. It originates on the me-

dial surface of the head of the fibula and the ventral tibia. It merges with a flat, shiny tendon to insert into the tarsals. It is not shown in the figure.

11.   The **flexor hallucis longus** (also not illustrated) is a long muscle that lies lateral to the tibialis posterior. It originates from the posterior tibia and passes downward to the ankle. It is a uniformly broad muscle in the cat. As in humans, it is a flexor of the great toe.

12.   Prepare your cat for storage and clean the area as instructed in the box on p. 752 before leaving the laboratory. ∎

Dissection Review

Many human muscles are modified from those of the cat (or any quadruped) as a result of the requirements of an upright posture. The following questions refer to these differences.

1. How does the human trapezius muscle differ from the cat's?

   _____

   _____

2. How does the deltoid differ?

   _____

   _____

3. How do the extent and orientation of the human sartorius muscle differ from its relative position in the cat?

   _____

   _____

4. Explain these differences in terms of differences in function.

   _____

   _____

5. The human rectus abdominis is definitely divided by four transverse tendons (tendinous intersections). These tendons are absent or difficult to identify in the cat. How do these tendons affect the human upright posture?

   _____

   _____

6. Match the terms in column B to descriptions in column A.

Column A		Column B	
_____ 1.	to separate muscles	a.	dissect
_____ 2.	to fold back a muscle	b.	embalm
_____ 3.	to cut through a muscle	c.	reflect
_____ 4.	to preserve tissue	d.	transect

Dissection of Cat Spinal Nerves

Objective

To identify on a dissected animal the musculocutaneous, radial, median, and ulnar nerves of the upper limb and the femoral, saphenous, sciatic, common peroneal, and tibial nerves of the lower limb.

Materials

❑ Disposable gloves
❑ Dissecting instruments and tray
❑ Animal specimen from previous dissection
❑ Embalming fluid
❑ Paper towels

The cat has 38 or 39 pairs of spinal nerves (as compared to 31 in humans). Of these, 8 are cervical, 13 thoracic, 7 lumbar, 3 sacral, and 7 or 8 caudal.

A complete dissection of the cat's spinal nerves would be extraordinarily time-consuming and exacting and is not warranted in a basic anatomy and physiology course. However, it is desirable for you to have some dissection work to complement your study of the anatomical charts. Thus at this point you will carry out a partial dissection of the brachial plexus and lumbosacral plexus and identify some of the major nerves.

See Exercise 21 of this manual for a discussion of human spinal nerves.

Activity 1:
Dissecting Nerves of the Brachial Plexus

1.   Don disposable gloves. Place your cat specimen on the dissecting tray, dorsal side down. Reflect the cut ends of the left pectoralis muscles to expose the large brachial plexus in the axillary region (Figure D2.1). Use forceps to carefully clear away the connective tissue around the exposed nerves as far back toward their points of origin as possible.

2.   The **musculocutaneous nerve** is the most superior nerve of this group. It splits into two subdivisions that run under the margins of the coracobrachialis and biceps brachii muscles. Trace its fibers into the ventral muscles of the arm it serves.

3.   Locate the large **radial nerve** inferior to the musculocutaneous nerve. The radial nerve serves the dorsal muscles of the arm and forearm. Follow it into the three heads of the triceps brachii muscle.

4.   In the cat, the **median nerve** is closely associated with the brachial artery and vein. It courses through the arm to supply the ventral muscles of the forearm (with the exception of the flexor carpi ulnaris and the ulnar head of the flexor digitorum profundus). It also innervates some of the intrinsic hand muscles, as in humans.

5.   The **ulnar nerve** is the most posterior of the large brachial plexus nerves. Follow it as it travels down the forelimb, passing over the medial epicondyle of the humerus, to supply the flexor carpi ulnaris and the ulnar head of the flexor digitorum profundus (and the hand muscles). ■

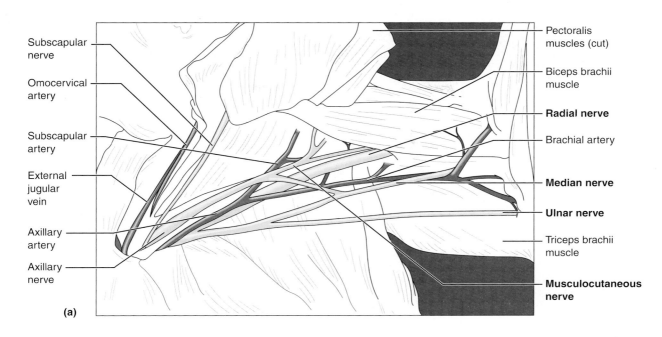

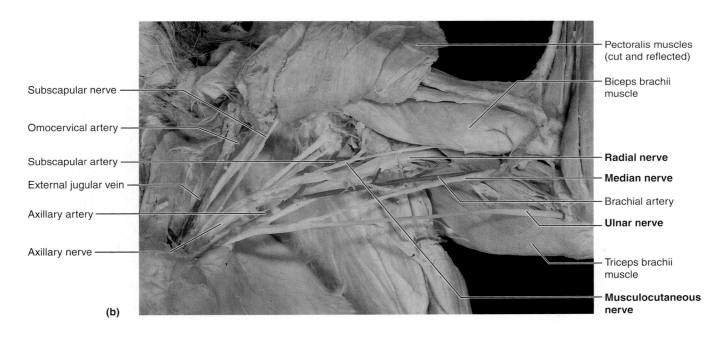

Figure D2.1   Brachial plexus and major blood vessels of the left forelimb of the cat, ventral aspect. (a) Diagrammatic view. **(b)** Photograph.

Activity 2:
Dissecting Nerves of the Lumbosacral Plexus

1.   To locate the **femoral nerve** arising from the lumbar plexus, first identify the *femoral triangle,* which is bordered by the sartorius and adductor muscles of the anterior thigh

(Figure D2.2). The large femoral nerve travels through this region after emerging from the psoas major muscle in close association with the femoral artery and vein. Follow the nerve into the muscles and skin of the anterior thigh, which it supplies. Notice also its cutaneous branch in the cat, the **saphenous nerve,** which continues down the anterior medial surface of the thigh (with the great saphenous artery and vein) to supply the skin of the anterior shank and foot.

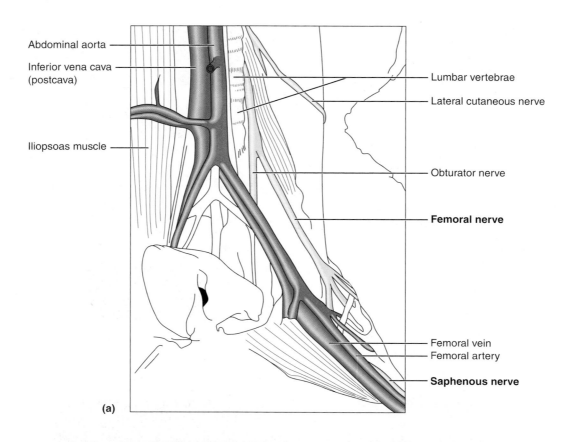

Abdominal aorta

Inferior vena cava (postcava)

Iliopsoas muscle

Lumbar vertebrae

Lateral cutaneous nerve

Obturator nerve

Femoral nerve

Femoral vein
Femoral artery
Saphenous nerve

(a)

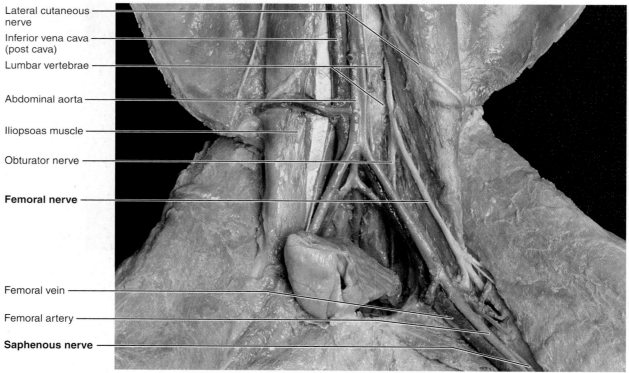

Lateral cutaneous nerve

Inferior vena cava (post cava)

Lumbar vertebrae

Abdominal aorta

Iliopsoas muscle

Obturator nerve

Femoral nerve

Femoral vein

Femoral artery

Saphenous nerve

Figure D2.2   Lumbar plexus of the cat, ventral aspect. (a) Diagrammatic view. **(b)** Photograph.

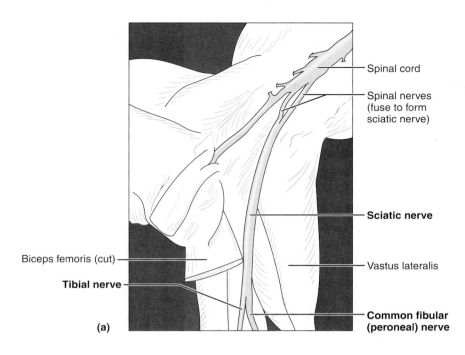

(a)

Spinal cord

Spinal nerves
(fuse to form
sciatic nerve)

Sciatic nerve

Vastus lateralis

**Common fibular
(peroneal) nerve**

Biceps femoris (cut)

Tibial nerve

**Figure D2.3 Sacral plexus
of the cat, dorsal aspect.**
(a) Diagrammatic view.
(b) Photograph.

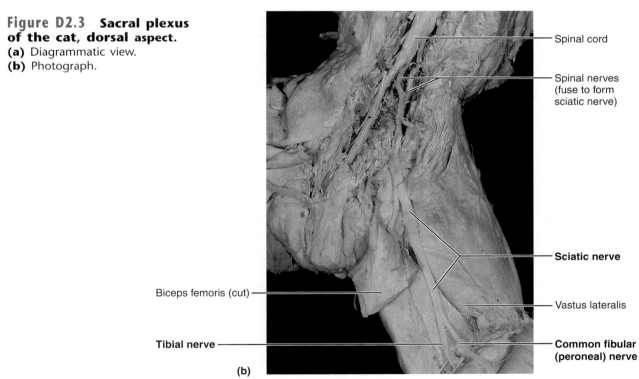

(b)

Spinal cord

Spinal nerves
(fuse to form
sciatic nerve)

Sciatic nerve

Vastus lateralis

**Common fibular
(peroneal) nerve**

Biceps femoris (cut)

Tibial nerve

2.   Turn the cat ventral side down so you can view the posterior aspect of the lower limb (Figure D2.3). Reflect the ends of the transected biceps femoris muscle to view the large cordlike sciatic nerve. The **sciatic nerve** arises from the sacral plexus and serves the dorsal thigh muscles and all the muscles of the leg and foot. Follow the nerve as it travels down the posterior thigh lateral to the semimembranosus muscle. Note that just superior to the gastrocnemius muscle of the calf, it divides into its two major branches, which serve the leg.

3.   Identify the **tibial nerve** medially and the **common fibular (peroneal) nerve,** which curves over the lateral surface of the gastrocnemius.

4.   When you have finished making your observations, wrap the cat for storage and clean all dissecting tools and equipment before leaving the laboratory according to the boxed instruction on p. 752. ■

Dissection Review

1. From anterior to posterior, put the nerves issuing from the brachial plexus in their proper order (i.e., the median, musculo-cutaneous, radial, and ulnar nerves).

   _____

   _____

2. Which of the nerves named above serves the cat's forearm extensor muscles? _____ Which serves the

   forearm flexors? _____

3. Just superior to the gastrocnemius muscle, the sciatic nerve divides into its two main branches, the _____

   and _____ nerves.

4. What name is given to the cutaneous nerve of the cat's thigh? _____

Identification of Selected Endocrine Organs of the Cat

Activity 1:
Opening the Ventral Body Cavity

1.   Don gloves and then obtain your dissection animal. Place the animal on the dissecting tray, ventral side up. Using scissors, make a longitudinal median incision through the ventral body wall. Begin your cut just superior to the midline of the pubic bone and continue it anteriorly to the rib cage. Check the incision guide provided in Figure D3.1 as you work along.

2.   Angle the scissors slightly (1.3 cm, or ½ inch) to the right or left of the sternum, and continue the cut through the rib cartilages (just lateral to the body midline), to the base of the throat. Your instructor may have you use heavier bone cutters to cut through the rib cartilages.

3.   Make two lateral cuts on both sides of the ventral body surface, anterior and posterior to the diaphragm, which separates the thoracic and abdominal parts of the ventral body cavity. *Leave the diaphragm intact.* Spread the thoracic walls laterally to expose the thoracic organs.

4.   Make an angled lateral cut on each side of the median incision line just superior to the pubic bone, and spread the flaps to expose the abdominal cavity organs. ■

Activity 2:
Identifying Organs

A helpful adjunct to identifying selected endocrine organs of the cat is a general overview of ventral body cavity organs as shown in Figure D3.2. (See Exercises 27 and 28A of this manual for a discussion of the human endocrine system.) Since you will study the organ systems housed in the ventral body cavity in later units, the objective here is simply to identify the most important organs and those that will help you to locate the desired endocrine organs (marked *). A schematic showing the relative positioning of several of the animal's endocrine organs is provided in Figure D3.3.

Before leaving the lab, prepare your animal for storage as instructed on p. 752. Then clean and dry all dissecting equipment, wash down your lab bench, and properly dispose of your gloves.

Objectives

1. To prepare the cat for observation by opening the ventral body cavity.

2. To identify and name the major endocrine organs on a dissected cat.

Materials

❑ Plastic gloves
❑ Dissection instruments and tray
❑ Animal specimen from previous dissections
❑ Bone cutters
❑ Embalming fluid
❑ Paper towels

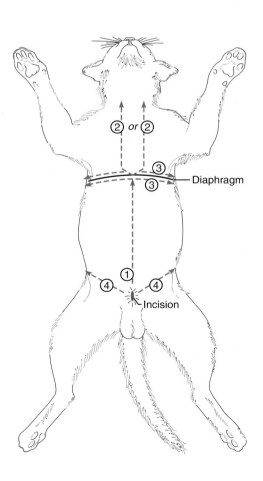

Figure D3.1   Incisions to be made in opening the ventral body cavity of a cat. Numbers indicate sequence.

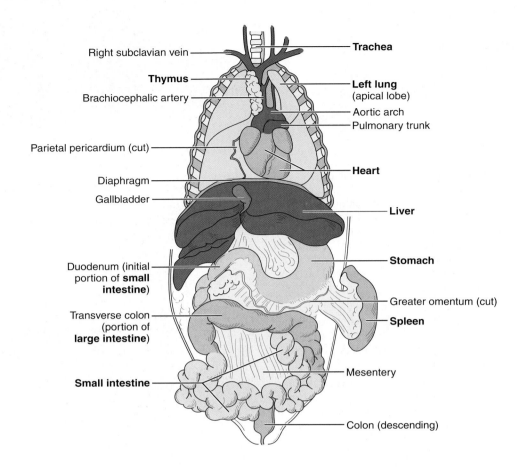

Figure D3.2 **Ventral body cavity organs of the cat.** Superficial view with greater omentum removed.

Neck and Thoracic Cavity Organs

Trachea: The windpipe; runs down the midline of the throat and then divides just anterior to the lungs to form the bronchi, which plunge into the lungs on either side.

*Thyroid: Its dark lobes straddle the trachea (see Figure D3.3). This endocrine organ's hormones are the main hormones regulating the body's metabolic rate.

*Thymus: Glandular structure superior to and partly covering the heart. The thymus is intimately involved (via its hormones) in programming the immune system. If you have a young cat, the thymus will be quite large. In old cats, most of this organ has been replaced by fat.

Heart: In the mediastinum enclosed by the pericardium.

Lungs: Paired organs flanking the heart.

Abdominal Cavity Organs

Liver: Large multilobed organ lying under the umbrella of the diaphragm.

• Lift the drapelike, fat-infiltrated greater omentum covering the abdominal organs to expose the following organs:

Stomach: Dorsally located sac to the left side of the liver.

Spleen: Flattened brown organ curving around the lateral aspect of the stomach.

Small intestine: Tubelike organ continuing posteriorly from the stomach.

Large intestine: Taking a U-shaped course around the small intestine to terminate in the rectum.

• Lift the first section of the small intestine with your forceps; you should see the pancreas situated in the delicate mesentery behind the stomach. This gland is extremely important in regulating blood sugar levels.

*Pancreas: Diffuse gland lying deep to and between the small intestine and stomach (see Figure D3.3).

• Push the intestines to one side with a probe to reveal the deeper organs in the abdominal cavity.

Kidneys: Bean-shaped organs located toward the dorsal body wall surface and behind the peritoneum (see Figure D3.3).

*Adrenal glands: Seen above and medial to each kidney, these small glands produce corticosteroids important in preventing stress and abnormalities of water and electrolyte balance in the body.

*Gonads (ovaries or testes): Sex organs producing sex hormones. The location of the gonads is illustrated in Figure D3.3, but their identification is deferred until the reproductive system organs are considered (Exercise 42 and Dissection Exercise 9). ■

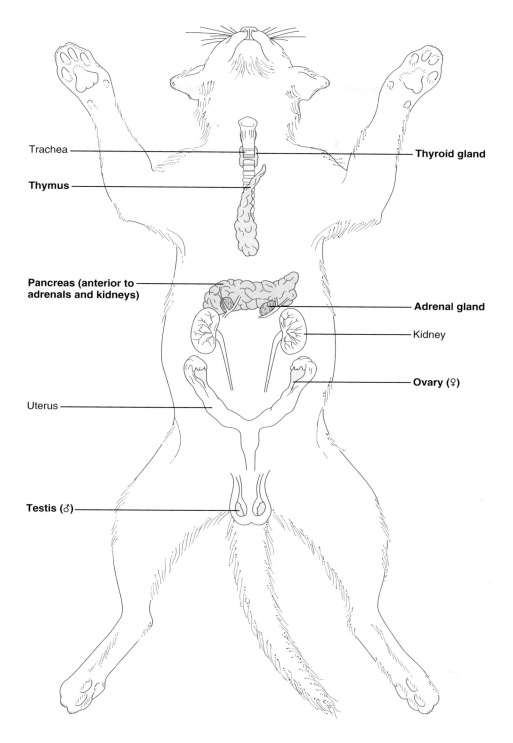

Figure D3.3 Endocrine organs in the cat.

Dissection Review

1. How do the locations of the endocrine organs in the cat compare with those in the human?

   _____

   _____

2. Name two endocrine organs located in the neck region: _____ and _____

3. Name three endocrine organs located in the abdominal cavity.

   _____

   _____

4. Given the assumption (not necessarily true) that human beings have more stress than cats, which endocrine organs would you expect to be relatively larger in humans?

   _____

5. Cats are smaller animals than humans. Which would you expect to have a (relatively speaking) more active thyroid gland—

   cats or humans? _____ Why? (We know we are asking a lot with this one, but give it a whirl.)

   _____

   _____

Dissection of the Blood Vessels of the Cat

I f Dissection Exercise 3 was conducted, you have already opened your animal's ventral body cavity and identified many of its organs. In such a case, begin this exercise with the activity "Preparing to Identify the Blood Vessels" on page 779. See Exercise 32 of this manual for a discussion of the anatomy of the human blood vessels.

Objectives

1. To identify several of the most important blood vessels of the cat.

2. To point out anatomical differences between the vascular system of the human and the laboratory dissection specimen.

Materials

- ❑ Disposable gloves
- ❑ Dissecting instruments and tray
- ❑ Animal specimen from previous dissections
- ❑ Bone cutters
- ❑ Scissors
- ❑ Embalming fluid
- ❑ Paper towels

Activity 1:
Opening the Ventral Body Cavity

1. Don gloves and then obtain your dissection animal. Place the animal on the dissecting tray, ventral side up. Using scissors and Figure D4.1 as a guide, make a longitudinal incision through the ventral body wall. Begin just superior to the midline of the pubic bone, and continue the cut anteriorly to the rib cage.

2. Angle the scissors slightly (1.3 cm, or ½ inch) to the right or left of the sternum, and continue the cut through the rib cartilages just lateral to the body midline, to the base of the throat. Your instructor may have you use heavier bone cutters to cut through the rib cartilages.

3. Make two lateral cuts on both sides of the ventral body surface, anterior and posterior to the diaphragm. *Leave the diaphragm intact.* Spread the thoracic walls laterally to expose the thoracic organs.

4. Make an angled lateral cut on each side of the median incision line just superior to the pubic bone and spread the flaps to expose the abdominal cavity organs. ■

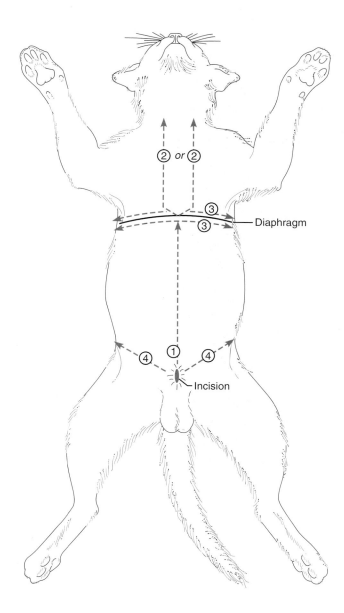

Figure D4.1 **Incisions to be made in opening the ventral body cavity of a cat.** Numbers indicate sequence.

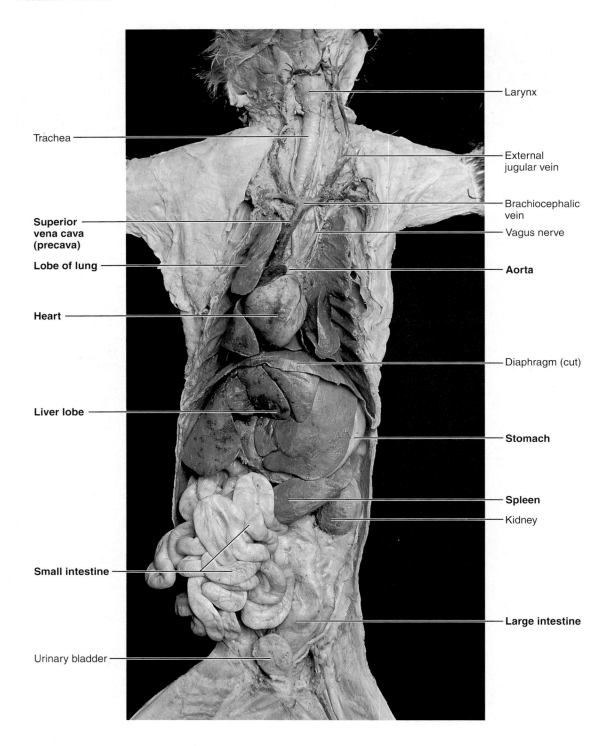

Trachea

Superior vena cava (precava)

Lobe of lung

Heart

Liver lobe

Small intestine

Urinary bladder

Larynx

External jugular vein

Brachiocephalic vein

Vagus nerve

Aorta

Diaphragm (cut)

Stomach

Spleen

Kidney

Large intestine

Figure D4.2 Ventral body cavity organs of the cat. (Greater omentum has been removed.)

Activity 2:
Preliminary Organ Identification

A helpful prelude to identifying and tracing the blood supply of the various organs of the cat is a preliminary identification of ventral body cavity organs shown in Figure D4.2. Since you will study the organ systems contained in the ventral cavity in later units, the objective here is simply to identify the most important organs. Using Figure D4.2 as a guide, identify the following body cavity organs:

Thoracic Cavity Organs

Heart: In the mediastinum enclosed by the pericardium.

Lungs: Flanking the heart.

Thymus: Superior to and partially covering the heart. (See Figure D3.2, page 774.) The thymus is quite large in young cats but is largely replaced by fat as cats age.

Abdominal Cavity Organs

Liver: Posterior to the diaphragm.

• Lift the large, drapelike, fat-infiltrated greater omentum covering the abdominal organs to expose the following:

Stomach: Dorsally located and to the left side of the liver.

Spleen: A flattened, brown organ curving around the lateral aspect of the stomach.

Small intestine: Continuing posteriorly from the stomach.

Large intestine: Taking a **U**-shaped course around the small intestine and terminating in the rectum. ■

Activity 3:
Preparing to Identify the Blood Vessels

1.   Carefully clear away any thymus tissue or fat obscuring the heart and the large vessels associated with the heart. Before identifying the blood vessels, try to locate the *phrenic nerve* (from the cervical plexus), which innervates the diaphragm. The phrenic nerves lie ventral to the root of the lung on each side, as they pass to the diaphragm. Also attempt to locate the *vagus nerve* (cranial nerve X) passing laterally along the trachea and dorsal to the root of the lung.

2.   Slit the parietal pericardium and reflect it superiorly. Then, cut it away from its heart attachments. Review the structures of the heart. Notice its pointed inferior end (apex) and its broader superior portion. Identify the two *atria,* which appear darker than the inferior *ventricles.*

3.   Identify the **aorta,** the largest artery in the body, issuing from the left ventricle. Also identify the *coronary arteries* in the sulcus on the ventral surface of the heart; these should be injected with red latex. (As an aid to blood vessel identification, the arteries of laboratory dissection specimens are injected with red latex; the veins are injected with blue latex. Exceptions to this will be noted as they are encountered.)

4.   Identify the two large venae cavae—the superior and inferior venae cavae—entering the right atrium. The superior vena cava is the largest dark-colored vessel entering the base of the heart. These vessels are called the **precava** and **postcava,** respectively, in the cat. The caval veins drain the same relative body areas as in humans. Also identify the **pulmonary trunk** (usually injected with blue latex) extending anteriorly from the right ventricle and the right and left pulmonary arteries. Trace the **pulmonary arteries** until they enter the lungs. Locate the **pulmonary veins** entering the left atrium and the ascending aorta arising from the left ventricle and running dorsally to the precava and to the left of the body midline. ■

Activity 4:
Identifying the Arteries of the Cat

Refer to Figure D4.3 and to the summary photo in Figure D4.6 on page 785 as you study the arterial system of the cat.

1.   Reidentify the aorta as it emerges from the left ventricle. As you observed in the dissection of the sheep heart, the first branches of the aorta are the **coronary arteries** (see Figure 30.8, p. 329), which supply the myocardium. The coronary arteries emerge from the base of the aorta and can be seen on the surface of the heart. Follow the aorta as it arches (aortic arch), and identify its major branches. In the cat, the aortic arch gives off two large vessels, the **brachiocephalic artery** and the **left subclavian artery.** The brachiocephalic artery has three major branches, the right subclavian artery and the right and left common carotid arteries. (Note that in humans, the left common carotid artery and left subclavian artery are direct branches off the aortic arch.)

2.   Follow the **right common carotid artery** along the right side of the trachea as it moves anteriorly, giving off branches to the neck muscles, thyroid gland, and trachea. At the level of the larynx, it branches to form the **external** and **internal carotid arteries.** The internal carotid is quite small in the cat and it may be difficult to locate. It may even be absent. The distribution of the carotid arteries parallels that in humans.

3.   Follow the **right subclavian artery** laterally. It gives off four branches, the first being the tiny **vertebral artery,** which along with the internal carotid artery provides the arterial circulation of the brain. Other branches of the subclavian artery include the **costocervical trunk** (to the costal and cervical regions), the **thyrocervical trunk** (to the shoulder), and the **internal mammary artery** (serving the ventral thoracic wall). As the subclavian passes in front of the first rib it becomes the **axillary artery.** Its branches, which may be difficult to identify, supply the trunk and shoulder muscles. These are the **ventral thoracic artery** (the pectoral muscles), the **long thoracic artery** (pectoral muscles and latissimus dorsi), and the **subscapular artery** (the trunk muscles). As the axillary artery enters the arm, it is called the **brachial artery,** and it travels with the median nerve down the length of the humerus. At the elbow, the brachial artery branches to produce the two major arteries serving the forearm and hand, the **radial** and **ulnar arteries.**

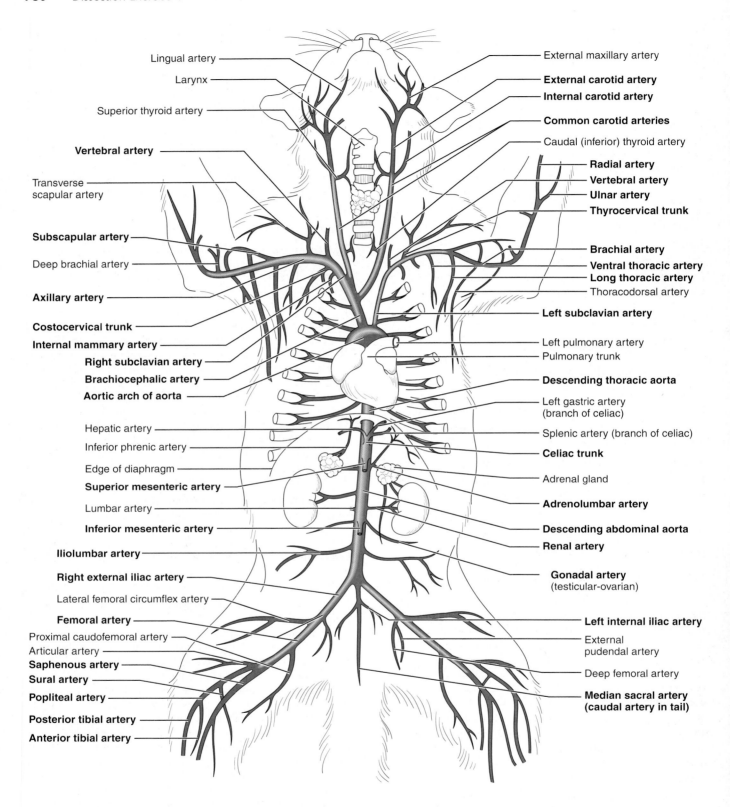

Lingual artery

Larynx

Superior thyroid artery

Vertebral artery

Transverse
scapular artery

Subscapular artery

Deep brachial artery

Axillary artery

Costocervical trunk

Internal mammary artery

Right subclavian artery

Brachiocephalic artery

Aortic arch of aorta

Hepatic artery

Inferior phrenic artery

Edge of diaphragm

Superior mesenteric artery

Lumbar artery

Inferior mesenteric artery

Iliolumbar artery

Right external iliac artery

Lateral femoral circumflex artery

Femoral artery

Proximal caudofemoral artery

Articular artery

Saphenous artery

Sural artery

Popliteal artery

Posterior tibial artery

Anterior tibial artery

External maxillary artery

External carotid artery

Internal carotid artery

Common carotid arteries

Caudal (inferior) thyroid artery

Radial artery

Vertebral artery

Ulnar artery

Thyrocervical trunk

Brachial artery

Ventral thoracic artery

Long thoracic artery

Thoracodorsal artery

Left subclavian artery

Left pulmonary artery

Pulmonary trunk

Descending thoracic aorta

Left gastric artery
(branch of celiac)

Splenic artery (branch of celiac)

Celiac trunk

Adrenal gland

Adrenolumbar artery

Descending abdominal aorta

Renal artery

Gonadal artery
(testicular-ovarian)

Left internal iliac artery

External
pudendal artery

Deep femoral artery

Median sacral artery
(caudal artery in tail)

Figure D4.3 Arterial system of the cat. (See also Figure D4.6 on page 785.)

4.   Return to the thorax, lift the left lung, and follow the course of the *descending aorta* through the thoracic cavity. The esophagus overlies it along its course. Notice the paired intercostal arteries that branch laterally from the aorta in the thoracic region.

5.   Follow the aorta through the diaphragm into the abdominal cavity. Carefully pull the peritoneum away from its ventral surface and identify the following vessels:

Celiac trunk: The first branch diverging from the aorta immediately as it enters the abdominal cavity; supplies the stomach, liver, gallbladder, pancreas, and spleen. (Trace as many of its branches to these organs as possible.)

Superior mesenteric artery: Immediately posterior to the celiac trunk; supplies the small intestine and most of the large intestine. (Spread the mesentery of the small intestine to observe the branches of this artery as they run to supply the small intestine.)

Adrenolumbar arteries: Paired arteries diverging from the aorta slightly posterior to the superior mesenteric artery; supply the muscles of the body wall and adrenal glands.

Renal arteries: Paired arteries supplying the kidneys.

Gonadal arteries (testicular or ovarian): Paired arteries supplying the gonads.

Inferior mesenteric artery: An unpaired thin vessel arising from the ventral surface of the aorta posterior to the gonadal arteries; supplies the second half of the large intestine.

Iliolumbar arteries: Paired, rather large arteries that supply the body musculature in the iliolumbar region.

External iliac arteries: Paired arteries which continue through the body wall and pass under the inguinal ligament to the hindlimb.

6.   After giving off the external iliac arteries, the aorta persists briefly and then divides into three arteries: the two **internal iliac arteries** which supply the pelvic viscera, and the **median sacral artery.** As the median sacral artery enters the tail, it comes to be called the **caudal artery.** (Note that there is no common iliac artery in the cat.)

7.   Trace the external iliac artery into the thigh, where it becomes the **femoral artery.** The femoral artery is most easily identified in the *femoral triangle* at the medial surface of the upper thigh. Follow the femoral artery as it courses through the thigh (along with the femoral vein and nerve) and gives off branches to the thigh muscles. (These various branches are indicated on Figure D4.3.) As you approach the knee, the **saphenous artery** branches off the femoral artery to supply the medial portion of the leg. The femoral artery then descends deep to the knee to become the **popliteal artery** in the popliteal region. The popliteal artery in turn gives off two main branches, the **sural artery** and the **posterior tibial artery,** and continues as the **anterior tibial artery.** These branches supply the leg and foot. ■

Activity 5:
Identifying the Veins of the Cat

Refer to Figure D4.4 on page 782 and to summary Figure D4.6 on page 785 as you study the venous system of the cat. Keep in mind that the vessels are named for the region drained, not for the point of union with other veins. (As you continue with the dissection, notice that not all vessels shown on Figure D4.4 are discussed.)

1.   Reidentify the **precava** as it enters the right atrium. Trace it anteriorly to identify veins that enter it.

Azygos vein: Passing directly into its dorsal surface; drains the thoracic intercostal muscles.

Internal thoracic (mammary) veins: Drain the chest and abdominal walls.

Right vertebral vein: Drains the spinal cord and brain; usually enters right side of precava approximately at the level of the internal mammary veins but may enter the brachiocephalic vein in your specimen.

Right and left brachiocephalic veins: Form the precava by their union.

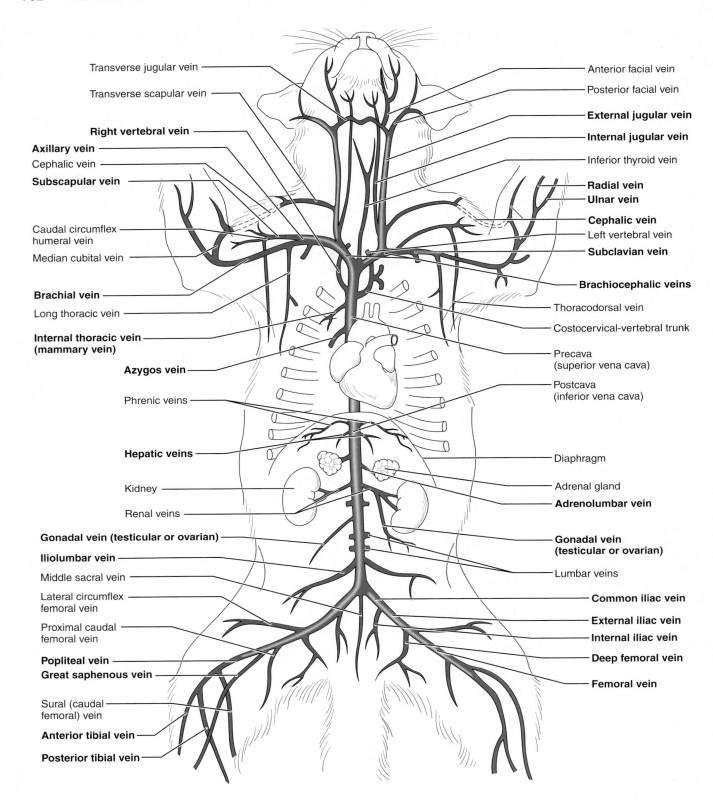

Transverse jugular vein

Transverse scapular vein

Right vertebral vein

Axillary vein
Cephalic vein
Subscapular vein

Caudal circumflex
humeral vein
Median cubital vein

Brachial vein
Long thoracic vein

**Internal thoracic vein
(mammary vein)**

Azygos vein

Phrenic veins

Hepatic veins

Kidney

Renal veins

Gonadal vein (testicular or ovarian)
Iliolumbar vein
Middle sacral vein
Lateral circumflex
femoral vein
Proximal caudal
femoral vein
Popliteal vein
Great saphenous vein

Sural (caudal
femoral) vein
Anterior tibial vein
Posterior tibial vein

Anterior facial vein
Posterior facial vein
External jugular vein
Internal jugular vein
Inferior thyroid vein
Radial vein
Ulnar vein
Cephalic vein
Left vertebral vein
Subclavian vein

Brachiocephalic veins
Thoracodorsal vein
Costocervical-vertebral trunk

Precava
(superior vena cava)

Postcava
(inferior vena cava)

Diaphragm

Adrenal gland
Adrenolumbar vein

**Gonadal vein
(testicular or ovarian)**
Lumbar veins

Common iliac vein

External iliac vein
Internal iliac vein
Deep femoral vein

Femoral vein

Figure D4.4   Venous system of the cat. (See also Figure D4.6 on page 785.)

2.   Reflect the pectoral muscles, and trace the brachio-cephalic vein laterally. Identify the two large veins that unite to form it—the external jugular vein and the subclavian vein. Notice this differs from what is seen in humans where the brachiocephalic veins are formed by the union of the internal jugular and subclavian veins.

3.   Follow the **external jugular vein** as it courses anteriorly along the side of the neck to the point where it is joined on its medial surface by the **internal jugular vein.** The internal jugular veins are small and may be difficult to identify in the cat. Notice the difference in cat and human jugular veins. The internal jugular is considerably larger in humans and drains into the subclavian vein. In the cat, the external jugular is larger, and the internal jugular vein drains into it. Several other vessels drain into the external jugular vein (transverse scapular vein draining the shoulder, facial veins draining the head, and others). These are not discussed here but are shown on the figure and may be traced if time allows. Also, identify the *common carotid artery,* since it accompanies the internal jugular vein in this region, and attempt to find the *sympathetic trunk,* which is located in the same area running lateral to the trachea.

4.   Return to the shoulder region and follow the course of the **subclavian vein** as it moves laterally toward the arm. It becomes the **axillary vein** as it passes in front of the first rib and runs through the brachial plexus, giving off several branches, the first of which is the **subscapular vein.** The subscapular vein drains the proximal part of the arm and shoulder. The four other branches that receive drainage from the shoulder, pectoral, and latissimus dorsi muscles are shown in the figure but need not be identified in this dissection.

5.   Follow the axillary vein into the arm, where it becomes the **brachial vein.** You can locate this vein on the medial side of the arm accompanying the brachial artery and nerve. Trace it to the point where it receives the **radial** and **ulnar veins** (which drain the forelimb) at the inner bend of the elbow. Also locate the superficial **cephalic vein** on the dorsal side of the arm. It communicates with the brachial vein via the median cubital vein in the elbow region and then enters the transverse scapular vein in the shoulder.

6.   Reidentify the **postcaval vein**, and trace it to its passage through the diaphragm. Notice again as you follow its course that the **intercostal veins** drain into a much smaller vein lying dorsal to the postcava, the **azygos vein.**

7.   Attempt to identify the **hepatic veins** entering the postcava from the liver. These may be seen if some of the anterior liver tissue is scraped away where the postcava enters the liver.

8.   Displace the intestines to the left side of the body cavity, and proceed posteriorly to identify the following veins in order. All of these veins empty into the postcava and drain the organs served by the same-named arteries. In the cat, variations in the connections of the veins to be located are common, and in some cases the postcaval vein may be double below the level of the renal veins. If you observe deviations, call them to the attention of your instructor.

Adrenolumbar veins: From the adrenal glands and body wall.

Renal veins: From the kidneys (it is common to find two renal veins on the right side).

Gonadal veins (testicular or ovarian veins): The left vein of this venous pair enters the left renal vein anteriorly.

Iliolumbar veins: Drain muscles of the back.

Common iliac veins: Unite to form the postcava.

The common iliac veins are formed in turn by the union of the **internal iliac** and **external iliac veins.** The more medial internal iliac veins receive branches from the pelvic organs and gluteal region whereas the external iliac vein receives venous drainage from the lower extremity. As the external iliac vein enters the thigh by running beneath the inguinal ligament, it receives the **deep femoral vein,** which drains the thigh and the external genital region. Just inferior to that point, the external iliac vein becomes the **femoral vein,** which receives blood from the thigh, leg, and foot. Follow the femoral vein down the thigh to identify the **great saphenous vein,** a superficial vein that courses up the inner aspect of the calf and across the inferior portion of the gracilis muscle (accompanied by the great saphenous artery and nerve) to enter the femoral vein. The femoral vein is formed by the union of this vein and the popliteal vein. The **popliteal vein** is located deep in the thigh beneath the semimembranosus and semitendinosus muscles in the popliteal space accompanying the popliteal artery. Trace the popliteal vein to its point of division into the **posterior** and **anterior tibial veins,** which drain the leg.

9.   In your specimen, trace the hepatic portal drainage depicted in Figure D4.5. Locate the **hepatic portal vein** by removing the peritoneum between the first portion of the small intestine and the liver. It appears brown due to coagulated blood, and it is unlikely that it or any of the vessels of this circulation contain latex. In the cat, the hepatic portal vein is formed by the union of the gastrosplenic and superior mesenteric veins. (In the human, the hepatic portal vein is formed by the union of the splenic and superior mesenteric veins.) If possible, locate the following vessels, which empty into the hepatic portal vein.

Gastrosplenic vein: Carries blood from the spleen and stomach; located dorsal to the stomach.

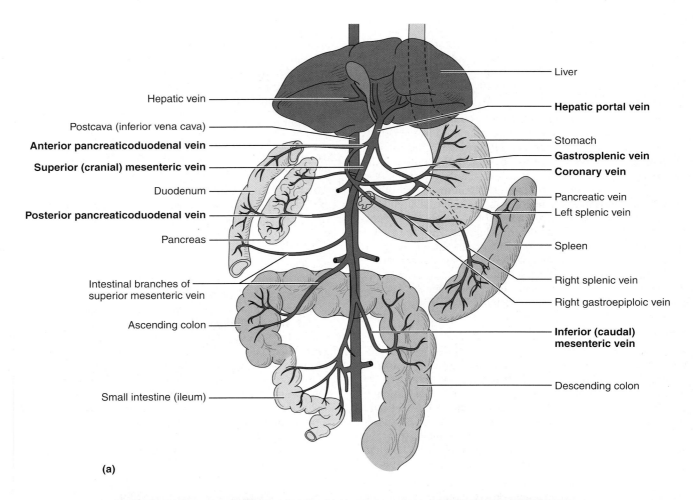

(a)

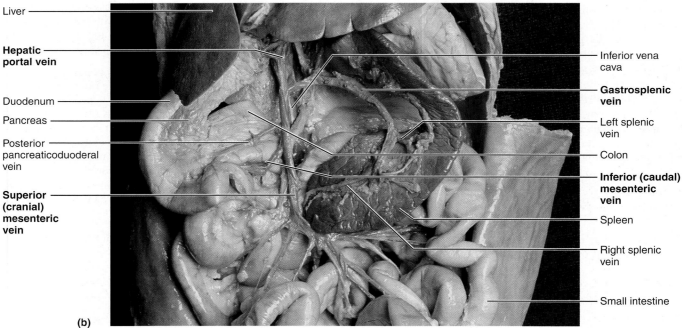

(b)

Figure D4.5 **Hepatic portal circulation of the cat.** **(a)** Diagrammatic view. **(b)** Photograph of hepatic portal system of the cat, midline to left lateral view, just posterior to the liver and pancreas. Intestines have been pulled to the left side of the cat. The mesentery of the small intestine has been partially dissected to show the veins of the portal system.

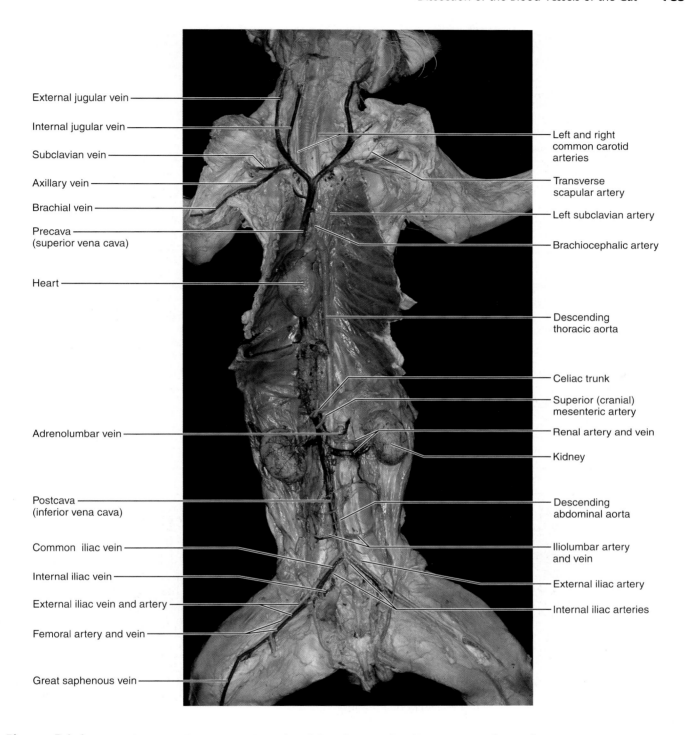

External jugular vein

Internal jugular vein

Subclavian vein

Axillary vein

Brachial vein

Precava
(superior vena cava)

Heart

Adrenolumbar vein

Postcava
(inferior vena cava)

Common iliac vein

Internal iliac vein

External iliac vein and artery

Femoral artery and vein

Great saphenous vein

Left and right
common carotid
arteries

Transverse
scapular artery

Left subclavian artery

Brachiocephalic artery

Descending
thoracic aorta

Celiac trunk

Superior (cranial)
mesenteric artery

Renal artery and vein

Kidney

Descending
abdominal aorta

Iliolumbar artery
and vein

External iliac artery

Internal iliac arteries

Figure D4.6   Cat dissected to reveal major blood vessels. (Summary Figure.)

Superior (cranial) mesenteric vein: A large vein draining the small and large intestines and the pancreas.

Inferior (caudal) mesenteric vein: Parallels the course of the inferior mesenteric artery and empties into the superior mesenteric vein. In humans, this vessel merges with the splenic vein.

Coronary vein: Drains the lesser curvature of the stomach.

Pancreaticoduodenal veins (anterior and posterior): The anterior branch empties into the hepatic portal vein; the posterior branch empties into the superior mesenteric vein. (In humans, both of these are branches of the superior mesenteric vein.)

If the structures of the lymphatic system of the cat are to be studied during this laboratory session, turn to Dissection Exercise 5 for instructions to conduct the study. Otherwise, properly clean your dissecting instruments and dissecting pan, and wrap and tag your cat for storage as described in the box on page 752. ■

Dissection Review

1. What differences did you observe between the origins of the left common carotid arteries in the cat and in the human?

   _____

   _____

   _____

   Between the origins of the internal and external iliac arteries?

   _____

   _____

   _____

   _____

2. How do the relative sizes of the external and internal jugular veins differ in the human and the cat?

   _____

   _____

   _____

3. In the cat the inferior vena cava is called the _____

   and the superior vena cava is referred to as the _____

4. Define the following terms.

   ascending aorta: _____

   aortic arch: _____

   descending thoracic aorta: _____

   descending abdominal aorta: _____

The Main Lymphatic Ducts of the Cat

Activity:
Identifying the Main Lymphatic Ducts of the Cat

1. Don disposable gloves. Obtain your cat and a dissecting tray and instruments. Because lymphatic vessels are extremely thin-walled, it is difficult to locate them in a dissection unless the animal has been triply injected (with yellow or green latex for the lymphatic system). However, the large thoracic duct can be localized and identified. See Exercise 35 of this manual for a discussion of the human lymphatic system.

2. Move the thoracic organs to the side to locate the **thoracic duct.** Typically it lies just to the left of the mid-dorsal line, abutting the dorsal aspect of the descending aorta. It is usually about the size of pencil lead and red-brown with a segmented or beaded appearance caused by the valves within it. Trace it anteriorly to the site where it passes behind the left brachiocephalic vein and then bends and enters the venous system at the junction of the left subclavian and external jugular veins. If the veins are well injected, some of the blue latex may have slipped past the valves and entered the first portion of the thoracic duct.

3. While in this region, also attempt to identify the short **right lymphatic duct** draining into the right subclavian vein, and notice the collection of lymph nodes in the axillary region.

Objective

To compare and contrast lymphatic structures of the cat to those of a human.

Materials

- ❑ Disposable gloves
- ❑ Dissecting instruments and tray
- ❑ Animal specimen from previous dissections
- ❑ Embalming fluid
- ❑ Paper towels

4. If the cat is triply injected, trace the thoracic duct posteriorly to identify the **cisterna chyli,** the saclike enlargement of its distal end. This structure, which receives fat-rich lymph from the intestine, begins at the level of the diaphragm and can be localized posterior to the left kidney.

5. When you finish identifying these lymphatic structures, clean the dissecting instruments and tray, and properly wrap the cat and return it to storage. ■

Dissection Review

1. How does the cat's lymphatic drainage pattern compare to that of humans? _____

_____

2. What is the role of

a. the thoracic duct? _____

_____

b. the right lymphatic duct? _____

_____

Dissection of the Respiratory System of the Cat

Objective

To identify the major respiratory system organs in a dissected animal.

Materials

- ❑ Disposable gloves
- ❑ Dissecting instruments and tray
- ❑ Animal specimen from previous dissections
- ❑ Embalming fluid
- ❑ Paper towels
- ❑ Stereomicroscope

In this dissection exercise, you will be examining both the gross and fine structure of respiratory system organs. Don disposable gloves and then obtain your dissection animal, and dissecting tray and instruments. See Exercises 36 and 37A of this manual for a discussion of the human respiratory system.

Activity 1:
Identifying Organs of the Respiratory System

1. Examine the external nares, oral cavity, and oral pharynx. Use a probe to demonstrate the continuity between the oral pharynx and the nasal pharynx above.

2. After securing the animal to the dissecting tray dorsal surface down, expose the more distal respiratory structures by retracting the cut muscle and rib cage. Do not sever nerves and blood vessels located on either side of the trachea if these have not been studied. If you have not previously opened the thoracic cavity, make a medial longitudinal incision through the neck muscles and thoracic musculature to expose and view the thoracic organs (see Figure D4.1, page 777).

3. Using the orientation Figure D6.1 and the photo in Figure D6.2 as guides, identify the structures named in items 3 through 5. Examine the **trachea,** and determine by finger examination whether the cartilage rings are complete

or incomplete posteriorly. Locate the **thyroid gland** inferior to the larynx on the trachea. Free the **larynx** from the attached muscle tissue for ease of examination. Identify the **thyroid** and **cricoid cartilages** and the flaplike **epiglottis.** Find the **hyoid bone,** located anterior to the larynx. Make a longitudinal incision through the ventral wall of the larynx and locate the *true* and *false vocal cords* on the inner wall.

4. Locate the large *right* and *left common carotid arteries* and the *internal jugular veins* on either side of the trachea (see Figure D4.5, page 784). Also locate a conspicuous white band, the *vagus nerve,* which lies alongside the trachea, adjacent to the common carotid artery.

5. Examine the contents of the thoracic cavity. Follow the trachea as it bifurcates into two *primary bronchi,* which plunge into the **lungs.** Note that there are two *pleural cavities* containing the lungs and that each lung is composed of many lobes. In humans there are three lobes in the right lung and two in the left. How does this compare to what is seen in the cat?

_____

_____

Identify the *pericardial sac* containing the heart located in the mediastinum (if it is still present). Examine the *pleura,* and note its exceptionally smooth texture.

6. Locate the **diaphragm** and the **phrenic nerve.** The phrenic nerve, clearly visible as a white "thread" running along the pericardium to the diaphragm, controls the activity of the diaphragm in breathing. Lift one lung and find the esophagus beneath the parietal pleura. Follow it through the diaphragm to the stomach. ■

Activity 2:
Observing Lung Tissue Microscopically

Make a longitudinal incision in the outer tissue of one lung lobe beginning at a primary bronchus. Attempt to follow part of the respiratory tree from this point down into the smaller subdivisions. Carefully observe the cut lung tissue (under a stereoscope, if one is available), noting the richness of the vascular supply and the irregular or spongy texture of the lung. ■

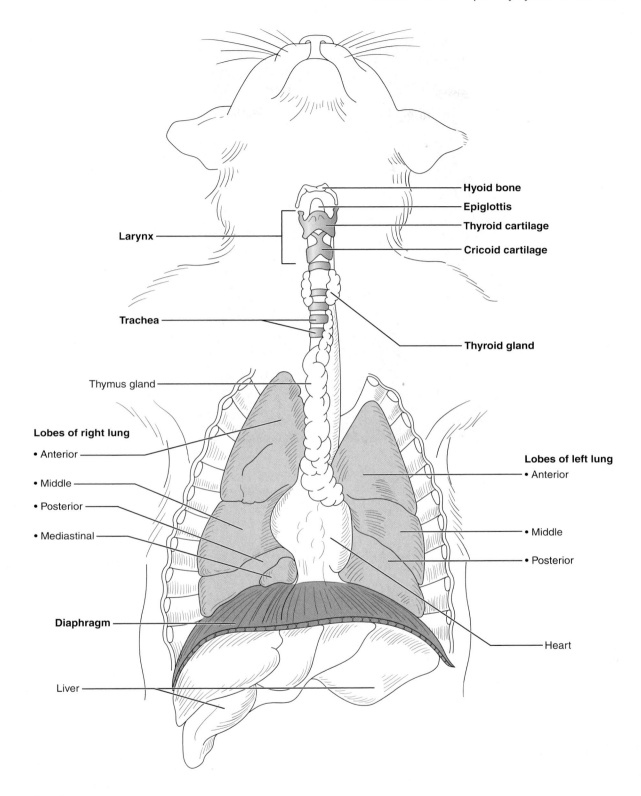

Figure D6.1 Respiratory system of the cat. (See also the photo in Figure D6.2.)

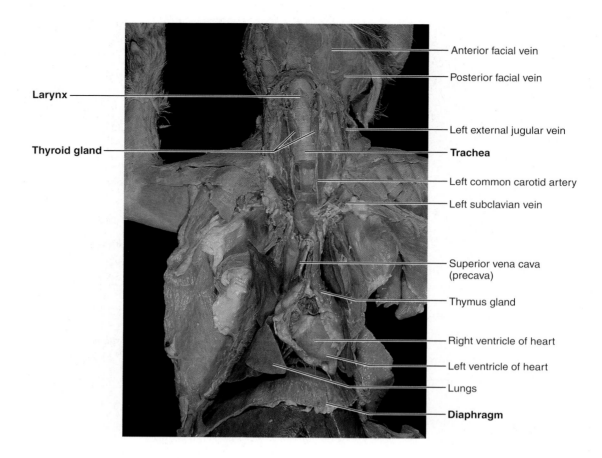

Figure D6.2 **Photograph of the respiratory system of the cat.**

Dissection Review

1. Are the cartilaginous rings in the cat trachea complete or incomplete?

    _____

2. Compare the number of right and left lung lobes in cats and humans.

    _____

    _____

3. Describe the appearance of the bronchial tree in the cat lung.

    _____

4. Describe the appearance of lung tissue under the dissection microscope.

    _____

    _____

Dissection of the Digestive System of the Cat

D on gloves and obtain your dissection animal. Secure it to the dissecting tray, dorsal surface down. Obtain all necessary dissecting instruments. If you have completed the dissection of the circulatory and respiratory systems, the abdominal cavity is already exposed and many of the digestive system structures have been previously identified. However, duplication of effort generally provides a good learning experience, so all of the digestive system structures will be traced and identified in this exercise. See Exercise 38 of this manual for a discussion of the human digestive system.

Objectives

1. To identify on a dissected animal the organs composing the alimentary canal, and to name their subdivisions if any.
2. To name and identify the accessory organs of digestion in the dissection animal, and to indicate their function.

Materials

- ❑ Disposable gloves
- ❑ Dissecting instruments and tray
- ❑ Animal specimen from previous dissections
- ❑ Bone cutters
- ❑ Hand lens
- ❑ Embalming fluid
- ❑ Paper towels

If the abdominal cavity has not been previously opened, make a midline incision from the rib cage to the pubic symphysis as shown in Figure D7.1. Then make four lateral cuts—two parallel to the rib cage and two at the inferior margin of the abdominal cavity so that the abdominal wall can be reflected back while you examine the abdominal contents. Observe the shiny membrane lining the inner surface of the abdominal wall, which is the **parietal peritoneum.**

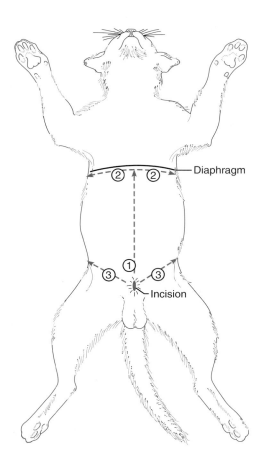

Figure D7.1   Incisions to be made in opening the ventral body cavity of the cat. Numbers indicate sequence.

Activity 1:
Identifying Alimentary Canal Organs

1. Using Figure D7.2, locate the abdominal alimentary canal structures.

2. Identify the large reddish brown **liver** just beneath the diaphragm and the greater omentum covering the abdominal contents. The greater omentum assists in regulating body temperature and its phagocytic cells help to protect the body. Notice that the greater omentum is riddled with fat deposits. Lift the greater omentum, noting its two-layered structure and attachments, and lay it to the side or remove it to make subsequent organ identifications easier. Does the liver of the cat have the same number of lobes as the human liver?

_____

3. Lift the liver and examine its inferior surface to locate the **gallbladder,** a dark greenish sac embedded in the liver's ventral surface. Identify the **falciform ligament,** a delicate layer of mesentery separating the main lobes of the liver (right and left median lobes) and attaching the liver superiorly to the abdominal wall. Also identify the thickened area along the posterior edge of the falciform ligament, the *round ligament,* or *ligamentum teres,* a remnant of the umbilical vein of the embryo.

4. Displace the left lobes of the liver to expose the **stomach.** Identify the esophagus as it enters the stomach and the cardiac, fundic, body, and pyloric regions of the stomach. What is the general shape of the stomach?

_____

Locate the **lesser omentum,** the serous membrane attaching the lesser curvature of the stomach to the liver and identify the large tongue-like spleen curving around the greater curvature of the stomach.

Make an incision through the stomach wall to expose the inner surface of the stomach. Can you see the **rugae**? (When the stomach is empty, its mucosa is thrown into large folds called rugae. As the stomach fills, the rugae gradually disappear and are no longer visible.) Identify the **pyloric sphincter** at the distal end of the stomach.

5. Lift the stomach and locate the **pancreas,** which appears as a grayish or brownish diffuse glandular mass in the mesentery. It extends from the vicinity of the spleen and greater curvature of the stomach and wraps around the duodenum. Attempt to find the **pancreatic duct** as it empties into the duodenum at a swollen area referred to as the **hepatopancreatic ampulla.** Tease away the fine connective tissue, locate the **bile duct** close to the pancreatic duct, and trace its course superiorly to the point where it diverges into the **cystic duct** (gallbladder duct) and the **common hepatic duct** (duct from the liver). Notice that the duodenum assumes a looped position.

6. Lift the **small intestine** to investigate the manner in which it is attached to the posterior body wall by the **mesentery.**

Observe the mesentery closely. What types of structures do you see in this double peritoneal fold?

_____

Other than providing support for the intestine, what other functions does the mesentery have?

_____

_____

Trace the course of the small intestine from its proximal, (duodenal) end to its distal (ileal) end. Can you see any obvious differences in the external anatomy of the small intestine from one end to the other?

_____

With a scalpel, slice open the distal portion of the ileum and flush out the inner surface with water. Feel the inner surface with your fingertip. How does it feel?

_____

Use a hand lens to see if you can see any **villi** and to locate the areas of lymphatic tissue called **Peyer's patches,** which appear as scattered white patches on the inner intestinal surface. See also Plate 41 in the Histology Atlas.

Return to the duodenal end of the small intestine. Make an incision into the duodenum. As before, flush the surface with water, and feel the inner surface. Does it feel any different than the ileal mucosa?

_____ If so, describe the difference. _____

_____

_____

Use the hand lens to observe the villi. What differences do you see in the villi in the two areas of the small intestine?

_____

_____

7. Make an incision into the junction between the ileum and cecum to locate the ileocecal valve. Observe the **cecum,** the initial expanded part of the large intestine. (Lymph nodes may have to be removed from this area to observe it clearly.) Does the cat have an appendix?

_____

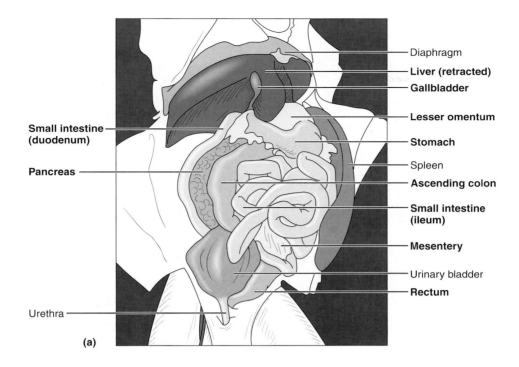

Diaphragm
Liver (retracted)
Gallbladder
Lesser omentum
Stomach
Spleen
Ascending colon
Small intestine (ileum)
Mesentery
Urinary bladder
Rectum
Urethra
Small intestine (duodenum)
Pancreas

(a)

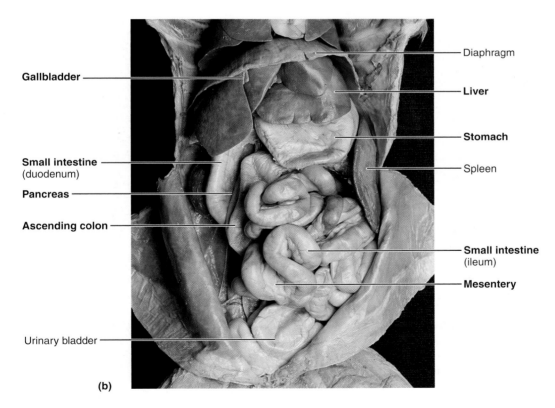

Diaphragm
Liver
Stomach
Spleen
Small intestine (ileum)
Mesentery
Urinary bladder
Gallbladder
Small intestine (duodenum)
Pancreas
Ascending colon

(b)

Figure D7.2   Digestive organs of the cat. (a) Diagrammatic view. **(b)** Photograph. The greater omentum has been cut from its attachment to the stomach.

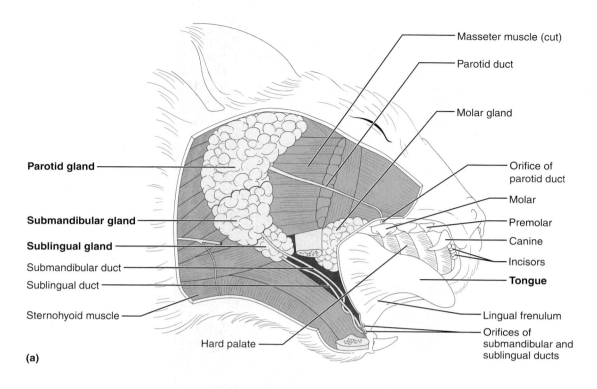

(a)

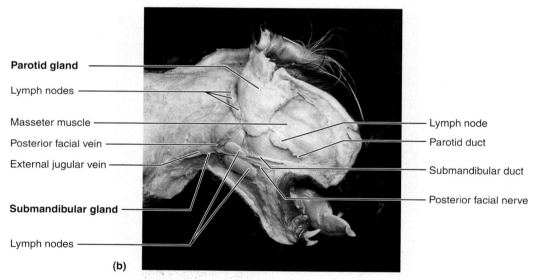

(b)

Figure D7.3   Salivary glands of the cat. (a) Diagrammatic view. **(b)** Photograph.

8.   Identify the short ascending, transverse, and descending portions of the **colon** and the **mesocolon,** a membrane that attaches the colon to the posterior body wall. Trace the descending colon to the **rectum,** which penetrates the body wall, and identify the **anus** on the exterior surface of the specimen.

Identify the two portions of the peritoneum, the parietal peritoneum lining the abdominal wall (identified previously) and the visceral peritoneum, which is the outermost layer of the wall of the abdominal organs (serosa). ■

Activity 2:
Exposing and Viewing the Salivary Glands and Oral Cavity Structures

1.   To expose and identify the **salivary glands,** which secrete saliva into the mouth, remove the skin from one side of the head and clear the connective tissue away from the angle of the jaw, below the ear, and superior to the masseter muscle.

Many dark, kidney-shaped lymph nodes are in this area and you should remove them if they obscure the salivary glands which are light tan and lobular in texture. The cat possesses five pairs of salivary glands, but only those glands described in humans are easily localized and identified (Figure D7.3). Locate the **parotid gland** on the cheek just inferior to the ear. Follow its duct over the surface of the masseter muscle to the angle of the mouth. The **submandibular gland** is posterior to the parotid, near the angle of the jaw, and the **sublingual gland** is just anterior to the submandibular gland within the lower jaw. The ducts of the submandibular and sublingual glands run deep and parallel to each other and empty on the side of the frenulum of the tongue. These need not be identified on the cat.

2. To expose and identify the structures of the oral cavity, cut through the mandiblar angle with bone cutters to free the lower jaw from the maxilla.

Identify the **hard** and **soft palates,** and use a probe to trace the bony hard palate to its posterior limits. Note the transverse ridges, or *rugae,* on the hard palate, which play a role in holding food in place while chewing.

Do these appear in humans? _____

Does the cat have a uvula? _____

Identify the **oropharynx** at the rear of the oral cavity and the palatine tonsils on the posterior walls at the junction between the oral cavity and oropharynx. Identify the **tongue** and rub your finger across its surface to feel the papillae. Some of the papillae, especially at the anterior end of the tongue, should feel sharp and bristly. These are the filiform papillae, which are much more numerous in the cat than in humans. What do you think their function is?

_____

Locate the **lingual frenulum** attaching the tongue to the floor of the mouth. Trace the tongue posteriorly until you locate the **epiglottis,** the flap of tissue that covers the entrance to the respiratory passageway when swallowing occurs. Identify the **esophageal opening** posterior to the epiglottis.

Observe the **teeth** of the cat. The dental formula for the adult cat is as follows:

$$\frac{3,1,3,1}{3,1,2,1} \times 2 = 30$$

What differences in diet and mode of food-getting explain the difference between cat and human dentition?

_____

_____

3. Prepare your cat for storage, wash the dissecting tray and instruments, and discard your gloves before continuing or leaving the laboratory. ■

Dissection Review

1. Compare the appearance of tongue papillae in cats and humans. _____

_____

2. Compare the number of lobes of the liver in cats and humans. _____

_____

3. Does the cat have a uvula? _____ An appendix? _____

4. Give an explanation for the different adult dental formulas in cats and humans.

_____

_____

5. How do the villi differ in the duodenum and the ileum? Explain.

_____

_____

Dissection of the Urinary System of the Cat

Objective

To identify on a dissection specimen the urinary system organs, and to describe the general function of each.

Materials

❑ Disposable gloves
❑ Dissecting instruments and tray
❑ Animal specimen from previous dissections
❑ Hand magnifying lens
❑ Embalming fluid
❑ Paper towel

The structures of the reproductive and urinary systems are often considered together as the *urogenital system,* since they have common embryological origins. However, the emphasis in this dissection is on identifying the structures of the urinary tract (Figures D8.1 and D8.2) with only a few references to contiguous reproductive structures. The anatomy of the reproductive system is studied in Dissection Exercise 9. See Exercise 40 of this manual for a discussion of the human urinary system.

Activity:
Identifying Organs of the Urinary System

1. Don gloves. Obtain your dissection specimen, and place it ventral side up on the dissecting tray. Reflect the abdominal viscera (most importantly the small intestine) to locate the kidneys high on the dorsal body wall (Figure D8.1). Note that the **kidneys** in the cat, as well as in the human, are retroperitoneal (behind the peritoneum). Carefully remove the peritoneum, and clear away the bed of fat that invests the kidneys. Then locate the adrenal (suprarenal) glands that lie superiorly and medial to the kidneys.

2. Identify the **renal artery** (red latex injected), the **renal vein** (blue latex injected), and the ureter at the hilus region of the kidney. (You may find two renal veins leaving one kidney in the cat but not in humans.)

3. To observe the gross internal anatomy of the kidney, slit the connective tissue *renal capsule* encasing a kidney and peel it back. Make a mid-frontal cut through the kidney and examine one cut surface with a hand lens to identify the granular *cortex* and the central darker *medulla* which will appear striated. Notice that the cat's renal medulla consists of just one pyramid as compared to the multipyramidal human kidney.

4. Trace the tubelike **ureters** to the **urinary bladder,** a smooth muscular sac located superiorly to the small intestine. If your cat is a female, be careful not to confuse the ureters with the uterine tubes, which lie superior to the bladder in the same general region (see Figure D8.1). Observe the sites where the ureters enter the bladder. How would you describe the entrance point anatomically?

_____

_____

5. Cut through the bladder wall, and examine the region of the urethral exit to see if you can discern any evidence of the *internal sphincter.*

6. If your cat is a male, identify the prostate gland (part of the male reproductive system), which encircles the urethra distal to the neck of the bladder (Figure D8.2). Notice that the urinary bladder is somewhat fixed in position by ligaments.

7. Using a probe, trace the urethra as it exits from the bladder to its terminus in the **urogenital sinus,*** a common chamber into which both the vagina and the urethra empty in the female cat, or into the penis of the male. Dissection to expose the urethra along its entire length should not be done at this time because of possible damage to the reproductive structures, which you will study in Dissection Exercise 9.

8. Before cleaning up the dissection materials, observe a cat of the opposite sex. Prepare your cat for storage as described in the box on page 752. ■

*In the human female, the vagina and the urethra have separate external openings.

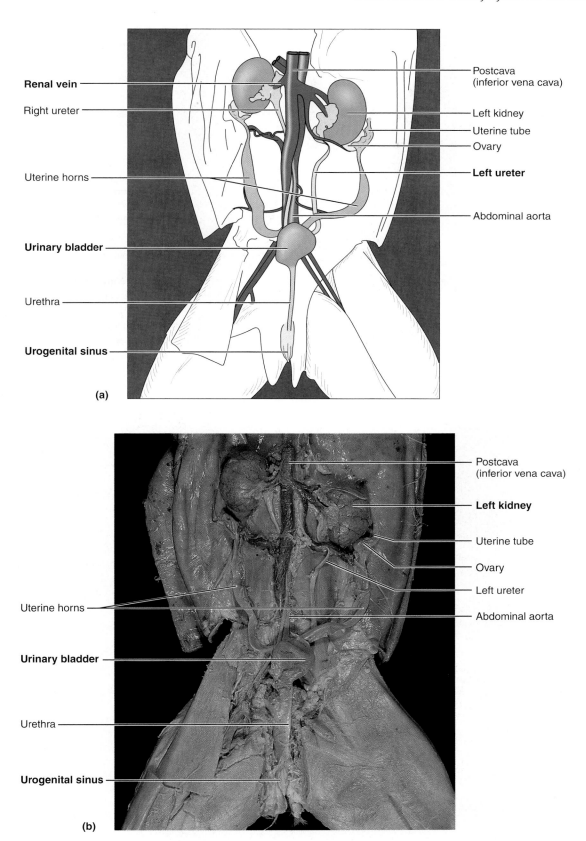

Renal vein

Right ureter

Uterine horns

Urinary bladder

Urethra

Urogenital sinus

Postcava
(inferior vena cava)

Left kidney

Uterine tube

Ovary

Left ureter

Abdominal aorta

(a)

Postcava
(inferior vena cava)

Left kidney

Uterine tube

Ovary

Left ureter

Abdominal aorta

Uterine horns

Urinary bladder

Urethra

Urogenital sinus

(b)

Figure D8.1   Urinary system of the female cat. (Reproductive structures are also indicated.)
(a) Diagrammatic view. **(b)** Photograph of female urogenital system.

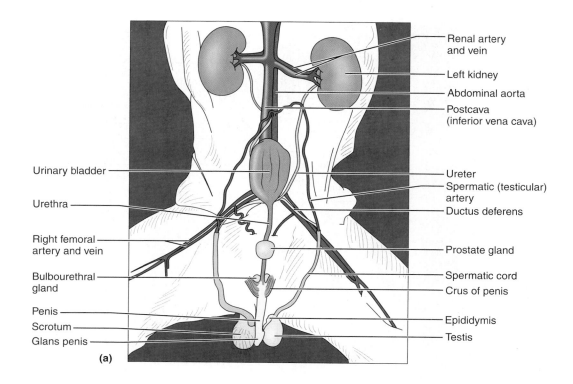

(a)

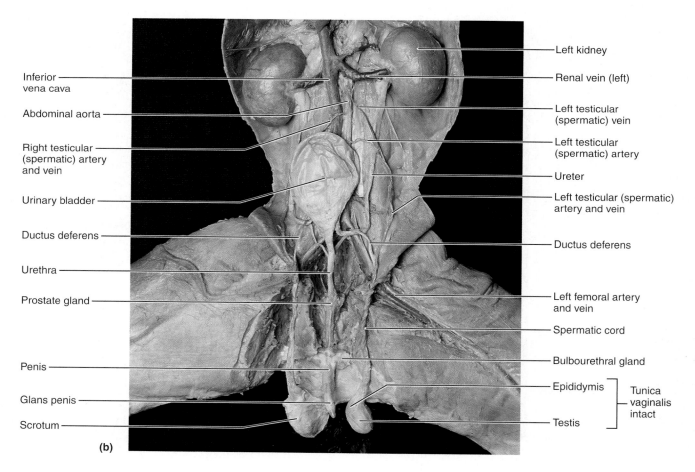

(b)

Figure D8.2 **Urinary system of the male cat.** (Reproductive structures are also indicated.)
(a) Diagrammatic view. **(b)** Photograph of male urogenital system.

Dissection Review

1. a.   How does the position of the kidneys in the cat differ from their position in humans?

    _____

    _____

    b.   In what way is the position similar?

    _____

    _____

2. Distinguish between a ureter and the urethra.

    _____

    _____

3. How does the site of urethral emptying in the female cat differ from its termination point in the human female?

    _____

    _____

4. What is a urogenital sinus?

    _____

    _____

5. What gland encircles the neck of the bladder in the male? _____ Is this part of the urinary system?

    _____ What is its function? _____

    _____

    _____

6. Compare the location of the adrenal glands in the cat to the location in humans.

    _____

    _____

Dissection of the Reproductive System of the Cat

Objectives

1. To identify the major reproductive structures of the male and female dissection animal.

2. To recognize and discuss pertinent differences between the reproductive structures of humans and the dissection animal.

Materials

- ❑ Disposable gloves
- ❑ Dissecting instruments and tray
- ❑ Animal specimen from previous dissections
- ❑ Bone cutters
- ❑ Small metric rulers (for female cats)
- ❑ Embalming fluid
- ❑ Paper towels

D on gloves, and obtain your cat, a dissecting tray, and the necessary dissecting instruments. After you have completed the study of the reproductive structures of your specimen, observe a cat of the opposite sex. (The following instructions assume that the abdominal cavity has been opened in previous dissection exercises.) See Exercise 42 of this manual for a discussion of the human reproductive system.

Activity 1:
Identifying Organs of the Male Reproductive System

Refer to Figure D9.1 as you identify the male structures.

1. Identify the **penis,** and notice the prepuce covering the glans. Carefully cut through the skin overlying the penis to expose the cavernous tissue beneath, then cross section the penis to see the relative positioning of the three cavernous bodies.

2. Identify the **scrotum,** and then carefully make a shallow incision through the scrotum to expose the **testes.** Notice the abundant connective tissue stretching between the inner wall of the scrotum and testis surface and that the scrotum is divided internally.

3. Lateral to the medial aspect of the scrotal sac, locate the **spermatic cord,** which contains the testicular (spermatic) artery, vein, and nerve, as well as the ductus deferens, and follow it up through the inguinal canal into the abdominal cavity. (It is not necessary to cut through the pelvic bone; a slight tug on the spermatic cord in the scrotal sac region will reveal its position in the abdominal cavity.) Carefully loosen the spermatic cord from the connective tissue investing it, and follow its course as it travels superiorly in the pelvic cavity. Then follow the **ductus deferens** as it loops over the ureter,* and then courses posterior to the bladder and enters the prostate gland. Using bone cutters, carefully make an incision through the pubic symphysis to follow the urethra.

4. Notice that the **prostate gland,** an enlarged whitish mass abutting the urethra, is comparatively smaller in the cat than in the human, and it is more distal to the bladder. (In the human, the prostate is immediately adjacent to the base of the bladder.) Carefully slit open the prostate gland to follow the ductus deferens to the urethra, which exits from the bladder midline. The male cat urethra, like that of the human, serves as both a urinary and sperm duct. In the human, the ductus deferens is joined by the duct of the seminal vesicle to form the ejaculatory duct, which enters the prostate. Seminal vesicles are not present in the cat.

5. Trace the **urethra** to the proximal ends of the cavernous tissues of the penis, each of which is anchored to the ischium by a band of connective tissue called the **crus** of the penis. The crus is covered ventrally by the ischiocavernosus muscle and the **bulbourethral gland** lies beneath it.

6. Once again, turn your attention to the testis. Cut it from its attachment to the spermatic cord and carefully slit open the **tunica vaginalis** capsule enclosing it. Identify the **epididymis** running along one side of the testis. Make a longitudinal cut through the testis and epididymis. Can you see the tubular nature of the epididymis and the rete testis portion of the testis with the naked eye? ■

*This position of the spermatic cord and ductus deferens is due to the fact that during fetal development, the testis was in the same relative position as the ovary is in the female. In its descent, it passes laterally and ventrally to the ureter.

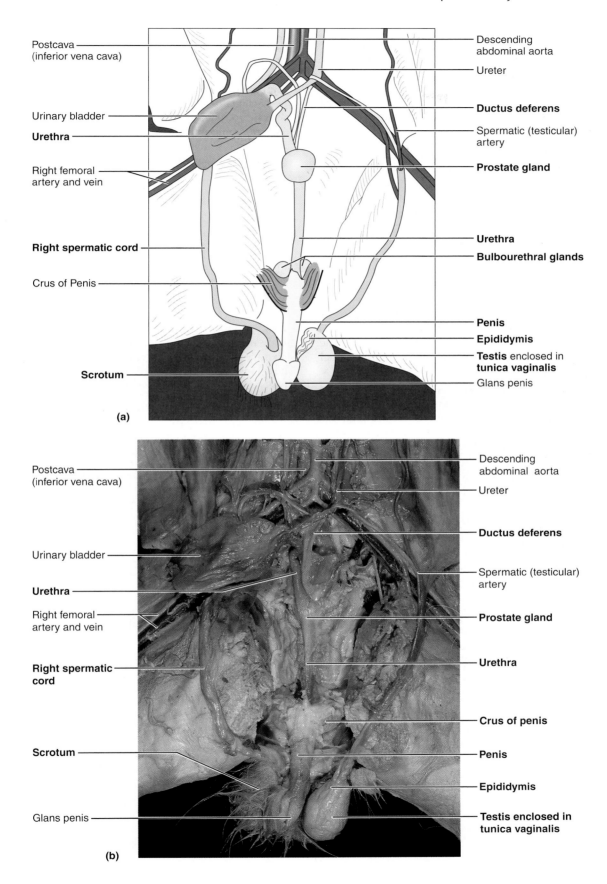

Figure D9.1   Reproductive system of the male cat. (a) Diagrammatic view. **(b)** Photograph.

Activity 2:
Identifying Organs of the Female Reproductive System

Refer to Figure D9.2 showing a dissection of the urogenital system of the female cat as you identify the structures described below.

1.   Unlike the pear-shaped simplex, or one-part, uterus of the human, the uterus of the cat is Y-shaped (bipartite, or bicornuate) and consists of a **uterine body** from which two **uterine horns** (cornua) diverge. Such an enlarged uterus enables the animal to produce litters. Examine the abdominal cavity, and identify the bladder and the body of the uterus lying just dorsal to it.

2.   Follow one of the uterine horns as it travels superiorly in the body cavity. Identify the thin mesentery (the *broad ligament*), which helps anchor it and the other reproductive structures to the body wall. Approximately halfway up the length of the uterine horn, it should be possible to identify the more important *round ligament,* a cord of connective tissue extending laterally and posteriorly from the uterine horn to the region of the body wall that would correspond to the inguinal region of the male.

3.   Examine the **uterine tube** and **ovary** at the distal end of the uterine horn just caudal to the kidney. Observe how the funnel-shaped end of the uterine tube curves around the ovary. As in the human, the distal end of the tube is fimbriated, or fringed, and the tube is lined with ciliated epithelium. The uterine tubes of the cat are tiny and much shorter than in the human. Identify the **ovarian ligament,** a short thick cord that extends from the uterus to the ovary and anchors the ovary to the body wall. Also observe the *ovarian artery* and *vein* passing through the mesentery to the ovary and uterine structures.

4.   Return to the body of the uterus and follow it caudad to the bony pelvis. Use bone cutters to cut through the median line of the pelvis (the pubic symphysis), cutting carefully so you do not damage the urethra deep to it. Expose the pelvic region by pressing the thighs dorsally. Follow the uterine body caudally to where it narrows to its sphincterlike cervix, which protrudes into the vagina. Note the point where the urethra draining the bladder and the **vagina** enter a common chamber, the **urogenital sinus.** How does this anatomical arrangement compare to that seen in the human female?

_____

_____

5.   On the cat's exterior, observe the **vulva,** which is similar to the human vulva. Identify the slim **labia majora** surrounding the urogenital opening.

6.   To determine the length of the vagina, which is difficult to ascertain by external inspection, slit through the vaginal wall just superior to the urogenital sinus and cut toward the body of the uterus with scissors. Reflect the cut edges, and identify the muscular cervix of the uterus. Approximately how long is the vagina of the cat? (Measure the distance between the urogenital sinus and the cervix.)

_____

7.   When you have completed your observations of both male and female cats, clean your dissecting instruments and tray and properly wrap the cat for storage as described in the box on page 752. ■

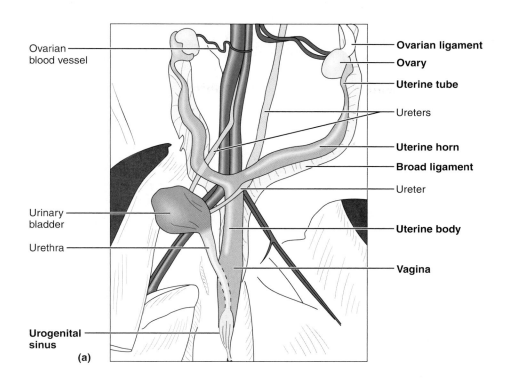

Ovarian blood vessel

Ovarian ligament
Ovary
Uterine tube

Ureters

Uterine horn
Broad ligament

Ureter

Urinary bladder

Urethra

Uterine body

Vagina

Urogenital sinus

(a)

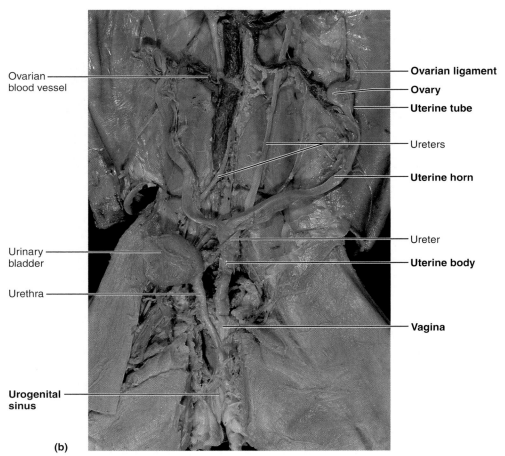

Ovarian blood vessel

Ovarian ligament
Ovary
Uterine tube

Ureters

Uterine horn

Ureter

Urinary bladder

Urethra

Uterine body

Vagina

Urogenital sinus

(b)

Figure D9.2 Reproductive system of the female cat. (a) Diagrammatic view. **(b)** Photograph.

Dissection Review

1. The female cat has a _____ uterus; that of the human female is _____.

    Explain the difference in structure of these two uterine types. _____

    _____

    _____

    _____

2. What reproductive advantage is conferred by the feline uterine type?

    _____

    _____

3. Cite differences noted between the cat and the human relative to the following structures:

    uterine tubes or oviducts _____

    _____

    site of entry of ductus deferens into the urethra _____

    _____

    _____

    location of the prostate gland _____

    _____

    _____

    seminal vesicles _____

    _____

    urethral and vaginal openings in the female _____

    _____

    _____

    _____

    _____

The Metric System

Measurement	Unit and abbreviation	Metric equivalent	Metric to English conversion factor	English to metric conversion factor
Length	1 kilometer (km)	= 1000 (10^3) meters	1 km = 0.62 mile	1 mile = 1.61 km
	1 meter (m)	= 100 (10^2) centimeters = 1000 millimeters	1 m = 1.09 yards 1 m = 3.28 feet 1 m = 39.37 inches	1 yard = 0.914 m 1 foot = 0.305 m
	1 centimeter (cm)	= 0.01 (10^{-2}) meter	1 cm = 0.394 inch	1 foot = 30.5 cm 1 inch = 2.54 cm
	1 millimeter (mm)	= 0.001 (10^{-3}) meter	1 mm = 0.039 inch	
	1 micrometer (μm) [formerly micron (μ)]	= 0.000001 (10^{-6}) meter		
	1 nanometer (nm) [formerly millimicron (mμ)]	= 0.000000001 (10^{-9}) meter		
	1 angstrom (Å)	= 0.0000000001 (10^{-10}) meter		
Area	1 square meter (m^2)	= 10,000 square centimeters	1 m^2 = 1.1960 square yards	1 square yard = 0.8361 m^2
			1 m^2 = 10.764 square feet	1 square foot = 0.0929 m^2
	1 square centimeter (cm^2)	= 100 square millimeters	1 cm^2 = 0.155 square inch	1 square inch = 6.4516 cm^2
Mass	1 metric ton (t)	= 1000 kilograms	1 t = 1.103 ton	1 ton = 0.907 t
	1 kilogram (kg)	= 1000 grams	1 kg = 2.205 pounds	1 pound = 0.4536 kg
	1 gram (g)	= 1000 milligrams	1 g = 0.0353 ounce 1 g = 15.432 grains	1 ounce = 28.35 g
	1 milligram (mg)	= 0.001 gram	1 mg = approx. 0.015 grain	
	1 microgram (μg)	= 0.000001 gram		
Volume (solids)	1 cubic meter (m^3)	= 1,000,000 cubic centimeters	1 m^3 = 1.3080 cubic yards 1 m^3 = 35.315 cubic feet	1 cubic yard = 0.7646 m^3 1 cubic foot = 0.0283 m^3
	1 cubic centimeter (cm^3 or cc)	= 0.000001 cubic meter = 1 milliliter	1 cm^3 = 0.0610 cubic inch	1 cubic inch = 16.387 cm^3
	1 cubic millimeter (mm^3)	= 0.000000001 cubic meter		
Volume (liquids and gases)	1 kiloliter (kl or kL)	= 1000 liters	1 kL = 264.17 gallons	1 gallon = 3.785 L 1 quart = 0.946 L
	1 liter (l or L)	= 1000 milliliters	1 L = 0.264 gallons 1 L = 1.057 quarts	
	1 milliliter (ml or mL)	= 0.001 liter = 1 cubic centimeter	1 ml = 0.034 fluid ounce 1 ml = approx. $\frac{1}{4}$ teaspoon 1 ml = approx. 15–16 drops (gtt.)	1 quart = 946 ml 1 pint = 473 ml 1 fluid ounce = 29.57 ml 1 teaspoon = approx. 5 ml
	1 microliter (μl or μL)	= 0.000001 liter		
Time	1 second (s)	= $\frac{1}{60}$ minute		
	1 millisecond (ms)	= 0.001 second		
Temperature	Degrees Celsius (°C)		$°F = \frac{9}{5}°C + 32$	$°C = \frac{5}{9}(°F - 32)$

A.D.A.M.® Interactive Anatomy Correlations

Appendix B lists correlations of Dissectible Anatomy images in the A.D.A.M.® Interactive Anatomy (AIA) program with exercises in this manual. To start the AIA program, insert the AIA CD in your CD-ROM drive. Double-click the Interactive Anatomy 3.0 application icon located in the Interactive Anatomy folder on your hard drive. From the Introduction screen, click Dissectible Anatomy. From the open dialog, click Open. To change anatomical views, click the View button drop-down menu in the tool bar, and select Anterior,

Posterior, Lateral, or Medial. Click on the Structure List to launch the List Manager (Mac only) or choose from the list of available structures (Win only).

Note that AIA also offers Atlas Anatomy and 3-D Anatomy. Take some time to explore these additional features of AIA.

After you click Open from the open dialog, the following image appears:

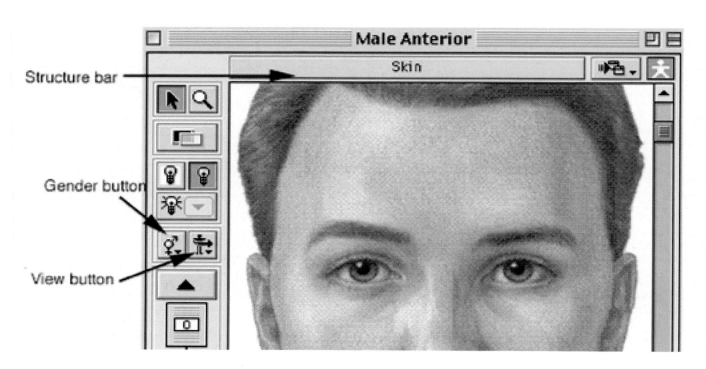

Exercise 1
The Language of Anatomy

To illustrate a coronal plane
View: Anterior
Structure: Skull-coronal section

To illustrate a midsagittal plane
View: Medial
Structure: Skin

To illustrate a ventral body cavity
View: Anterior
Structure: Diaphragm

To illustrate serous membranes of the ventral body cavity
View: Anterior
Structure: Pericardial sac, Parietal peritoneum, Peritoneum

To illustrate a parietal pleura
View: Medial
Structure: Costal parietal pleura diaphragmatic

Exercise 8
Classification of Covering and Lining Membranes

To illustrate parietal pleural membranes
View: Anterior
Structure: Parietal pleura

Exercise 10
The Axial Skeleton

To illustrate bones of the cranium and face
View: Anterior
Structure: Skull

To illustrate bones of the cranium
View: Posterior
Structure: Bones—coronal section

To illustrate bones of the cranium and face
View: Lateral
Structure: Skull

To illustrate hyoid bone
View: Lateral
Structure: Hyoid bone

To illustrate paranasal sinuses
View: Anterior
Structure: Mucosa of maxillary, Frontal, Sphenoidal sinuses, Ethmoidal sinus

To illustrate a vertebral column
View: Anterior
Structure: Intervertebral disc

To illustrate a posterior vertebral column
View: Posterior
Structure: Intervertebral disc

To illustrate a vertebral column and intervertebral discs
View: Medial
Structure: Sacrum

To illustrate a sacrum and lumbar vertebrae
View: Posterior
Structure: Sacrum

To illustrate a bony thorax
View: Anterior
Structure: Ribs

Exercise 11
The Appendicular Skeleton

To illustrate a pectoral girdle
View: Anterior
Structure: Clavicle

To illustrate a pectoral girdle
View: Posterior
Structure: Scapula

To illustrate a humerus
View: Anterior
Structure: Humerus

To illustrate an ulna
View: Anterior
Structure: Ulna

To illustrate bones of the wrist and hand
View: Anterior
Structure: Bones of hand

To illustrate a female pelvis click on the Gender button and choose Female

View: Anterior
Structure: Bones—coronal section

To illustrate a male pelvis click on the Gender button and choose Male
View: Anterior
Structure: Bones—coronal section

To illustrate a femur
View: Anterior
Structure: Femur

To illustrate a tibia
View: Anterior
Structure: Tibia

To illustrate bones of the foot
View: Anterior
Structure: Bones of the foot

Exercise 13
Articulations and
Body Movements

To illustrate a synovial joint of the knee
View: Anterior
Structure: Synovial capsule of knee joint

To illustrate a synovial joint capsule of the hip
View: Anterior
Structure: Synovial joint capsule of the hip

Exercise 15
Gross Anatomy of the
Muscular System

To illustrate muscles of the face
View: Anterior
Structure: Orbicularis oculi muscle

To illustrate muscles of mastication
View: Anterior
Structure: Masseter muscle

To illustrate superficial muscles of the neck
View: Lateral
Structure: Platysma muscle, Sternocleidomastoid muscle

To illustrate deep muscles of the neck
View: Lateral
Structure: Strap muscles

To illustrate thorax and shoulder muscles
View: Lateral
Structure: Pectoralis major muscle, Serratus anterior muscle

To illustrate thorax muscles
View: Anterior
Structure: External intercostal muscles, Internal intercostal muscle

To illustrate abdominal wall
View: Anterior
Structure: Rectus abdominis muscle, External abdominal oblique muscle, Internal abdominal oblique muscle

To illustrate thorax muscles
View: Lateral
Structure: Latissimus dorsi muscle

To illustrate posterior muscles of the trunk
View: Posterior
Structure: Rhomboideus muscle

To illustrate muscles associated with the vertebral column
View: Posterior
Structure: Semispinalis muscle, Splenius muscle

To illustrate muscles of the humerus that act on the forearm
View: Posterior
Structure: Brachialis muscle

To illustrate anterior muscles of the forearm that act on the hand and fingers
View: Anterior
Structure: Flexor carpi radialis muscle, Palmaris longus muscle, Flexor carpi ulnaris muscle, Flexor digitorum superficialis muscle

To illustrate deep muscles of the forearm that act on the hand and fingers
View: Posterior
Structure: Abductor pollicis longus muscle

To illustrate muscles acting on the thigh
View: Anterior
Structure: Sartorius muscle

To illustrate quadriceps
View: Anterior
Structure: Rectus femoris muscle, Vastus lateralis muscle, Vastus medialis muscle, Vastus intermedius muscle, Tensor fasciae latae muscle

To illustrate muscles acting on the thigh and originating on the pelvis
View: Posterior
Structure: Gluteus maximus muscle, Gluteus medius muscle, Gluteus minimus muscle

To illustrate hamstrings
View: Posterior
Structure: Long head of the biceps femoris muscle, Semitendinosus muscle, Semimembranosus muscle

To illustrate superficial muscles acting on the foot and ankle
View: Posterior
Structure: Gastrocnemius muscle, Soleus muscle, Popliteus muscle, Tibialis posterior muscle

To illustrate muscles acting on the foot and ankle
View: Anterior
Structure: Tibialis anterior muscle, Extensor digitorum longus muscle, Extensor hallucis longus muscle

Exercise 19
Gross Anatomy of the Brain and Cranial Nerves

To illustrate a cerebrum
View: Anterior
Structure: Skull—coronal section

To illustrate a cerebrum
View: Lateral
Structure: Brain

To illustrate cranial nerves
View: Lateral
Structure: Cranial nerves

To illustrate a vagus nerve
View: Lateral
Structure: Vagus nerve {CN X}

To illustrate phrenic and vagus nerves
View: Anterior
Structure: Phrenic and vagus nerves {CN X}

Exercise 21
Spinal Cord, Spinal Nerves, and the Autonomic Nervous System

To illustrate a spinal cord
View: Posterior
Structure: Spinal cord

To illustrate deep nerve plexuses and intercostal nerves
View: Anterior
Structure: Deep nerve plexuses and inter-costal nerves

To illustrate a brachial plexus and branches
View: Anterior
Structure: Brachial plexus

To illustrate a central nervous system and sacral plexus
View: Medial
Structure: Central nervous system and sacral plexus

To illustrate a sciatic nerve and branches
View: Medial
Structure: Sciatic nerve and branches

To illustrate a tibial nerve
View: Posterior
Structure: Tibial nerve and branches

To illustrate autonomic nerve plexuses
View: Medial
Structure: Autonomic nerve plexuses

To illustrate a sympathetic trunk
View: Anterior
Structure: Sympathetic trunk

Exercise 24
Special Senses: Vision

To illustrate muscles and external anatomy of the eye
View: Anterior
Structure: Muscles of the eye

To illustrate eye muscles
View: Lateral
Structure: Eye muscles—medial

Exercise 27
Functional Anatomy of the Endocrine Glands

To illustrate a pituitary gland
View: Lateral
Structure: Pituitary gland

To illustrate a thyroid gland
View: Anterior
Structure: Thyroid gland

To illustrate a suprarenal gland
View: Anterior
Structure: Suprarenal {Adrenal} gland

To illustrate a pancreas
View: Anterior
Structure: Pancreas

To illustrate ovaries click on the Gender button and choose Female
View: Medial
Structure: Ovary

To illustrate testes click on the Gender button and choose Male
View: Anterior
Structure: Testis

To illustrate a thymus gland
View: Anterior
Structure: Thymus gland

Exercise 30
Anatomy of the Heart

To illustrate a heart
View: Anterior
Structure: Heart

To illustrate fibrous pericardium
View: Anterior
Structure: Pericardiacophrenic vein

To illustrate visceral pericardium
View: Anterior
Structure: Epicardium

To illustrate heart chambers and heart valves
View: Anterior
Structure: Heart—cut section

To illustrate coronary arteries
View: Anterior
Structure: Coronary arteries

Exercise 32
Anatomy of Blood Vessels

To illustrate an aortic arch and branches
View: Anterior
Structure: Aortic arch and branches

To illustrate common carotid arteries
View: Anterior
Structure: Common carotid arteries

To illustrate major branches of the descending aorta
View: Anterior
Structure: Celiac trunk and branches

To illustrate a descending thoracic aorta
View: Anterior
Structure: Descending thoracic aorta

To illustrate an abdominal aorta and branches
View: Anterior
Structure: Abdominal aorta and branches

To illustrate an aortic arch and branches
View: Medial
Structure: Aortic

To illustrate veins draining into the vena cavae
View: Lateral
Structure: Venae Cavae and tributaries

To illustrate pulmonary circulation
View: Anterior
Structure: Pulmonary arteries

To illustrate arterial supply of the brain
View: Lateral
Structure: Aortic arch and branches

To illustrate hepatic portal circulation
View: Anterior
Structure: Portal vein and tributaries

Exercise 33
Human Cardiovascular Physiology: Blood Pressure and Pulse Determination

To illustrate the position of the heart and valves in the thoracic cavity
View: Anterior
Structure: Heart—cut section

To illustrate the pulse points
View: Anterior
Structure: Radial artery, Deep femoral artery

Exercise 35A
The Lymphatic System and Immune Response

To illustrate lymphatic vessels and lymphoid organs
View: Anterior
Structure: Lymph vessels

To illustrate a thoracic duct
View: Anterior
Structure: Thoracic duct

To illustrate axillary and cervical lymph nodes
View: Anterior
Structure: Axillary and cervical lymph nodes

To illustrate a thymus gland
View: Anterior
Structure: Thymus gland

To illustrate a spleen
View: Anterior
Structure: Spleen

To illustrate palatine glands and tonsils
View: Anterior
Structure: Palatine glands and tonsils

Exercise 36
Anatomy of the Respiratory System

To illustrate an upper respiratory tract
View: Medial
Structure: Nasal conchae

To illustrate an upper respiratory tract
View: Lateral
Structure: Mediastinal parietal pleura of right pleural cavity

To illustrate a larynx
View: Anterior
Structure: Thyroid gland

To illustrate an epiglottis
View: Anterior
Structure: Epiglottis

To illustrate lower respiratory structures
View: Medial
Structure: Right lung

To illustrate lower respiratory structures
View: Anterior
Structure: Trachea

To illustrate lungs
View: Anterior
Structure: Lungs

To illustrate lungs—coronal section
View: Anterior
Structure: Lungs—coronal section

To illustrate a right lung
View: Lateral
Structure: Right lung

To illustrate a parietal pleura
View: Anterior
Structure: Parietal pleura

To illustrate a diaphragm
View: Anterior
Structure: Diaphragm

To illustrate a trachea
View: Lateral
Structure: Trachea

Exercise 38
Anatomy of the Digestive System

To illustrate an oral cavity
View: Lateral
Structure: Esophagus

To illustrate tonsils
View: Anterior
Structure: Palatine tonsil

To illustrate salivary glands
View: Lateral
Structure: Parotid gland, Parotid duct, Deep salivary glands

To illustrate an esophagus
View: Lateral
Structure: Esophagus

To illustrate a stomach
View: Anterior
Structure: Stomach, Stomach—coronal section

To illustrate a stomach
View: Lateral
Structure: Stomach

To illustrate an ileum
View: Anterior
Structure: Ileum

To illustrate a duodenum
View: Anterior
Structure: Duodenum

To illustrate a transverse colon
View: Anterior
Structure: Transverse colon

To illustrate an ascending and descending colon
View: Anterior
Structure: Ascending colon, Descending colon

To illustrate a colon
View: Medial
Structure: Colon

To illustrate teeth
View: Anterior
Structure: Skull

To illustrate a bile duct, liver, and gallbladder
View: Anterior
Structure: Bile duct {Common bile duct}, Liver—coronal section, Gallbladder

To illustrate a pancreas
View: Anterior
Structure: Pancreas

Exercise 40
Anatomy of the Urinary System

To illustrate kidneys
View: Anterior
Structure: Kidney, Kidney—longitudinal section

To illustrate a ureter
View: Anterior
Structure: Ureter

To illustrate a urinary bladder
View: Anterior
Structure: Urinary bladder

To illustrate a female urethra click on the Gender button and choose Female
View: Medial
Structure: Urethra

To illustrate a male urethra click on the Gender button and choose Male
View: Medial
Structure: Urinary bladder and prostate gland, Urethra

Exercise 42
Anatomy of the Reproductive System

To illustrate testes click on the Gender button and choose Male
View: Anterior
Structure: Testis

To illustrate a penis click on the Gender button and choose Male
View: Anterior
Structure: Penis

To illustrate a uterus click on the Gender button and choose Female
View: Anterior
Structure: Uterus

To illustrate mammary glands click on the Gender button and choose Female
View: Anterior
Structure: Breast

Credits

ILLUSTRATIONS

Exercise 1
1.2, 1.4, 1.6, 1.7: Imagineering. 1.3, 1.5: Precision Graphics. 1.8: Adapted from Marieb and Mallatt, *Human Anatomy,* 3e, F1.10, © Benjamin Cummings, 2003.

Exercise 3
3.2–3.4, Activity 3: Precision Graphics.

Exercise 4
4.1, 4.2: Imagineering. 4.3: Tomo Narashima. 4.4: Adapted from Campbell, Reece, and Mitchell, *Biology,* 5e, F12.5, © Benjamin Cummings 1999. Table 4.1: Precision Graphics.

Exercise 5A
5A.1: Precision Graphics. 5A.4: Nadine Sokol/Imagineering.

Exercise 6
6.1, 6.3, 6.5–6.7: Imagineering. 6.2, 6.8: Precision Graphics. 6.4: Kristin Otwell/Imagineering.

Exercise 7
7.1: Tomo Narashima. 7.2, 7.4, 7.6–7.9: Imagineering.

Exercise 8
8.1, 8.2: Imagineering.

Exercise 9
9.1: Laurie O'Keefe. 9.2–9.5, Table 9.1: Imagineering.

Exercise 10
10.1–10.9, 10.13: Nadine Sokol. 10.10, 10.14: Kristin Otwell. 10.11: Vincent Perez/Kristin Mount. 10.12, 10.17: Laurie O'Keefe. 10.15, 10.16: Imagineering.

Exercise 11
11.1–11.7a, 11.8, Table 11.1: Laurie O'Keefe. 11.9a: Kristin Otwell. 11.9b: Imagineering.

Exercise 12
12.1a,b: Nadine Sokol.

Exercise 13
13.1, 13.5, 13.6: Precision Graphics. 13.3, 13.4, 13.7, Table 13.1: Imagineering. 13.8. 13.9: Barbara Cousins.

Exercise 14
14.1, 14.2, 14.5: Imagineering. 14.3, 14.4: Raychel Ciemma.

Exercise 15
15.1: Adapted from Martini, *Fundamentals of Anatomy & Physiology,* 4e, F11.1, Upper Saddle River, NJ: Prentice-Hall, © Frederic H. Martini, 1998. 15.2–15.12, 15.14, 15.15: Raychel Ciemma. 15.13: Wendy Hiller Gee.

Exercise 16A
16A.1–16A.4: Precision Graphics. 16A.5, 16A.6, 16A.10–16A.12: Imagineering. 16A.7–16A.9, 16A.13–16A.18: Biopac Systems.

Exercise 17
17.1, 17.2, 17.5, 17.7b: Precision Graphics. 17.3, 17.6: Imagineering. 17.7a: Charles W. Hoffman.

Exercise 18A
18A.1–18A.4: Precision Graphics.

Exercise 19
19.7b, 19.8c, 19.9, 19.11, 19.13: Precision Graphics. 19.1, 19.2, 19.4, 19.5, 19.7a, 19.8a,b: Imagineering.

Exercise 20
20.1b, 20.2, 20.3: Imagineering. 20.4–20.7: Biopac Systems.

Exercise 21
21.1–21.3, 21.5a, 21.6–21.15: Imagineering. 21.5b: Stephanie McCann. 21.16–21.22: Biopac Systems.

Exercise 22
22.1, 22.2, 22.3, 22.7: Imagineering. 22.8, 22.9: Biopac Systems.

Exercise 23
23.2: Imagineering.

Exercise 24
24.1: Charles W. Hoffman. 24.2–24.4, 24.8, 24.9: Imagineering. 24.7: Shirley Bortoli. 24.10, 24.11: Precision Graphics.

Exercise 25
25.1: Charles W. Hoffman. 25.2, 25.3, 25.5, 25.7, 25.8: Imagineering. 25.4: Precision Graphics.

Exercise 26
26.1, 26.2a,b: Imagineering. 26.2c,d: Adapted from Marieb and Mallatt, *Human Anatomy,* 3e, F16.1, © Benjamin Cummings, 2003.

Exercise 27
27.1, 27.2: Imagineering. 27.3: Precision Graphics

Exercise 28A
28.1: Imagineering.

Exercise 29
29.1, 29.6, Table 29.1: Imagineering. 29.2, 29.3: Precision Graphics.

Exercise 30
30.1: Wendy Hiller Gee. 30.2, 30.3, 30.6, 30.10: Barbara Cousins. 30.4, 30.5: Imagineering. 30.8: Precision Graphics.

Exercise 31
31.1: Barbara Cousins. 31.2–31.4: Precision Graphics. 31.5, 31.6: Imagineering. 31.7–31.12: Biopac Systems.

Exercise 32
32.1: Adapted from Tortora and Grabowski, *Principles of Anatomy and Physiology,* 9e, F21.1, New York: Wiley, © Biological Sciences Textbooks and Sandra Reynolds Grabowski, 2000. 32.2, 32.7, 32.14: Imagineering. 32.3–32.6, 32.8–32.13: Barbara Cousins. 32.15: Kristin Mount.

Exercise 33A
33A.1, 33A.3–33A.5: Imagineering. 33A.2, 33A.9: Precision Graphics. 33A.6–33A.8: Biopac Systems.

Exercise 34A
34A.1, 34A.2, 34A.4, 34A.6: Precision Graphics. 34A.3: Imagineering. 34A.5: Biopac Systems.

Exercise 35A
35.1a: Adapted from Marieb and Mallatt, *Human Anatomy,* 3e, F20.1, © Benjamin Cummings, 2003. 35.1b,c, 35.2, 35.3, 35.4, 35.5a: Imagineering. 35.5b, 35.6: Precision Graphics.

Exercise 36
36.1–36.7: Imagineering.

Exercise 37A
37A.1, 37A.2, 37A.7–37A.10, 37A.12, 37A.15: Imagineering. 37A.5, 37A.6: Precision Graphics. 37A.11, 37A.13, 37A.14: Biopac Systems.

Exercise 38
38.1:Kristin Mount. 38.2: Adapted from Seeley, Stephens, and Tate, *Anatomy & Physiology,* 4e, F24.2, New York: WCB/McGraw-Hill, © McGraw-Hill, 1998. 38.3, 38.4: Cyndie Wooley. 38.5a: Kristin Otwell. 38.5c,d, 38.7, 38.8, 38.11, 38.12, 38.14: Imagineering. 38.6, 38.9, 38.13, 38.15: Precision Graphics. 38.10: Karl Miyajima.

Exercise 39A
39A.1: Imagineering. 39A.2, Digestion Tables: Precision Graphics.

Exercise 40
40.1a, 40.2: Linda McVay. 40.1c, 40.3–40.5: Imagineering. 40.6: Precision Graphics.

Exercise 41A
41A.1–41A.2: Precision Graphics.

Exercise 42
42.1, 42.2, 42.5: Imagineering. 42.4: Carla Simmons. 42.7: Martha Blake.

Exercise 43
43.1, 43.2, 43.5: Precision Graphics. 43.3, 43.4, 43.7: Imagineering.

Exercise 44
44.1, 44.2, 44.3: Imagineering.

Exercise 46
46.3: Raychel Ciemma. 46.5, 46.7, 46.9, 46.10, 46.13: Imagineering. 47.19: Precision Graphics.

Cat Dissection Exercises
D1.1, D3.1, D3.3, D4.1, D7.1: Precision Graphics. D2.1, D2.3, D3.2, D4.3–D4.5, D6.1, D7.2, D7.3, D8.1, D8.2, D9.1, D9.2: Kristin Mount. D2.2: Imagineering.

Fetal Pig Dissection Exercises
D1.3–D1.8, D2.2, D3.1, D3.2, D4.1–D4.5, D6.2, D7.1, D7.2, D8.1, D8.2, D9.1, D9.2: Kristin Mount.

PhysioEx Exercises
Opening screens: Cadre Design.

PHOTOGRAPHS
Exercise 1
1.1, 1.4,1: Jenny Thomas, Benjamin Cummings. 1.4a: Simon Fraser, Royal Victoria Infirmary, Newcastle Upon Tyne/Science Photo Library/Photo Researchers. 1.4b: Science Photo Library/Photo Researchers. 1.4c: CNRI/Science Photo Library/Photo Researchers. 1.7b: Custom Medical Stock.

Exercise 2
2.1a–d, 2.2, 2.3a, 2.4a, 2.5b–c: Elena Dorfman, Benjamin Cummings. 2.3b, 2.4b,c, 2.5a, 2.6a–c: Robert A. Chase. 2.7: Carolina Biological Supply/Phototake.

Exercise 3
3.1: Leica. 3.5: Victor Eroschencko, Benjamin Cummings. 3.6: Swift Instruments.

Exercise 4
4.1b: Don Fawcett/Science Source/Photo Researchers. 4.4a–f: Ed Reschke.

Exercise 5A
5A.2a–c: Richard Megna/Fundamental Photographs. 5A.3a: Keith R. Porter/Science Source/Photo Researchers. 5A.3b: Mohandas Narla, Lawrence Berkeley Laboratory. 5A.3c: David M. Phillips/Visuals Unlimited.

Exercise 6
6.3a: G. W. Willis/Visuals Unlimited. 6.3b,e,f,h, 6.5d,h,i, 6.6c: Allen Bell, University of New England; Benjamin Cummings. 6.3c: Cabisco/Visuals Unlimited. 6.3d: R. Calentine/Visuals Unlimited. 6.3g: Richard Kessel/Visuals Unlimited. 6.5a,b,f,g,j,k, 6.6b: Ed Reschke. 6.5c: Carolina Biological Supply/Visuals Unlimited. 6.5e: Ed Reschke/Peter Arnold. 6.6a: Eric Graves/Photo Researchers. 6.7: Biphoto Associates/Photo Researchers.

Exercise 7
7.2a: Dennis Strete/Fundamental Photographs. 7.3: Benjamin Cummings. 7.4b: Carolina Biological Supply/Phototake. 7.4d: Manfred Kage/Peter Arnold. 7.5a: Marian Rice. 7.5b: From *Gray's Anatomy* by Henry Gray, © Churchill Livingstone, UK. 7.7a: Cabisco/Visuals Unlimited. 7.7b: John D. Cunningham/Visuals Unlimited.

Exercise 8
8.2b: Gilbert Faure/Science Photo Library/Photo Researchers.

Exercise 9
9.3c: Allen Bell, University of New England; Benjamin Cummings. 9.4: Ed Reschke.

Exercise 10
10.4: From *A Stereoscopic Atlas of Human Anatomy* by David L. Bassett. 10.5: R. T. Hutchings. 10.9c: Robert A. Chase.

Exercise 11
11.5b: Department of Anatomy and Histology, University of California, San Francisco. 11.7b, Table 11.1: From *A Stereoscopic Atlas of Human Anatomy* by David L. Bassett.

Exercise 12
12.1c,d: R. T. Hutchings. 12.2a,b: Jack Scanlon, Holyoke Community College, MA.

Exercise 13
13.2: Robert A. Chase. 13.8d: L. Bassett/Visuals Unlimited. 13.9b: From *A Stereoscopic Atlas of Human Anatomy* by David L. Bassett.

Exercise 14
14.4b: John D. Cunningham/Visuals Unlimited.

Exercise 15
15.4b, 15.8b, 15.13b: Robert A. Chase. 15.5a, 15.9a: From *A Stereoscopic Atlas of Human Anatomy* by David L. Bassett. 15.11f: L. Bassett/Visuals Unlimited.

Exercise 17
17.2c: Triarch/Visuals Unlimited. 17.3c: Don Fawcett/Photo Researchers. 17.4: Victor Eroschenko, University of Iowa; Benjamin Cummings.

Exercise 19
19.2c: Robert A. Chase. 19.3: Mark Nielsen, University of Utah; Benjamin Cummings. 19.4a: R. T. Hutchings. 19.5b: Pat Lynch/Photo Researchers. 19.6a,b, 19.7c, 19.10: From *A Stereoscopic Atlas of Human Anatomy* by David L. Bassett. 19.11b, 19.13b, 19.14: Elena Dorfman, Benjamin Cummings. 19.12: Sharon Cummings, University of California, Davis; Benjamin Cummings.

Exercise 20
20.1a: Alexander Tsiaras/Science Source/Photo Researchers.

Exercise 21
21.1b,c,d: From *A Stereoscopic Atlas of Human Anatomy* by David L. Bassett. 21.4: Victor Eroschenko, Benjamin Cummings.

Exercise 22
22.4, 22.5, 22.6: Richard Tauber, Benjamin Cummings.

Exercise 24
24.3b: From *A Stereoscopic Atlas of Human Anatomy* by David L. Bassett. 24.4b: Ed Reschke/Peter Arnold. 24.5b: Stephen Spector; courtesy of Charles Thomas, Kansas University Medical Center; Benjamin Cummings. 24.6: Elena

Dorfman, Benjamin Cummings. 24.12a,b: Richard Tauber, Benjamin Cummings. 24.13: Don Wong/Science Source/Photo Researchers.

Exercise 25
25.6a–c: Richard Tauber, Benjamin Cummings.

Exercise 26
26.2d: Carolina Biological Supply/Phototake.

Exercise 29
29.4a–c, 29.5a–d: Elena Dorfman, Benjamin Cummings. 29.6b: Meckes and Ottawa/Photo Researchers. 29.7: Jack Scanlon, Holyoke Community College; Benjamin Cummings.

Exercise 30
30.3b: From *A Stereoscopic Atlas of Human Anatomy* by David L. Bassett. 30.3c: Lennart Nilsson, *The Body Victorious,* New York: Dell, © Boehringer Ingelheim International GmbH. 30.3d: L. Bassett/Visuals Unlimited. 30.7: Ed Reschke. 30.8a,b; 30.9: Wally Cash, Kansas State University; Benjamin Cummings.

Exercise 32
32.1a: Gladden Willis/Visuals Unlimited.

Exercise 35
35.3b: Biophoto Associates/Photo Researchers.

Exercise 36
36.1b, 36.5a: From *A Stereoscopic Atlas of Human Anatomy* by David L. Bassett. 36.5b: Richard Tauber, Benjamin Cummings. 36.6b: University of San Francisco. 36.7a: Ed Reschke/Peter Arnold. 36.7b: Carolina Biological Supply/Phototake.

Exercise 37A
37A.3, 37A.4a,b: Elena Dorfman, Benjamin Cummings.

Exercise 38
38.5b: From *Color Atlas of Histology* by Leslie P. Garner and James L. Hiatt, © Williams and Wilkins, 1990. 38.7a,c, 38.14b: From *A Stereoscopic Atlas of Human Anatomy* by David L. Bassett. 38.8d: LUMEN Histology, Loyola University Medical Education Network.

Exercise 40
40.3a: From *A Stereoscopic Atlas of Human Anatomy* by David L. Bassett. 40.7: Biophoto Associates/Photo Researchers.

Exercise 42
42.2b,c: Ed Reschke. 42.3: Roger Wagner, University of Delaware. 42.6: Biodisc/Visuals Unlimited.

Exercise 43
43.2b: Dennis Strete, Benjamin Cummings. 43.4b: Ed Reschke. 43.6a–c: Victor Eroschencko, Benjamin Cummings.

Exercise 45
45.1: CNRI/SPL/Photo Researchers. 45.2.1: Llewellyn/Uniphoto Picture Agency. 45.2.2: Marc Martinelli/The Image Bank. 45.2.3, 45.2.4: Ogust/Image Works. 45.2.5: Boisvieux/Explorer/Photo Researchers. 45.2.6, 45.2.7, 45.2.8: Anthony Loveday, Benjamin Cummings. 45.3: Carolina Biological Supply.

Exercise 46
46.1a,b, 46.2, 46.3a, 46.4, 46.6a,b, 46.8, 46.11a,b, 46.12, 46.13a, 46.15a,b, 46.16–46.18, 46.20, 46.21a–d, 46.22: Jenny Thomas, Benjamin Cummings. 46.14: Paul Waring/BioMed Arts Associates.

Histology Atlas
PLATES 11, 24, 29, 30, 34, 36, 39, 51: Dennis Strete, Benjamin Cummings. PLATES 1, 5, 6, 7, 15, 26, 27, 37, 40–42, 50: Nina Zanetti, Benjamin Cummings. PLATES 2, 4, 9, 10, 12–14, 16–19, 20, 22, 23, 25, 33, 35, 38, 43–49, 52, 54–63: Victor Eroschenko, Benjamin Cummings. PLATE 3: Manfred Kage/Peter Arnold. PLATE 8: Ed Reschke/Peter Arnold. PLATE 21: Carolina Biological Supply/Phototake. PLATE 28: LUMEN Histology, Loyola University Medical Education Network. PLATE 31: John Cunningham/Visuals Unlimited. PLATE 32: Marian Rice. PLATE 53: M. Abbey/Visuals Unlimited.

Human Anatomy Atlas
PLATES A, B: Elena Dorfman, Benjamin Cummings. PLATES C–F, H, J, O: R. T. Hutchings. PLATES G, I, K–N: Robert A. Chase.

Cat Dissection Exercises
D1.2, D1.3, D1.4, D1.7, D1.13, D4.2: Elena Dorfman, Benjamin Cummings. D1.5, D1.6, D1.8–D1.11, D1.12a,b, D2.1b, D2.2b, D2.3b, D4.5b, D4.6, D6.2, D8.1b, D8.2b, D9.1b, D9.2b: Paul Waring/BioMed Arts Associates. D7.2b, D7.3b: Jack Scanlan, Holyoke Community College; Benjamin Cummings.

Fetal Pig Dissection Exercises
D1.1, D1.2: Jack Scanlan, Holyoke Community College; Benjamin Cummings. D1.3b, D1.4b, D1.5b, D1.6b, D1.7b, D1.8b, D2.1, D4.1b, D4.2b, D4.3b, D4.4b, D6.1, D6.2b, D7.1b, D7.2b, D8.1b, D8.2b, D9.1b, D9.2b: Elena Dorfman, Benjamin Cummings.

Index